The Folk Song Abecedary

The
Folk Song

By James F. Leisy

Hawthorn Books, Inc.   *Publishers*   New York

Abecedary

Musical Autography by Alfredo Seville

TO EMILY

3715

CONTENTS

FOREWORD

I don't think I've said anything to offend a listener. I hope not. And it's possible he might find these pages entertaining, or at least educational. He might even get the idea, as Hermes Nye put it, "that folk singing *is* an art and not just an old man in ragged overalls leaning up against a turnip hoe somewhere in East Virginia, singing 'Barbara Allen' to the man from the University with the portable tape-recorder." But the listener without-whom-we-cannot-afford-to-be is not the person I had centrally in mind when I put this book together. I was thinking of that wide, wonderful, and diverse cross section of humanity — those folks who get itchy fingers and a tickle in the throat when an opportunity comes along to *do* something about folk music: those middle-aged accountants, high school dropouts, part-time executives, full-time intellectuals, classroom teachers, trapped technicians, bored bankers, radicals, moderates, mavericks, and misfits, who maintain their sanity in the age of instant music by doing it themselves — the hard way. I've tried to make life easier for them by putting some of the hard choices they have to make all together between the covers of one book.

I've tried to show some of the diversity and the dynamics of the twentieth-century American folk song heritage. The songs — ballads and southern mountain songs, Negro spirituals and blues, songs of the cowboys and hoboes and prospectors and railroad men and sailors, topical songs based on sensational calamities, protest songs of laborers — indicate the richness and the range of our tradition. The performance variations and alternatives I have suggested emphasize the dynamic quality of that tradition.

For those who want mainly to learn and perform these songs, I have included popular, standard, contemporary versions — and suggested ways of changing, adapting, and enhancing them. I have also tried to point out significant lyrical, melodic, and harmonic subtleties that might be overlooked by the casual performer. For those who want to hear how others perform and interpret the songs, I have listed and sometimes described available recordings. To encourage deeper involvement and broader understanding, I have suggested creative activities and research projects and have provided information about the mood, idiom, and contextual reference.

The general introduction to the book describes and discusses the various classes, or genres, that make up this collection. Although the songs themselves are arranged alphabetically, I have emphasized relationships and interrelationships throughout. In the introductory commentaries prefacing each song, I have pointed out thematic, melodic, and textual relationships and shown how these elements are borrowed from one song for another and how new songs are developed from these elements. In addition, I have identified the genre to which the songs belong and, in the index, have cross-referenced the songs by genre. For instance, under the classification "murder ballads" the various murder ballads in the collection are listed—so that you can explore similarities within these groupings. The indexed categories may also be an aid in programming.

The introductory commentaries provide background information: the customs, folkways, settings, circumstances, and historical events reflected in the songs; some of the controversies over the "proper" interpretation of some of the songs; definitions of obsolete words or references; the use of symbols. Some of the commentaries present the thoughts of leading folk specialists on various aspects of the songs. And from time to time I involve the reader in research processes—scholarly sleuthing into the background, development, and meaning of the songs. For those who will want to go beyond the scope of this book for more information and understanding, the bibliography provides a convenient guide to further study.

All of these suggestions are intended only as a point of departure. The ultimate performance of a song is the responsibility of the reader. Spontaneity and creativity are essential ingredients in a vital folk music tradition, and we can keep our tradition vital by avoiding slavish imitation of others. You will get a lot more enjoyment out of music when you exercise your own creativity and ingenuity to come up with your own unique way of performing a song. Don't worry about hurting folk music—no one has succeeded yet. No one knows where the conscious interest and the commercial exploitation of the current folk music scene will take us. But they aren't likely to do any more harm than the extensive commercialization (by the backroom printer and the sidewalk vendor) that has already taken place. (And that dates back almost to the time the invention of the printing press made mass-media circulation possible and profitable.) The question is whether the tradition is as safe in the hands of the neighborhood minstrel (surrounded by records, books, radio, television, and folk song societies, workshops, festivals, and magazines) as it was in the hands of the medieval minstrel, the forecastle entertainer, the street singer, and the backwoods banjoist. I think it is. If his interpretation lacks intrinsic and lasting appeal, it will die with him. The song itself lives on. And even in 2066 you'll be able to find someone in a remote corner of East Megalopolis who never heard of all the to-do about folk music but who learned a few verses of "Barbara Allen" from his daddy and will be glad to run through them for the man from the University with the supersonic recorder.

ACKNOWLEDGMENTS

A family enthusiasm for singing first sparked my interest in folk music. My father's interest and professional activities in the broad field of folklore deepened my involvement. And early contact with folk music specialists like William Owens and John Lomax made an enthusiast of me before I was old enough to appreciate the depth and significance of their contributions. Ultimately, I became a devoted student of the work of Francis James Child, Cecil James Sharp, Phillips Barry, Frank Clyde Brown, Vance Randolph, B. A. Botkin, and the many other scholars and collectors who have contributed so much to the preservation and understanding of our folk music heritage. I have learned much from the performers themselves — particularly Sam Hinton. Irwin Silber and his *Sing Out* (which is more an institution than a magazine) have contributed greatly to my education. A host of unsung, but singing, heroes have provided me with encouragement and a living laboratory for the study of contemporary singing. They include Jim McDaniel, Jack Thornton, Burton Newmark, and my three young aficionados, Jamie, Scot, and Becky. I am indebted to Fawcett World Library and to the Sam Fox Publishing Company, publishers of my earlier books, *Hootenanny Tonight!* and *Folk Song Fest*, for permission to reprint some material which originally appeared in those volumes. This particular book owes more to Dorothy Ohliger than anyone else. Her sharp eye and deft questioning always demanded more and better instead of less and easier. She also taught me how to make a Hungarian omelette (first you steal an egg). It's not ethical, but it has advantages over laying one. And all of the responsibilities in that department belong to me — not the good-hearted accessories named above.

James F. Leisy

Portola Valley, California

INTRODUCTION

Folk songs, depending on your definition preference, are songs that have that certain sound — that ring of truth; songs of the people, by the people, and for the people; songs that were fashioned by ordinary folk (and maybe some extraordinary folk) and passed on to other ordinary folk, refashioned a little, and then passed on again. You may insist that "they must have been submitted to the process of oral transmission," must be the "product of evolution" and dependent "on the circumstances of continuity, variation, and selection." You may even require a certain specific number of years for that evolutionary process to have taken place before the song qualifies, by your standards, as a folk song. Or you may be willing to lower the barriers a little — or a whole lot — to let some of your favorites into the hallowed inner circle. It's fashionable to disagree about the definition of folk song. If you're going to be or already are a folk song insider, you really should take a position and argue heatedly for it. It helps to pass the time while you are replacing a broken E string on your guitar.

It would be nice to have a universally acceptable definition for folk songs. Perhaps one of these days we shall. In the meantime, it may be more rewarding to focus our attention on some of the areas in which there is general agreement. Many of us have a keen interest in the songs themselves, their entertainment value, and their cultural significance. Quite possibly you'll agree with folklorist Bruno Nettl that "in folklore the most important works of music are probably those which are especially closely tied to the culture and which therefore are the most accurate expressions of its nature and character." That factor in itself makes folk music interesting — and significant — to anyone who is interested in folks and their culture. The folk themselves may or may not care that deeply at any given time or place, but a good many of them have been convinced all along that, whatever you call it or say about it, folk music is entertaining. There are those who argue—with good cause— that musical expression is essential to human existence and that it is, therefore, a much more precious item than many imagine or are willing to admit. But even if you're not absolutely certain that it is essential to soothe the savage breast tunefully, you're probably in favor of entertainment. And who is to say that entertainment isn't essential to human existence.

The vital role of music in the lives of human beings is reflected in its religious and ceremonial uses by primitive people. And contemporary primitives have been observed to sing and invent songs as a seemingly necessary part of hunting, fishing, and other activities. The primitive uses of music have led to considerable speculation among specialists concerning the essential role of music for primitives as a special form of communication with the supernatural. When you look at any advanced culture, you find that musical habits have a firm hold and all sorts of songs are being sung by all kinds of people for any number of more "earthy" purposes. You find children singing as they play, playing as they sing, and combining the two in singing games. The singing game is just a shuffle or two away from singing and dancing, or dancing while someone else sings or plays a song designed for dancing. Young lovers and old may be found living or reliving romantic overtures to the accompaniment of a traditional love song. And a lot of work just doesn't get done without a song to lighten the load.

Folk songs reflect the traditions and the heritage of the people. They are also strongly influenced by the music and the musical styles of the society's most cultivated musicians. The folk musician and the cultivated musician aren't as far apart as many think, and each shows evidence of having at least an inner ear open unconsciously to the other.

The contemporary American folk song heritage is an expression of America's nature and character, its melting-pot culture, its diverse and dynamic qualities. As we go racing through the last half of the twentieth century, recovering from the greatest revival of conscious interest in folk music the world has ever known, we can't help but be aware of the countless blessings the movement has brought us. We've collected, preserved, and dished out (though frequently in too gross a serving) a folk song potpourri fine enough—and varied enough—to fit every taste. The diversity must have been inevitable from the beginning. The main body of songs and singing styles came originally from different and distinctive cultures—predominantly British and African. As an American culture and personality developed, the songs and singing styles became part of a new and dynamic native tradition—a living singing tradition that continues to change, to blend, and to grow.

When the early settlers began to establish the thirteen colonies on the eastern coast of the United States, they brought British folk music with them. These traditions are the oldest and most extensive found among white Americans. The folk music of the less than one million Indians who were here first has never been fused with the white American heritage.

The traditional English and Scottish ballads were an important and interesting part of the British folk music brought to this country in the early days. This ballad tradition survived, perhaps thrived, in its purest form in the mountain regions of New England and the Appalachians in the South. Scholars have traced these ballads back as far as the fifteenth and sixteenth centuries in a ballad-singing tradition that is very much older than any one of the ballads traced. The most important work done in this field was by the nineteenth-century American scholar Francis James Child, who collected and published over 1,300 variants of 305 ballads.

The ballad is a narrative song in which a story is told in several stanzas. The older versions sometimes required over a hundred verses to tell the story; the versions of contemporary balladeers tend to run shorter in length. The stories deal with universal themes of romance, adventure, battle, the supernatural, and so on, as well as with historical events. George Lyman Kittredge, Child's brilliant student and successor, describes the ballad as "a song that tells a story, or — to take the other point of view — a story told in song . . . a short narrative poem, adapted for singing, simple in plot and metrical structure, divided into stanzas, and characterized by complete impersonality so far as the author or singer is concerned."

Most ballad scholars and singers have stressed the importance of singing the ballads in a straightforward, detached manner. They feel that any dramatics by the singer detract from the emotional impact and the dramatic tension supplied by the plot of the story itself. Traditionally, ballads were sung without accompaniment, although occasionally the dulcimer, the guitar, the banjo, and other plucked instruments have been used to accompany ballad singing. Today, the guitar is probably the most widely used instrument for accompaniment. When accompaniment is used, the style is simple and quiet, usually with very little harmonic change in the chording of the instrument. In the more isolated mountain areas, many singers retain a very old European style of singing the ballads. In this style the melody is embellished through the addition of grace notes and other ornaments that are not essential but add interest to the melodic line.

The history and legend of man have recorded many disasters both great and small. A very important part of that record is the folk song or ballad that inevitably crops up after a disaster or calamity, and lives on in oral tradition to tell its cheerless tale. Many of these ballads and songs began as cheap commercial songs, printed on one side of a broad sheet of paper and peddled through the streets like newspapers. This commercial-song business flourished in Europe and America for several centuries and was the forerunner of the popular-song industry of today. Executions and spectacular murders and other crimes were appealing to the commercial ballad makers of yesteryear, who relied heavily on sensationalism and timeliness to sell their wares. Of the many ballads written about the sinking of the *Titanic*, one contained a date line a day ahead of the disaster. Distortion and confusion of fact cannot be entirely blamed on the folk process, although it contributed its share; the peddlers were much more interested in fast sales than they were in accuracy and objectivity — and quality. Consequently, the quality of these *broadside* (or *stall*, or *street*) ballads and songs was generally bad, and very few of them survived. Those that have survived have been shaped, refined, and improved by the folk process and accorded an important place in our folk song literature.

Benjamin Franklin, well known for his many and varied talents, was a broadside-ballad composer at the early age of nine: "My brother put me on composing occasional ballads. One was called the Lighthouse Tragedy; the other was a sailor's song on the taking of Teach [Blackbeard, the pirate]. They were wretched stuff, in the Grub Street ballad style; and when they were printed he sent me about the town to sell them. The first sold wonderfully, the event being recent, having made a great noise. . . ."

From the singing traditions of sailors, both at work and at play, we have inherited a distinctive body of folk songs. The work songs were called chanteys (pronounced "shanties").

The origin of chanteying is typically obscured by the lack of written records of its early history and development. The earliest-known recorded reference to singing at sea may be found in a fifteenth-century manuscript, *The Book of the Wanderings of Brother Felix Fabri* (a Dominican friar). A translation of this old manuscript (Fabri's account of his voyage to Palestine aboard a Venetian galley) is located in the Library of the Palestine Pilgrims' Text Society in London. Brother Fabri refers to those "who sing when work is going on, because work at sea is very heavy, and is only carried on by a concert between one who sings out orders and the laborers who sing in response." There is reason to believe that the earliest singing at sea was probably a very simple vocalization or "singing out" by individuals as they worked. These individual efforts then led to group songs or chants.

One of the simplest and most natural forms of group singing involves a solo phrase or line followed by a simple, standardized response from the group. This solo with choral response is a basic form common to many types of folk singing—the spiritual, the field song, the singing game or dance, as well as the sea chantey.

The art of chanteying achieved its highest development in the early nineteenth century aboard American and British ships engaged in the vigorous, highly competitive merchant (or packet) trade that flourished on the high seas as the industrial revolution began to dominate the activity ashore. A thriving competitive environment, which attracted men of vigor and action, combined with the relative isolation of life aboard ship, no doubt contributed much to the attention given to chanteying and to the elaboration and quality that evolved. The nineteenth century was truly the era of superb ships and seamen, and the same can be said of their songs. That era ended when technological advances in ship construction made the old square-rigger obsolete.

The chanteys varied in form from simple one-line solos with a short response to more elaborate constructions—multiple solo lines with longer choral responses, or songs sung entirely in chorus (see "The Drunken Sailor"). To a great extent the kind of chantey used depended on the kind of work being done. The solo lines were sung by the chanteyman (an able-bodied seaman with a talent for singing, remembering songs, and improvising), and the responses were sung by the crew as they worked. Although most of the chanteys were fairly standardized in form, content, and tune, the chanteyman sang freely in his own individual style and improvised both words and music with considerable variation from established patterns. He used unique embellishments, unusual stresses and holds, and special effects to add interest and color to his singing. The choruses were sung in unison to established melodic patterns, although Negro crews were known to harmonize. The chanteys were rarely accompanied instrumentally; sometimes, however, a fiddler or an accordionist would play along when he could be spared from the work itself for this luxury.

Although the chanteys grew out of the life and work of the sailor and were essentially created and developed on the job, ideas, phrases, and tunes were frequently borrowed from songs learned ashore. These inspirations came from many sources, including English, Irish, American, and Negro traditions. Borrowed songs and ideas were quickly remolded to fit the new environment, so that "after a number of years, they became unconsciously influenced by the pungent, briny odor and surging roar and rhythm of the ocean."

In addition to the work songs, the sailor had his forecastle (foc's'l) songs and ballads, which helped pass the evenings on the long, lonely voyages and accompanied roistering while in port. In *Roll and Go, Songs of American Sailormen,* Joanna C. Colcord describes a typical setting for the leisure-time singing of the sailor aboard ship:

> When the day's work was over, supper eaten and the mess-kids put away, and the pipes or cheeks, as the case might be, filled with strong plug tobacco, came the sailor's time of leisure. During the "dog-watch," in the early evening, both watches were on deck, gathered about the main hatch in pleasant weather, or stowed away in sheltered spots when it was inclement. Singing, dancing and yarn-spinning were then the order of the day; cherished instruments were brought out, perhaps a squeaky fiddle, or an accordion, beloved of the sailor and hated, for some unknown reason, by every master mariner I ever knew. Happy the "crowd" that had a "nigger singer," for he had a repertoire all his own. Songs popular ashore had their place in these evening concerts, of course — sentimental songs for choice — but never the sailor songs so favored by amateurs ashore.*

Though the trail-driving American cowboy has vanished from the scene, his songs still live on. Between 1867 and 1890, over forty thousand cowboys took part in an enormous and hazardous enterprise — driving 10,000,000 cattle to northern markets, where they were sold for about $250,000,000. The cowboy, like the seaman, sang as he worked — and his songs have become part of our folk song tradition. Widespread interest in and enthusiasm for cowboy songs resulted largely from the work of John A. Lomax, who first brought them to national attention. In his 1910 publication, *Cowboy Songs and Other Frontier Ballads,* Lomax tells us:

> A trip up the trail made a distinct break in the monotonous life of the big ranches, often situated hundreds of miles from where the conventions of society were observed. The ranch community consisted usually of the boss, the straw-boss, the cowboys proper, the horse wrangler, and the cook — often a Negro. These men lived on terms of practical equality. Except in the case of the boss, there was little difference in the amounts paid each for his services. Society, then, was here reduced to its lowest terms. The work of the men, their daily experiences, their thoughts, their interests, were all in common. Such a community had necessarily to turn to itself for entertainment. Songs sprang up naturally, some of them tender and familiar lays of childhood, others original compositions, all genuine, however crude and unpolished. Whatever the most gifted man could produce must bear the criticism of the entire camp, and agree with the ideas of a group of men. In this sense, therefore, any song that came from such a group would be the joint product of a number of them, telling perhaps the story of some stampede they had all

*From *Roll and Go, Songs of American Sailormen* by Joanna C. Colcord. Copyright © MCMXXXVIII by W. W. Norton and Company, Inc., New York. Copyright renewed 1966 by the Boone County State Bank, Lebanon, Indiana.

fought to turn, some crime in which they all shared equally, some comrade's tragic death which they had all witnessed. The song-making did not cease as the men went up the trail. Indeed the songs were here utilized for very practical ends. Not only were sharp, rhythmic yells—sometimes beaten into verse—employed to stir up lagging cattle, but also during the long watches the night-guards, as they rode round and round the herd, improvised cattle lullabies which quieted the animals and soothed them to sleep. Some of the best of the so-called "dogie songs" seem to have been created for the purpose of preventing cattle stampedes—such songs coming straight from the heart of the cowboy, speaking familiarly to his herd in the stillness of the night.*

The cowboy borrowed many of his ideas and texts from poems, and many texts and tunes from older songs and other traditions and popular sources. The sea song was a favorite source, perhaps because of the similarity between life on the rolling, lonely prairie and that on the sea. The relaxed and uninhibited western singing style later merged with the hillbilly style of the southern mountains to lay the groundwork for country and western popular-music styles.

Traditional songs of the inhabitants of the southern mountain country may be found throughout this book. Since most of the early residents of the isolated mountain communities had come from the British Isles, they preserved almost intact the traditional songs and ballads of fifteenth- and sixteenth-century Britain. As the twentieth century approached, technological innovations in transportation and communication removed the natural barriers that separated these people from the rest of the world, and outside influences began to affect and change this traditional music. A new style and tradition then emerged—a style usually called hillbilly, mountain, or country music today. To the inexperienced ear "all of this music sounds alike," but it is actually composed of many distinguishable musical mixes, including the old ballad tradition, the Negro styles, the yodeling falsetto of Mexican hillbillies, the western singing style, and—more recently—the bluegrass style. The dominant singing style is derived from the traditional high-pitched singing style, with vocal ornamentations, that had been retained in the mountains from earlier British traditions. Harmonization usually consists of one voice above the melody lead and the frequent use of minor intervals.

This particular music is defined almost as much by the style in which it is accompanied as by the singing and the songs themselves. The fiddle had been played at country dances and hoedowns since the early days of the pioneers. The dance-music tradition of the British Isles provided the basis for the instrumental accompaniment and the style, and newer music was created in imitation of the tradition. Much of the fiddle style, imitative of the bagpipes, is distinctive in its use of double stops (two notes played simultaneously) and slides. Just prior to the Civil War, the minstrel show brought the banjo, originally derived from the three-stringed West African *bania*, to the mountains. A fifth, drone, string was added to the banjo, and the instrumental accompaniment for dancing began to grow when the banjo was tuned modally to accompany the fiddle in playing the melody between verses of a hoedown tune. The Spanish guitar and the mandolin from Greece and Italy were soon

*From *Cowboy Songs and Other Frontier Ballads,* Copyright © 1910, 1916 by Sturgis and Walton Company. The Macmillan Company, New York.

added. The autoharp, adapted from the German zither, the mouth harp, string bass, and the *dobro* (an unamplified Hawaiian steel guitar) all became acceptable instruments for mountain-country string bands. The actual instrumentation used in most bands depended on the availability of the instruments themselves, musicians who could play them, and the amount of money that could be earned to support the musicians.

The Negro in America—with his work songs, cries, whoops, hollers, play-party songs, spirituals, gospel songs, and blues—has created what is probably our most original and distinctive folk music. Negro music appears to be such a blending of the cultural elements brought to America that scholars will be arguing its basic makeup and subtleties for a long time. It was influenced first by traditional European and British music and musical styles and, later, by hillbilly, western, and urban traditions. And, of course, it has given as much to other traditions as it has borrowed. "But," says Harold Courlander (in *Negro Folk Music, U.S.A.*), "with all the permutations and combinations, there remains the reality that, taken as a whole, the Negro folk music idiom is an integral and somewhat separate phenomenon and has a character completely its own." There is uniqueness in the use of the "blues tonality" (flatted third and seventh notes) as well as other idiosyncrasies of tone, interval, rhythm, and harmony. There is uniqueness in the Negro's special vocal timbre, in his way of changing words for musical and rhythmic effects, in his special use of falsetto tones, of patting and handclapping as an accompaniment to singing, and of buzzing and rattling and "moaning and groaning" sounds.

The spiritual, or anthem, of the American Negro is generally considered the most important of the unique contributions he has made to the folk music world. Courlander describes this religious folk music as follows:

> Negro religious songs include a wide range of styles, idioms, and substance. There are staid, square-measured songs that strongly reflect white hymns of an earlier day; rocking and reeling songs that truly shake the rafters; two part prayer songs of polyphonous character; spirited tunes that are nothing less than marches; shouts that call for percussive effects by clapping and foot stamping; songs in which popular musical instruments such as tambourines, guitars, drums, and harmonicas provide instrumental dynamics; songs that are sung quietly and songs that put people on their feet; ecstatic moans and groans; religious songs of street singers that are almost indistinguishable from blues; strident gospel songs calling on sinners to reform; and songs which transpose scenes from the Bible into moving, immediate, colloquial, and, often, magnificently dramatic terms. So broad, indeed, is the realm of Negro religious music that the customary title "spiritual" is patently inadequate to describe it. In fact, this word is not used by some people who sing these songs, the term "anthem" being preferred.*

The simplest form of the spiritual, and the most common, is the leader-response structure that occurs, for instance, in the beautiful and majestic "Swing Low, Sweet Chariot." In more complex forms the response is lengthened into a full refrain—as in "Steal Away," in which the solo lines are followed by a chorus in harmony.

*From *Negro Folk Music, U.S.A.* by Harold Courlander. Copyright © 1963 Columbia University Press, New York.

The *blues*, though chiefly a product of the twentieth century, grew out of the "holler and the moan" with which the Negro accompanied his work. As the work song moved into the city along with the Negro, the blues evolved into a commercial product. It went on to become the very foundation of jazz, and its influence has been felt in almost every form of musical composition from the hillbilly songs of "Tin Pan Valley" in Tennessee to the most serious works of our major composers.

Despite, and probably accounting for, the universal appeal of the blues, it is highly personal in its conception. The blues, to the composer-singer, is a way of talking things over with himself. Probably more blues choruses have been composed for an audience of one than have ever been performed for the mass media of radio and the phonograph record. This may be one of the unique aspects of the blues as a folk song type. Although we are all collaborators in the composition of a folk song when we sing what we remember and make up what we have forgotten, few of us have the originality or talent to start from scratch with the entire composition. The blues provides a ready structure for original and primitive composition, particularly in its simplest form: the first line repeated twice, followed by a second, rhyming line to complete the thought or phrase. The repetition of the first line allows the composer-singer (or remembering singer) time to come up with the closing line. Some typical *floating blues verses* (verses that show up in first one song and then another) are:

When I had money, had friends from miles around.
When I had money, had friends from miles around.
Now ain't got no money, my friends cannot be found.

Sittin' in the jail house; face turned to the wall.
Sittin' in the jail house; face turned to the wall.
Red-headed woman was the cause of it all.

Michigan water it tastes like cherry wine.
Michigan water it tastes like cherry wine.
But this Nashville water it drinks like turpentine.

My gal's got teeth like a lighthouse on the sea.
My gal's got teeth like a lighthouse on the sea.
Every time she smiles she throws a light on me.

I wish I was a catfish, swimmin' in the sea.
I wish I was a catfish, swimmin' in the sea.
I'd have all the pretty women fishin' after me.

This here city is the best in this here land.
This here city is the best in this here land.
I got the world in a jug and the stopper in my hand.

Besides the sailor, the cowboy, and the Negro, many other working groups have added their songs to our tradition — the railroader, the farmer, the prospector, the miner, the pioneer, the lumberjack, the hobo, and the present-day industrial worker. Since the work was hard and conditions often rough and the pay low, many of the songs complained a little and protested a good deal. As a special class, however, the "protest song" is most closely associated with union activities of the 1930s. Most of the songs of social or political protest were so related to current situations that they quickly fell into disuse and disappeared. For this reason, most scholars do not consider many protest songs to be folk songs by definition. However, the folk song revival in this century owes much to the union singers and song leaders who mixed folk songs and union songs to provide a "voice of the people." By so doing, they laid a foundation in the 1930s and 1940s for the folk song revival heights of the 1950s and 1960s.

In twentieth-century America, all of the distinctive musical traditions we have discussed continue to blend with each other as cultural barriers are broken and blurred. The exchange of ideas, styles, and techniques continues apace. New adaptations, new variations, new songs emerge in new contexts. But they are clearly built upon the traditions of the past. The dynamic, evolutionary folk process in music lives—despite the lamentations and warnings of some folk music specialists, who fear that commercialization, mass circulation, and consciousness of the process will destroy it. But it is not the *doing*—the rearranging, the rewriting, the restyling, the borrowing —that we need fear. The folk process has always eliminated the mediocrity resulting from opportunistic attempts to capitalize commercially on folk music—and I am confident that it will continue to do so. We need fear only an apathetic response to folk music—*doing nothing* about it. But nothing on the contemporary scene suggests apathy. All of the evidence shows we are doing more than we've ever done before. Our concern for preserving the heritage of the past should not interfere with the building of a heritage for the future—and it won't.

A

*...the leafy
green dome*

*Can she bake
a cherry pie...*

*As I was going
to Derby...*

ABILENE

There's a saying in Texas that Dallas is where the East ends and Fort Worth is where the West begins. All you have to do to prove it is head out west from Dallas on Highway 80. The country looks different and it feels different. About one hundred and fifty-three miles west of Fort Worth you hit Abilene—and then you really know you're in the West. There's plenty of open space between towns and people. Folks out there don't stand on ceremony, and they're friendly to strangers if the strangers are down to earth and friendly too. When some unknown folk composer saw what some of the rest of the country was like, he expressed his sentiments in this blues-idiom song.

The first version below follows a traditional blues pattern and is easy to chord on the guitar. I learned the second version from my daughter, who learned it from her teacher, Richard Jaqua. You don't have to read music to follow the accompaniment. Just strum the chords in the circles and pick the runs in the rectangles. (The first measure reads: strum three times using a C chord and then pick out the bass run by plucking the A string while depressing it at the third fret, plucking the D string while it is open, and then plucking the D string while it is depressed at the first fret.) The arrangement is simplified for beginners, but you can make it more elaborate by varying the strum.

The first verse is usually sung as a chorus, at the beginning and after each of the other verses. There's nothing wrong with shortening the performance by leaving out some of the verses included here.

Recordings: Bob Gibson (Riverside, RLP 12 806); *Folk Song Festival Freaturing Walter Forbes* (RCA Victor, LPM 2670)—produced by Anita Kerr and Chet Atkins; and a pop-country version by George Hamilton IV (RCA Victor, 8184).

FIRST VERSION

2. I sit alone most every night
   Watching the trains as they pull out of sight.
   Don't I wish they'd carry me back
   To Abilene, my Abilene.

3. Old empty boxcar standing all alone;
   Wheels all rusted, it ain't no home;
   But it'll take me home
   To Abilene, my Abilene.

4. Been to Chicago, Frisco, too;
   New York City just won't do.
   So I'll be headin' back
   To Abilene, my Abilene.

5. Saw New York City in the drizzlin' rain;
   Headlights flickerin' on my window pane;
   Made me so lonesome for
   My Abilene, old Abilene.

6. Crowded city—ain't nothin' free—
   Nothin' in this town for me.
   So I'll be headin' home
   To Abilene, my Abilene.

SECOND VERSION

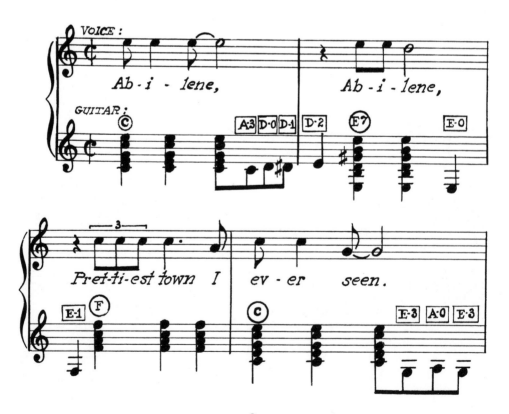

ACRES OF CLAMS

The tunes that survive the competitive struggle for attention—and retention—are few. It's a rare melody that holds an audience for a second hearing. And the ones that live through a few decades of changing fashions in music are extremely rare. Many songwriters recognize the value of these durable tunes and borrow them to enhance their own productions. It's a lot safer to collaborate with a proven melody than it is to gamble on an untested composer.

The Irish had a tune for a patriotic ballad, "Men of the West," which had the magic formula for longevity. The melody was first introduced in America in 1838, when it was imported with the lyric to a comic ditty, "Old Rosin the Beau." "Old Rosin" became a popular drinking song on the western frontier. In the 1840s the Whigs borrowed the tune for two campaign songs for Henry Clay, "The Mill-Boy of the Slashes":

> Come forward, ye brave sons of Neptune,
> Come forward without more delay,
> And rally around your protector,
> The statesman, the patriot, Clay.

and "Old Hal of the West":

> Hark! freedom peals far in her thunder,
> Her lightning no force can arrest,
> She drives the foul army asunder.
> "Hail, gallant old Hal o' the West!"

3

The Whigs and Old Hal, the orphan mill-boy from the Slashes district of Hanover County in Virginia, lost—but the tune survived the defeat (and the lyrics) to campaign again in 1860. This time the tune was on the winning side of one of the bitterest campaigns in history. The "winning" lyric to "Lincoln and Liberty" was written by F. A. Simpkins. It was back in the losers' column again in 1872 as a "Straight-out Democrat" against General Grant.

In the meantime, the gold fever in the far West had created conditions that led to the sentiments expressed in Judge Francis D. Henry's "Acres of Clams." It became the state song of Washington in 1889, when that state was formed.

And that's by no means the end of the story. You can't help but suspect that this fine old melody lingers on, in a different mood and altered form, in "Willow Garden" (see Index). It wouldn't surprise me at all if one of these days soon somebody came up with a new set of words.

Recordings: "Acres of Clams"—John Greenway (Riverside, RLP 12 619), Win Stracke (Bally, Bal 12013). Variations: "Rosin the Beau"—A. L. Lloyd (Riverside, RLP 12 618). "Lincoln and Liberty"—Hermes Nye (Folkways, FA 2187).

4

I have been fre-quent-ly sold. ——

2. For one who got rich by mining
   I saw there were hundreds grew poor;
   I made up my mind to try farming,
   The only pursuit that is sure.
   The only pursuit that is sure,
   The only pursuit that is sure,
   I made up my mind to try farming,
   The only pursuit that is sure.

3. I rolled up my grub in my blanket,
   I left all my tools on the ground,
   I started one morning to shank it
   For the country they call Puget Sound.
   For the country they call Puget Sound,
   For the country they call Puget Sound,
   I started one morning to shank it,
   For the country they call Puget Sound.

4. No longer the slave of ambition,
   I laugh at the world and its shams,
   And think of my happy condition
   Surrounded by acres of clams.
   Surrounded by acres of clams.
   Surrounded by acres of clams,
   And think of my happy condition
   Surrounded by acres of clams.

OLD ROSIN THE BEAU

1. I live for the good of my nation
   And my sons are all growing low;
   But I hope the next generation
   Will resemble old Rosin, the Beau.
   Resemble old Rosin, the Beau,
   Resemble old Rosin, the Beau,
   I hope that the next generation
   Will resemble old Rosin, the Beau.

   Continue, as above:

2. I've traveled this country over
   And now to the next I will go,
   For I know that good quarters await me
   To welcome old Rosin, the Beau.
       To welcome old Rosin, the Beau (etc.)

3. In the gay round of pleasures I've traveled.
   Nor will I behind leave a foe,
   And when my companions are jovial
   They will drink to old Rosin, the Beau.

4. But my life is now drawn to a closing,
   As all will at last be so.

So we'll take a full bumper at parting
To the name of old Rosin, the Beau.

5. When I'm dead and laid out on the counter,
The people all making a show,
Just sprinkle plain whiskey and water
On the corpse of old Rosin, the Beau.

6. Then pick me out six trusty fellows
And let them stand all in a row,
And dig a big hole in the meadow
And in it toss Rosin, the Beau.

7. Then bring out two little brown jugs:
Place one at my head and my toe;
And do not forget to scratch on them
The name of old Rosin, the Beau.

LINCOLN AND LIBERTY

1. Hurrah for the choice of the nation,
Our chieftain so brave and so true;
We'll go for the great reformation,
For Lincoln and liberty, too.

2. We'll go for the son of Kentucky,
The hero of Hoosierdom through;
The pride of the suckers* so lucky,
For Lincoln and liberty, too.

3. Our David's good sling is unerring,
The Slavocrats' giant he slew,
Then shout for the Freedom preferring,
For Lincoln and liberty, too.

4. They'll find what by felling and mauling
Our railmaker statesman can do;
For the people are everywhere calling
For Lincoln and liberty, too.

5. Then up with our banner so glorious,
The star-spangled red, white and blue,
We'll fight till our banner is victorious,
For Lincoln and liberty, too.

*A slang expression for natives of Illinois.

ALL GOD'S CHILDREN GOT SHOES

Scholars have taken a keen interest in symbolism in spirituals. The most extreme views envision composers working away constantly to create hidden double meanings for the in-group understanding and appreciation of the singers. In line with this principle, John Lovell, Jr., advanced this interpretation for "All God's Children Got Shoes":

"When I get to heav'm" means when I get free. It is a Walt Whitman "I," meaning any slave, present or future. If I personally don't, my children or

6

grandchildren or my friend on the other side of the plantation will. What a glorious sigh these people breathed when one of their group slipped through to freedom! What a tragic intensity they felt when one was shot down trying to escape! So, the group speaks in the group way, all for one, one for all. "When I get to heav'm, gonna put on my shoes," that means he has talents, abilities, programs manufactured, ready to wear. On Douglass' plantation the slaves bossed, directed, charted everything—horse-shoeing, cart-mending, plow-repairing, coopering, grinding, weaving, "all completely done by slaves." But he has much finer shoes than that which he has no choice to wear. He does not mean that he will outgrow work, but simply that he will make his work count for something, which slavery prevents. When he gets a chance, he says, he is going to "shout all over God's heav'm"—make every section of his community feel his power. He knows he can do it.*

John Greenway replies to this interpretation in *American Folk Songs of Protest:*

This is certainly a plausible interpretation of the spiritual, undeniably stimulating, and just possibly valid, but there is a good deal of speciousness in it too. The first sentence is plain enough in significance—"When I get to heav'm" means when I get free—and not too difficult to apprehend. But to continue probing for hidden meanings like this excerpt was utterly beyond the capacity of most slaves. To comprehend such symbolism as is contained in the last four sentences of Lovell's interpretation even after the meaning had been explained would impute to the slave an understanding of literary symbolism possessed by few people today who are trained to recognize such buried meanings. It makes of Uncle Tom an enigmatist as skillful as Dylan Thomas. If Lovell's conclusions are accepted, a theme of symbolic protest could be found in every spiritual, but too many spirituals and Negro religious songs are transparent conflations of biblical text and temporal application to make this theory tenable.

But it is just as rash to conclude that there is no symbolism in the spirituals as to state that they are all symbolic. The spirituals were all things to all men; of three Negroes singing "I Got Shoes," one Negro might interpret the shoes as his latent abilities, mordant in a slave society; another might see himself literally strolling through heaven in golden footwear; for the third singer the word "shoes" might not arouse any image in the extensional world whatever.†

With a few minutes of instruction and practice you can make any group sound like professionals by showing them how to harmonize using the tones of the chords on the *heaven* in measures eight, nine, ten, thirteen, fourteen, and sixteen in the simple arrangement below. Encourage hand clapping on the downbeats.

Recording: Lucretia West (Westminister, WP 6063).

*From "The Social Implications of the Negro Spiritual" by John Lovell, Jr., *Journal of Negro Education*, October 1939, pp. 641–642.
†From *American Folk Songs of Protest* by John Greenway. Copyright © 1953 by University of Pennsylvania Press, Philadelphia; 1965 by John Greenway.

I got a shoe, you got a shoe,

All God's chil-dren got shoes. When I get to Heav-en gon-na

put on my shoes, Im gon-na tromp all ov-er God's

(Melody)

Heav-en,— Heav-en,— Heav-en,—

(Harmony)

Ev-ry-bo-dy talk-in' 'bout Heav-en aint a-go-in' there,

Heav-en,— Heav-en,—Gonna tromp all ov-er God's Heav-en.

2. I got a robe, you got a robe,
   Gonna shout all over God's heaven.

3. I got a harp, you got a harp,
   Gonna play all over God's heaven.

4. I got a song, you got a song,
   Gonna sing all over God's heaven.

5. I got wings, you got wings,
   Gonna fly all over God's heaven.

8

ALL MY TRIALS

This lullaby-like spiritual seems to have a background similar to the one ascribed to "Kum Ba Ya" (see Index). Apparently it originated with a Baptist hymn current in the South after the Civil War and was carried into the folk tradition of the Bahamas on the boats plying between the West Indies and southern ports. Eventually, it was "rediscovered" and brought back to this country to become a favorite of twentieth-century folk song revivalists.

The Spaniards originally brought slaves to the West Indies, and it later became a center of the slave trade. The Negroes who worked on the boats provided a convenient transportation service for traditions between the Negroes on the plantations of the South and those in the West Indies.

Recordings: Joan Baez (Vanguard, VRS 9078); Cynthia Gooding (Elektra, EKL 107).

Hush, lit - tle ba - by, don't you cry. You know your moth-er is bound to die.___ All _____ my trials, Lord, soon be ov - er.

Chorus

Too late, my broth-er, too late, but nev - er mind. ___ All _____ my trials, Lord, soon be ov — er.

2. The river of Jordan is mighty cold.
   It chills the body but not the soul.
   All my trials, Lord, soon be over.

3. I've got a little book with pages three,
   And every page spells liberty.
   All my trials, Lord, soon be over. (*Chorus*)

4. If religion was a thing that money could buy,
   The rich would live and the poor would die.
   All my trials, Lord, soon be over.

5. There is a tree in paradise
   The Christians call the tree of life.
   All my trials, Lord, soon be over.

6. There's a little white dove a-flyin' in the blue;
   Gonna show what the power of love can do.
   All my trials, Lord, soon be over. (*Chorus*)

ALL THE GOOD TIMES

Many folk songs contain what are frequently called "floating verses" —verses that show up in almost the same wording and form in first one song and then another. This southern mountain song seems almost to have been fashioned by setting a series of floating verses to music. The tune has the same haunting, nostalgic quality found in "Goodnight, Irene" and "Beautiful, Beautiful Brown Eyes." I'm surprised it has never achieved the almost universal popularity those two songs enjoy. It has, however, long been a favorite of commercial country music devotees.

Recordings: Bill Clifton (Blue Ridge Records—collector's item); Lester Flatt and Earl Scruggs, with the title "Good Times Are Past and Gone" (Columbia, CL 1830); *Mountain Music, Bluegrass Style,* recorded by Mike Seeger (Folkways, FA 2318).

2. I wish to the Lord I'd never been born,
   Or had died when I was young;
   And never had seen your sparkling blue eyes
   Or heard your flattering tongue.

3. Oh, don't you see that distant train
   A-comin' round the bend.
   It'll take me away from this old town;
   Never to return again.

4. Oh, don't you see that lonesome dove
   That flies from pine to pine.
   He's mourning for his own true love
   Just like I mourn for mine.

ANNE BOLEYN

A lot of women have lost their heads over a man. One of the most famous was Anne Boleyn, who was beheaded in 1536 by Bluff King Hal. She was thirty-nine years old at the time and should have known better. But then, her life had been filled with more problems than most of us have to cope with. She had partial hexadactylism, a long word that means she had six fingers on one of her hands. The sixth finger was a stump covered by a nail turned up at the sides. She wore gloves whenever possible to hide her deformity. Legend tells us that Queen Catherine forced her to play cards without gloves in order to expose the deformity to King Henry and thereby gain revenge against her rival. Don't let the lack of universal spelling conventions in those times lead you into mispronouncing Boleyn. It rhymes with pullin'. Anne was the daughter of Sir Thomas Bullen, pronounced the same way. Nowadays the trend toward numbers may eliminate these problems. Instead of a name, you can have a simple-to-pronounce number like 304-569-7885. It's easy to remember, and you can always use "3", perhaps, as a nick-number. And if you prefer anonymity, you can substitute a pseudo-number for your real number.

This song is of uncertain, not folk, origin, but it has been popular with folk song revivalists in recent years.

Recordings: Alan Arkin (Elektra, EKL 21); Oscar Brand (Riverside, RLP 12-825); Dean Gitter (Riverside, RLP 12-636).

11

Anne Bo-leyn was once King Hen-ry's wife — Un-til he had the heads-man bob her hair — Ah, yes, he did her wrong years a-go, — And back she comes each night to tell him so. — With her head tucked un-der-neath her arm, she walks — the blood-y tower. — With her head tucked un-der-neath her arm at the mid-night hour. —

2. Now, when she goes to Henry she's for telling him what's for.
   Ah, yes, she's gonna show him for having split her gore.
   And just in case his headsman wants to give it an encore,
   She's got her head tucked underneath her arm. (*Chorus*)

3. Now, sometimes gay old King Henry throws a spread
   For all his pals and gals, a ghostly crew.
   Now the headsman carves the joint and cuts the bread,
   When in walks Anne Boleyn to queer the do. (*Chorus*)

4. Now the sentries think that Anne is carrying in a rugby ball.
   When dinner's done they'll push the chairs and table to the wall,
   And then they'll choose up sides and kick the queen around the hall,
   With her head tucked underneath her arm. (*Chorus*)

A-ROVING

When the long sea voyage ended and a sailor landed in port with his pockets full of hard-earned pay, he didn't have to think twice about who was going to help him spend it. And though the adventure usually ended the way it does in this old sea ballad, there was always another ship, another port, and another repetition of the same old story. "A-Roving" was probably adapted from a song that originated in the music halls, but the sailors made it their own and sang it both as a ballad and a work song. Since there are ports all over the world, there's no reason to stick to the same one each time you sing this song. Give Amsterdam, Liverpool, Frisco Bay, and all the rest a chance.

There are many versions of "A-Roving" that were passed around by British and American sailors. Many of these are too bawdy to be printed. The song has been found in Dutch, Flemish, and French oral tradition as well. One contemporary version follows the pattern of "Roll Me Over in the Clover" by starting out with:

> I put my hand upon her toe,
> Said she: "You're stooping mighty low."

Toe is then followed by the calf (to which she responds, "You're there by half"), and so on, ending with the denouement:

> 'Twas then she let her garments fall,
> Bless you, young women;
> Said she, "Young man, now you know it all."
> Oh, mind what I do say.
> I took one look and almost died,
> It was secret agent, Henry Hyde,
> I'll go no more a-roving with you, fair maid.

Recordings: Oscar Brand (Chesterfield, CMS 101); Paul Clayton (Tradition, TLP 1005); Alan Mills (Folkways, FA 2312); Milt Okun (Riverside, RLP 12-603).

you, fair maid. A - rov - ing, a - rov - ing Since

rov - ing's been my ru - i - en, I'll go no more a

rov— ing with you, fair maid.

2. The past six months I'd been to sea,
   Bless you, young women;
   The past six months I'd been to sea,
   Oh, mind what I do say.
   The past six months I'd been to sea,
   And, boys, this maid looked good to me.
   I'll go no more a-roving with you, fair maid.

3. Her cheeks were like the roses red,
   Bless you, young women;
   Her cheeks were like the roses red,
   Oh, mind what I do say.
   Her cheeks were like the roses red,
   And her eyes were like twin stars at night.
   I'll go no more a-roving with you, fair maid.

4. I met her walking on the strand,
   Bless you, young women;
   I met her walking on the strand,
   Oh, mind what I do say.
   I met her walking on the strand.
   I said "ahoy" and took her hand.
   I'll go no more a-roving with you, fair maid.

5. She said, "Young man, you're rather free,"
   Bless you, young women;
   She said, "Young man, you're rather free,"
   Oh, mind what I do say.
   She said, "Young man, you're rather free."
   And then turned around and walked with me.
   I'll go no more a-roving with you, fair maid.

6. I took this fair maid for a walk,
   Bless you, young women;
   I took this fair maid for a walk,
   Oh, mind what I do say.
   I took this fair maid for a walk,
   And we had such a lovin' talk.
   I'll go no more a-roving with you, fair maid.

Continue, as before:

7. And didn't I tell her stories, too,
Of the gold we found in Timbuctoo.

8. She swore that she'd be true to me,
But she spent my pay so fast and free.

9. Now scarce had I been gone to sea,
When a soldier took her on his knee.

THE ASH GROVE

This beautiful old Welsh melody provides an opportunity for beginning guitar players to practice a lot of simple chords pleasantly. It may also be played using only three chords (G, D7, and C), but the chords suggested below make it much more interesting. I've added a descant written by Alice Snyder Knuth of San Francisco State College. Get someone to play the descant along with you on a recorder, flute, or the bells. The Welsh version, "Llwyn On," has words too difficult for most of us (e.g., Ym Mhalas Llwyn On gynt, fe drigal pendefig). While the English words are too arty for my taste, they do seem to fit the mood and style of the song.

Recordings: William Clauson (RCA Victor, LPM 1286); Will Holt (Stinson, SLP 64).

The ash grove, how graceful, how plainly 'tis speaking. The

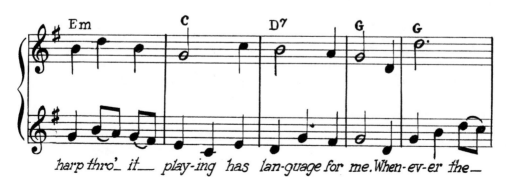

harp thro' it playing has language for me. When-ev-er the

15

light through its branch-es_ is_break-ing, A host of_ kind_

fac - es is gaz - ing on me The_

friends of_ my_ child-hood a-gain are_ be - fore me; Each

step wakes_ a _ mem'-ry as free-ly I roam;

With soft whis-pers la - den, Its leaves rus - tle_

o'er me, The ash-grove, the ash-grove a-lone is my home.

2. My laughter is over, my step loses lightness,
   Old countryside measures steal soft on my ears;
   I only remember the past and its brightness,
   The dear ones I mourn for again gather here.
   From out of the shadows their loving looks greet me,
   And wistfully searching the leafy green dome,
   I find other faces fond bending to greet me,
   The ash grove, the ash grove alone is my home.

B

*...the leafy
green dome*

*Can she bake
a cherry pie...*

*As I was going
to Derby...*

BAILIFF'S DAUGHTER OF ISLINGTON

This ballad is number 105 in the monumental collection of ballads made by Francis James Child in the latter part of the nineteenth century. It was a widely printed broadside ballad of the seventeenth century. This wide circulation in a virtually static form probably explains why little variation has taken place in the ballad despite the many years it has existed.

The return of the disguised lover is a classic theme that appears in other ballads as well. An amusing song current in American colleges uses the disguise gimmick in a different way and gets to the point a lot quicker:

> Don't cry, lady, I'll buy your wilted violets.
> Don't cry, lady, I'll buy your pencils, too.
> Don't cry, lady. Take off those dark brown glasses.
> Hello, mother, I knew it was you!

The structure of the melody provides a drawing-room atmosphere for twentieth-century ears. It suggests a harpsichord accompaniment to me, but if you don't have one handy you may be able to achieve a similar effect using an arpeggio accompaniment on the guitar.

Recordings: Paul Clayton (Folkways, FA 2106 and FA 2310); Richard Dyer-Bennet (Dyer-Bennet, DYB 2000); Cynthia Gooding (Elektra, EKL 107); Hermes Nye (Folkways, FA 2037).

2. She was coy, and she would not believe
   That he did love her so,
   No, nor at any time she would
   Any countenance to him show.

3. But when his friends did understand
   His fond and foolish mind,
   They sent him up to fair London,
   An apprentice for to bind.

4. And when he had been seven long years,
   And his love he had not seen,

"Many a tear have I shed for her sake
When she little thought of me."

5. All the maids of Islington
Went forth to sport and play,
All but the bailiff's daughter,
She secretly stole away.

6. She put off her gown of gray,
And put on her puggish attire.
She's up to fair London gone
Her true love to require.

7. As she went along the road,
The weather being hot and dry,
There was she aware of her true love,
At length came riding by.

8. She stepped to him as red as any rose,
And took him by the bridle ring:
"I pray you, kind sir, give me one penny,
To ease my weary limb."

9. "I prithee, sweet heart, canst thou tell me
Where that thou wast born?"
"At Islington, kind sir," said she,
"Where I have had many a scorn."

10. "I prithee, sweet heart, canst thou tell me
Whether thou dost know
The bailiff's daughter of Islington?"
"She's dead, sir, long ago."

11. "Then I will sell my goodly steed,
My saddle and my bow;
I will unto some far countree
Where no man doth me know."

12. "O stay, O stay, thou goodly youth,
She's alive, she is not dead;
Here she standeth by thy side,
And is ready to be thy bride."

13. "O farewell grief, and welcome joy,
Ten thousand times and more,
For now I have seen my own true love
That I tho't I should have seen no more."

BANKS OF THE OHIO

Murder ballads have been so popular in folk music that hundreds of them still survive, and books and collections are devoted to them alone. Murder balladeers often rewrote earlier ballads to describe a new crime; or at least borrowed a tune, words, or phrases to complete a new ballad. This borrowing practice sometimes makes it difficult to tell whether one ballad is a different ballad from another or simply a variation of the same one. "The Oxford Girl" is a famous British ballad with many variations in Britain and America. The name of the town has been changed frequently—not to protect the innocent but to provide local currency. "Banks of the Ohio" is either a variation of "The Oxford Girl" or an adaptation. In any event, the story is essentially the same, although the method of the murder differs and the descriptions in "The Oxford Girl" tend to be more gruesome:

> I heeded not one word she said
> But beat her more and more
> Till all the ground around us
> Stood in a bloody gore.

Both of these ballads (or versions of the same ballad) have been very popular with commercial hillbilly singers, but "Banks of the Ohio" has been favored by folk song revivalists. I've made a few melodic and textual changes from standard versions to arrive at the way it is presented here. It bothered me that, in the way the second verse is customarily sung, the girl never really said no and the boy took the mother's answer alone as his motive for the murder:

> I asked your mother for you, dear,
> And she said you were too young;
> Only say that you'll be mine—
> Happiness in my home you'll find.

(Then in the next two verses he proceeds to kill her without waiting for her answer.) I was convinced there was a missing verse—and I finally found one in the John Burch Blaylock Collection. I adapted that verse and used it (in the words that follow) to replace the second verse shown above.

Recordings: Paul Clayton (Riverside, RLP 12-615); The Kossoy Sisters (Tradition, TLP 1018); Bascom Lamar Lunsford (Folkways, FA 2040); Ed McCurdy (Elektra, EKP 108); Glenn Yarbrough (Tradition, TLP 1019); Harry and Jeanie West (in Smokey Mountain Ballads, Counterpoint Esoteric Records); Bill and Earl Bostick (RCA Camden, CAL 797).

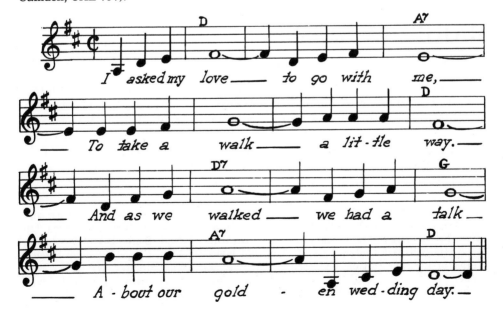

21

Chorus:

Then only say that you'll be mine,
In no other arms entwined.
Down beside where the waters flow,
On the banks of the Ohio.

2. I asked her would she marry me,
So in our home we'd happy be.
These fatal words she then did say:
"No man on earth shall marry me."

3. I held a knife against her breast,
And gently in my arms she pressed.
And then she cried: "Don't murder me.
I'm not prepared for eternity."

4. I took her by her pale white hand,
And led her where the waters stand.
And then I threw her in to drown
And watched her as she floated down.

5. Then I went home 'twixt twelve and one,
And cried: "My God, what have I done?
I've killed the only girl I love
Because she would not be my bride."

BARBARA ALLEN

This is an American version of one of the "giants" among the British ballads. Barbara is slighted by Willie (or William, if you prefer) in public and gets even by refusing to admit she loves him though he is on his deathbed. His death brings her such misery, however, that she soon joins him in the grave; and they are at last united, poetically, when the rose bush and the brier tie in a true-love knot (see discussion of "true love" with "Black Is the Color of My True Love's Hair," which is listed in the Index).

Recordings: Alfred Deller (Vanguard, VRS 479); Richard Dyer-Bennet (Stinson, SLP 35); Patrick Gainer (Folk Heritage Recording, DB 2122-3); Burl Ives (Decca, DL 5490); Ed McCurdy (Tradition, TLP 1003); Brownie McNeil (Sonic, B-16847-8); John Jacob Niles (RCA Camden, CAL 245); Susan Reed (Elektra, EKL 116); Jean Ritchie (Collector Limited Edition, CLE 1201 — three versions; Westminister, WP 6037); Pete Seeger (Folkways, FA 2319); Andrew Rowan Summers (Folkways, FA 2041); Josh White (London, LL 1147); Stan Wilson (Cavalier, CAV 5505).

In Scar-let town where I was born There lived a fair young maid-en.___ She was the fair-est of them_ all, And her name was Bar - b'ry Al - len.___

2. 'Twas in the merry month of May,
   When flowers were a-bloomin',
   Sweet Willie on his deathbed lay
   For the love of Barb'ry Allen.

3. He sent his servant to the town,
   The town that she did dwell in,
   Saying, "Master bid me to come here,
   If your name be Barb'ry Allen."

4. Then slowly, slowly she rose up,
   And slowly she went to him,
   And all she said when she got there:
   "Young man, I think you're dyin'."

5. "Oh, yes, I'm sick within my heart,
   And I never will get better,
   Until I know the love of one,
   The love of Barb'ry Allen."

6. "Oh, don't you remember the other day,
   When we were in the tavern,
   You drank a toast to the ladies all,
   But slighted Barb'ry Allen."

7. "Oh, yes, I know, I know it well,
   When we were in the tavern,
   I gave a toast to the ladies all,
   But my love to Barb'ry Allen."

8. He turned his face unto the wall,
   And death was with him dealin'.
   "Adieu, adieu, to all my friends,
   Be kind to Barb'ry Allen."

9. Then lightly she tripped down the stairs,
   He trembled like an aspen.

23

"'Tis vain, 'tis vain, my dear young man
To hone for Barb'ry Allen."

10. She walked out in the green, green fields,
    She heard his death bell knellin'.
    And every stroke they seemed to say:
    "Hardhearted Barb'ry Allen."

11. She looked to the east; she looked to the west;
    She saw his corpse a-comin',
    "Oh, set him down for me," she cried,
    "That I may gaze upon him."

12. The more she looked the more she grieved,
    Until she burst out cryin';
    Saying, "Pick me up and carry me home,
    For I feel like I am dyin'."

13. "Oh, father, dear, go dig my grave;
    Go dig it deep and narrow.
    Sweet Willie died for me today;
    I'll die for him tomorrow."

14. They buried Willie in the old churchyard
    And Barb'ry in the new one.
    From Willie's grave there grew a rose;
    From Barb'ry's a green brier.

15. They grew and grew to the old church wall
    Till they couldn't grow no higher;
    And there they tied in a true-love knot,
    The rose bush and the brier.

BEAUTIFUL, BEAUTIFUL
BROWN EYES

This plaintive hillbilly song ranks with "Goodnight, Irene" for good, old-fashioned group-singing appeal. It sounds like a simple little love song but the hard-luck verses give it a greater dimension and power. Certain commercialized versions have attempted to rob the song of this power:

Willie, oh Willie, I love you,
Love you with all my heart,
Tomorrow we're gonna be married
And never again be apart.

The rougher edges have not been removed from the version that follows. I've indicated a harmony part (the top notes) for the choruses. It's easy to teach this one to the harmonizers in a group in a few minutes. Girls sound good alone in the first two verses, with everyone singing in the third.

Wil-lie, oh Wil-lie, I love you, Love you with all my heart. To-mor-row we might have been mar-ried. But lik-ker has kept us a-part.

CHORUS:
Beau-ti-ful, beau-ti-ful brown eyes. Beau-ti-ful, beau-ti-ful brown eyes. Beau-ti-ful, beau-ti-ful brown eyes, I'll nev-er love blue eyes a-gain.

2. Seven long years I've been married.
   I wish I was single again.
   A woman never knows of her troubles
   Until she has married a man.

3. Down to the barroom he staggered,
   Staggered and fell at the door.
   The last words that he ever uttered:
   "I'll never drink likker no more."

BETTY AND DUPREE

Some unknown balladeer immortalized Betty and Dupree soon after Dupree was hanged. This is my favorite, melodically, of the many versions of the ballad now in circulation. One December day in 1921, Dupree picked out a diamond ring for Betty in an Atlanta jewelry store. As he left the store without having paid for the ring, a policeman attempted to stop him. Dupree shot the policeman with his forty-four. The law eventually caught up with Dupree in Detroit. He was returned to Atlanta, where he was tried, convicted, and hanged for the crime.

Recordings: Paul Clayton (Folkways, FA 2310); Brownie McGhee (Folkways, FA 2030); Josh White (ABC Paramount, ABC 124).

Bet-ty told Du-pree: "I want a dia-mond ring."
Bet-ty told Du-pree:
"I want a dia-mond ring."— Du-pree said:
"Oh, yes, Bet-ty, For you I'd do most an-y-thing."—

2. Dupree said: "Go to sleep. See what tomorrow brings."
Dupree said: "Go to sleep. See what tomorrow brings."
"Sure as the sun comes up, you'll get a diamond ring."

Continue, as above:

3. Now, Dupree he had a gun, it was a forty-four.
He stuck it in his pocket; went to the jewelry store.

4. Police they caught Dupree and took him off to jail.
He told 'em send for Betty to come and go his bail.

5. To the jailhouse Betty went; his face she could not see.
She asked the jailor, "Please, take him this note from me."

6. "They wouldn't let me in to let me see your face.
You know I love you, baby, but I just can't take your place."

7. Dupree he told the judge: "I'm not so brave and bold.
   The reason why I did it, I wanted Betty's jelly roll."

8. The judge he told Dupree: "Jelly roll done ruined you."
   "Your honor, set me free, with jelly roll I'm through."

9. The judge he told Dupree: "I think you quit too late.
   You shot a policeman and hangin' is your fate."

THE BIG ROCK CANDY MOUNTAIN

The old-time hobo is disappearing from the American scene, the victim of prosperity and technological progress. Where once there were countless thousands of freight train freeloaders roaming the country, cooking mulligan stew in "jungles" beside the tracks, the *Wall Street Journal* reports only 55 showed up this year for the 59th annual convention of the knights of the road at Britt, Iowa. This is not a sudden development. The forces working toward the extinction of the bindle stiff have been at work for some time. It's been many years, for example, since the phrase "riding the rods" had any meaning. Steel-framed boxcars now universally in use have no exterior bracing. And modern diesel locomotives accelerate so fast leaving the yards that a bum hardly has a chance to catch a grabiron and swing aboard. Besides, unless he stays in one place and maintains a mailing address like a working stiff, he can't collect his welfare check. It takes a lot of character, in today's circumstances, to remain true to the creed of the professional 'bo, to live in poverty and shirk work. The surviving 55 deserve to find the Big Rock Candy Mountain, with its cigarette trees and lemonade springs.

News story, 1959

For decades this little song was accepted as a charming one for "children in wonderland." But according to "Haywire Mac" McClintock, the busker (tramp entertainer) who claimed he wrote it (and "Hallelujah, I'm a Bum"), it's a song about the sales pitch used by "blowed-in-the-glass-stiffs . . . to snare a kid to do their begging and pander to their perversions . . . a kid who could not only beg handouts but who could bring in money for alcohol was a valuable piece of property for any jocker [experienced tramp] who could snare him. The decent hoboes were protective as long as they were around, but there were times when I fought like a wildcat or ran like a deer to preserve my independence and my virginity."

Preshuns (apprentice tramps) were recruited in the railroad yards of small towns. There, where poor children played, hoboes told them fabricated stories of the glamour of tramp life. "The Big Rock Candy Mountain" is a humorous exaggeration of one of these "ghost stories" of a hobo pied piper. The hoboes called these recruitment tales ghost stories because they bore the same relationship to reality that ghosts do.

Recordings: John Greenway (Riverside, RLP 12-619); Burl Ives (Decca, DL 5093 and DL 8080); Milt Okun (Baton, BL 1203); Pete Seeger (Folkways, FA 2320 and Disc, D 101); Paul Sykes (Crown, CLP 5057).

On a sum-mer day in the month of May A— bur-ly bum came hik-ing Down a shad-y lane thro' the sug-ar cane; He was look-ing for his lik-ing. As he roamed a-long he sang a song Of the land of milk and hon-ey,— Where a bum can stay for man-y a day, And he won't need an-y mon-ey. Oh, the buz-zin' of the bees in the cig-a-rette trees Near the sod-a wat-er foun-tain, At the lem-o-nade springs where the blue-bird sings on the big rock can-dy moun-tain.

2. Oh, a farmer and his son, they were on the run,
To the hayfield they were bounding.
Said the bum to the son, "Why don't you come
To that big rock candy mountain?"
So the very next day they hiked away,
The mile posts they kept counting,
But they never arrived at the lemonade tide
On the big rock candy mountain.

BILLY BARLOW

The hunting of the wren is an old British custom connected with the celebration of St. Stephen's Day. On Christmas Day the boys would catch the wren (he was supposed to be blind on that day). On the next day, St. Stephen's Day, they would carry the wren from door to door, asking for money to bury it. If anyone failed to pay up, they would bury the wren at that home's door—thus bringing bad luck to the inhabitants. There are two popular theories on how this ritual became a custom. One is that it grew out of a folk tale in which the wren became king of the birds by perching on the head of an eagle during a flying contest. The birds discovered they'd been tricked and have hunted the wren ever since. The other theory is that Christian missionaries inaugurated the custom as an anti-Druid measure. The Druids believed the wren was the king of birds. In most American versions the wren has been dropped in favor of a rat.

Recordings: Terrea Lea (Hifirecord, R 404); Alan Lomax (Tradition, TLP 1029); Pete Seeger (Folkways, FC 7001); Peggy Seeger (Topic, TOP 18 and Prestige, PR 13029).

2. What shall I hunt? says Risky Rob,
   What shall I hunt? says Robin to Bob,
   What shall I hunt? says Dan'l to Joe,
   Hunt for a rat, says Billy Barlow.

   Continue, as above:

3. How shall I get him? says Risky Rob, *etc.*
   Go borrow a gun, says Billy Barlow.

4. How shall I haul him? *etc.*
   Go borrow a wagon, says Billy Barlow.

5. How shall we divide him? *etc.*
   How shall we divide him? says Billy Barlow.

6. I'll take shoulder, says Risky Rob,
   I'll take side, says Robin to Bob,
   I'll take ham, says Dan'l to Joe,
   Tail bone mine, says Billy Barlow.

7. How shall we cook him? *etc.*
   How shall we cook him? says Billy Barlow.

8. I'll broil shoulder, says Risky Rob,
   I'll fry side, says Robin to Bob.
   I'll boil ham, says Dan'l to Joe,
   Tail bone raw, says Billy Barlow.

BILLIE MAGEE MAGAW

Long a favorite on the American campus (it appears in many college song-books of the nineteenth and twentieth centuries), "Billie Magee Magaw" is a descendant of an old British ballad, "The Three Ravens." It is number 26 in Francis James Child's famous collection of ballads. You can get an idea of the variation that has taken place by reading the following version from *Melismata. Musicall Phansies. Fitting the Court, Cittie, and Countrey Humours,* which appeared in London in 1611. Spelling conventions have changed considerably since that date.

> There were three rauens sat on a tree,
> Downe a downe, hay downe, hay downe,
> There were three rauens sat on a tree,
> With a downe,
> There were three rauens sat on a tree,
> They were as blacke as they might be.
> With a downe derrie, derrie, derrie, downe, downe.

For the rest of the verses I've provided only the key lines, omitting the repetitions:

> The one of them said to his mate,
> "Where shall we our breakfast take?"
>
> "Downe in yonder greene field,
> There lies a knight slain vnder his shield.
>
> "His hounds they lie downe at his feete,
> So well they can their master keepe.
>
> "His haukes they fly so eagerly,
> There's no fowle dare him come nie."
>
> Downe there comes a fallow doe,
> As great with yong as she might goe.
>
> She lift vp his bloudy hed,
> And kist his wounds that were so red.

She got him vp vpon her backe,
And carried him to earthen lake.

She buried him before the prime,
She was dead herselfe ere euen-song time.

God send euery gentleman,
Such haukes, such hounds, and such a leman.

An interesting project would be to develop your own version of the ballad by using elements from the older version above and the contemporary one below. You can get additional ideas from listening to the various records listed, which cover several variants of the ballad. If that sounds like too much work, just sing the contemporary version. The tune should be familiar. It's the same tune used for "When Johnny Comes Marching Home."

Recordings: Grace Creswell (Rebel, 411); Alfred Deller (Vanguard, VRS 479); Richard Dyer-Bennet (Stinson, SLP 35); Ed McCurdy (Riverside, RLP 12-601); Alan Mills (Folkways, FP 709); Hermes Nye (Folkways, FA 2305); John Runge (Riverside, RLP 12-814); Andrew Rowan Summers (Folkways, FA 2348).

Continue, as above:

2. Said one old crow unto his mate,
   "What shall we do for grub to ate?"

3. "There lies a horse on yonder plain,
   Who's by some cruel butcher slain.

4. "We'll perch ourselves on his backbone,
   And pick his eyes out one by one.

5. "The meat we'll eat before it's stale
   Till naught remains but bones and tail."

BILLY BOY

Some ballad scholars have linked "Billy Boy" with the classic ballad "Lord Randall." Although it is possible that "Billy Boy" started out as a parody or burlesque of "Lord Randall," there isn't sufficient similarity, or parody, in any of the contemporary versions to support this theory.

I've always found it difficult to resist tampering with a good idea when I see one. So I usually sing the last verse like this:

Can she sing a pretty song, Billy Boy, Billy Boy,
Can she sing a pretty song, charming Billy?
She can sing a pretty song
But she gets the words all wrong:
She's a mother and cannot leave her young thing.

Children—being less inhibited or critical than adults—like to make up verses to songs. The verses my children sing to "Billy Boy" run in the slapstick-comedy vein and seem to tickle their funny bones, even after constant repetition:

Did she take your hat and coat, Billy Boy, Billy Boy,
Did she take your hat and coat, charming Billy?
Yes she took my hat and coat
And she fed it to a goat,
She's a young thing and cannot leave her mother.

Here are some other punch lines they use:

Yes, she told me to come in
But she stuck me with a pin.

Yes, she offered me a drink
But she poured it down the sink.

Yes, she made for me a pie,
But she threw it in my eye.

Recordings: Paul Clayton (Stinson, SLP 70); Shep Ginandes (Elektra, EKL 7); John Langstaff (Tradition, TLP 1009); Ed McCurdy (Tradition, TLP 1027); Alan Mills (Folkways, FA 2312); Milt Okun (Riverside, RLP 12-603); Jean Ritchie and Oscar Brand (Riverside, RLP 12-646); Tom Scott (Coral, CRL 56056); Andrew Rowan Summers (Folkways, FA 2044).

2. Did she bid you to come in, Billy Boy, Billy Boy,
Did she bid you to come in, charming Billy?
Yes, she bade me to come in,
Let me kiss her on her chin,
She's a young thing and cannot leave her mother.

Continue, as above:

3. Did she set for you a chair?
   Yes, she set for me a chair,
   And the bottom wasn't there.

4. Can she bake a cherry pie?
   She can bake a cherry pie,
   Quick as a cat can wink her eye.

5. Can she make a feather bed?
   She can make a feather bed
   That will rise above your head.

6. How old is she?
   Three times six and four times seven,
   Twenty-eight and eleven.

7. Can she sing a pretty song?
   She can sing a pretty song
   But she gets the words all wrong.

BLACK IS THE COLOR
OF MY TRUE LOVE'S HAIR

The two different meanings attached to the expression "true love" in folk song may cause confusion at times. True love can refer to a loved one who is faithful and, thus, true. Or it can mean "my one and only *real* love." Often in folk song the true love—the one and only real love—turns out to be unfaithful. Apparently "Black Is the Color" started out a century or so back as a girl's song of unrequited love, complaining about an unfaithful man:

> Many a night I've been with you
> And never thought you'd be untrue.
> When I found out I cried aloud,
> Such faithless love as you followed.

Later on, in the most popular version of the twentieth century (with a melody composed by John Jacob Niles) it became a man's complaint—with these (traditional) words:

> Black, black, black is the color of my true love's hair,
> Her lips are like some rosy fair,
> The prettiest face and the neatest hands,
> I love the ground whereon she stands.
>
> I love my love and well she knows,
> I love the grass whereon she goes,
> If she on earth no more I see,
> I can't serve her as she has me.
>
> I go to Troublesome* to mourn and weep,
> But satisfied I never could sleep.
> I'll write to you in a few little lines.
> I'll suffer death ten thousand times.

*With poetic license, *Troublesome* is the name of a town.

34

So fare you well, my own true love,
The time has passed and I wish you well.
But still I hope the time will come
When you and I will be as one.

My version* takes the song in still another direction: a true-love song about true lovers that are true. This offers you three choices for performance: You may adapt the traditional words above, to make the song a girl's complaint; sing them as they are, as a man's complaint; or try the true, true-love version.

Recordings: Frances Archer and Beverly Gile (Disneyland, WDL 3023); William Clauson (RCA Victor, LPM 1286); Cisco Houston (Disc, D 103); Burl Ives (Stinson, SLP 1); Ed McCurdy (Dawn, DLP 1127); John Jacob Niles (RCA Camden, CAL 245); Susan Reed (Elektra, EKL 116); Jean Ritchie (Elektra, EKL 125); Bob Ross (Folkways, FA 2334); John Runge (Stinson, SLP 88); Pete Seeger (Folkways, FA 2321); Betty Vaiden Williams (Vanguard, VRS 9028).

2. We met in the springtime when the world was green,
   And love, as true as the world has seen,
   Began to grow as we both could see
   A love like ours was meant to be.

3. The spring and the summer, they were light and gay.
   When winter came it was cold and gray.
   And those were the dark, dark days we knew,
   But still our love was strong and true.

4. Black is the color of my true love's hair,
   Her lips are like a rose so fair.
   And my heart sings when I hold her hands.
   I love the ground whereon she stands.

BLOW THE CANDLES OUT

"Blow the Candles Out" is one of the most famous British broadside ballads of seduction. In this version the last verse holds out hope that the lover will return and presumably make an honest woman of the maiden. In some less romantic versions she has a baby nine months later:

> And she damned the very hour
> That she blowed the candle out.

Recordings: Theodore Bikel (Elektra, EKL 105); Oscar Brand (Audio Fidelity, ADFL 906); Richard Dyer-Bennet (Dyer-Bennet, DYB 2000); Tom Glazer (Mercury, MG 20007); Ewan MacColl (Riverside, RLP 12-605); Stan Wilson (Verve, MGV 2019); Cisco Houston (Disc, D 103).

When I was ap-pren-ticed in Lon - don, I went to see my dear. The can-dles all were burn-ing, the moon shone bright and clear. I knocked up-on her win - dow to ease her of her pain. She rose to let me in, then she barred the door a - gain.

2. I like your well behavior and thus I often say,
   I cannot rest contented whilst you are far away.
   The roads they are so muddy, we cannot gang about,
   So roll me in your arms, love, and blow the candles out.

3. Your father and your mother in yonder room do lie,
   A-huggin' one another, so why not you and I?
   A-huggin' one another without a fear or doubt,
   So roll me in your arms, love, and blow the candles out.

4. And if you prove successful, love, pray name it after me,
   Keep it neat and kiss it sweet, and daff it on your knee.
   When my three years are ended, my time it will be out,
   Then I will double my indebtedness by blowing the candles out.

BLOW THE MAN DOWN

Before the nineteenth century, sailing schedules across the Atlantic were irregular and not very dependable. The kind of service we are accustomed to today was first introduced in the early 1800s, when enterprising American shipping men began to operate faster ships on regular, tight schedules. The first and most famous of these hard-driving lines was the Black Ball Line, which operated a fleet of packet ships between New York and Liverpool. On the first and the sixteenth of each month one of these ships left each port without fail, fair weather or foul. The ships were small, strong, and well built and were superior to earlier vessels. The skippers were tough and capable men who drove their ships and crews harder and more relentlessly than ever before. It wasn't long before they dominated the carrying of mail, freight, and passengers across the Atlantic.

"Blow the Man Down" is one of the earliest, most famous, and most popular chanteys associated with the rugged packet ships. There are several versions of this halyard chantey, but they all reflect the iron discipline and brutality of the hard life aboard these "red-hot blood ships." The title itself sets the pace. *Blow* means *knock* or *strike,* and some of the earlier versions of the chantey were known by the title "Knock the Man Down."

Recordings: Oscar Brand (Audio Fidelity, AFLP 1884); Paul Clayton (Folkways, FA 2106); E. G. Huntington (Folkways, FA 2032); A. L. Lloyd and Ewan MacColl (Stinson, SLP 80); Alan Mills (Folkways, FA 2312); Pete Seeger (Folkways, FA 2175).

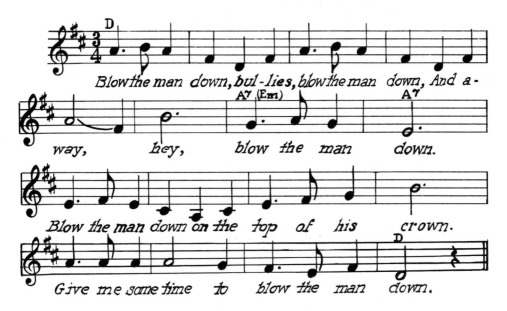

Blow the man down, bul-lies, blow the man down, And a-way, hey, blow the man down. Blow the man down on the top of his crown. Give me some time to blow the man down.

2. 'Twas on board a Black Baller I first served my time,
   And away, hey, blow the man down.
   And on the Black Baller I wasted my prime.
   Give me some time to blow the man down.

3. It's when a Black Baller's preparing for sea,
   And away, hey, blow the man down.

You'd split your sides laughing at the sights you would see,
Give me some time to blow the man down.

4. With the tinkers and tailors and soldiers and all,
   And away, hey, blow the man down.
   That ship as good seamen on board the Black Ball.
   Give me some time to blow the man down.

5. It's when a Black Baller is clear of the land,
   And away, hey, blow the man down.
   Our boatswain [bosun] then gives us the word of command.
   Give me some time to blow the man down.

6. "Lay aft!" is the cry "to the break of the poop!"
   And away, hey, blow the man down.
   "Or I'll help you along with the toe of my boot."
   Give me some time to blow the man down.

7. It's larboard and starboard on the deck you will sprawl,
   And away, hey, blow the man down.
   For "Kicking Jack Williams" commands the Black Ball.
   Give me some time to blow the man down.

8. Pay attention to orders, yes, you, one and all,
   And away, hey, blow the man down.
   For see right above you there flies the Black Ball.
   Give me some time to blow the man down.

9. It's when a Black Baller comes down to the dock,
   And away, hey, blow the man down.
   The lasses and lads to the pier-heads do flock.
   Give me some time to blow the man down.

*Another version was sung as a forecastle ballad
and is related to other sea ballads:*

1. As I was a-walking down Paradise Street,
   And away, hey, blow the man down.
   A saucy young damsel I chanced for to meet.
   Give me some time to blow the man down.

Continue, as above:

2. She was round in the counter and bluff in the bow,
   So I took in all sail and cried "Way enough now."

3. She backed her main topsail and gave me a sigh,
   And said she was busted and ready to die.

4. "Oh, Jack," said the maiden, "And will you stand treat?"
   "Well sure, my dear lady, let's walk down the street."

5. So I tailed her my flipper and took her in tow,
   And yardarm to yardarm away we did go.

6. She steered me through alleys and up to the bar,
   And had me quite groggy before we'd gone far.

7. She told of a clipper just ready for sea,
   And said she was waiting for sailors like me.

8. That spanking full-rigger to New York was bound,
   She was very well manned and very well found.

9. She slipped me her hawser and took me in tow,
   And soon I was anchored in Battery Row.

10. But soon as that packet was clear of the bar,
    The mate knocked me down with the end of a spar.

11. And so I was shanghaied aboard this old ship,
    She took all my money and gave me the slip.

12. I'll give you a warning before we belay,
    Don't ever take heed of what pretty girls say.

THE BOLL WEEVIL

In the 1890s the boll weevil crossed the border from Mexico and invaded Texas and the South, bringing ruin to the cotton crops. The ballad of the boll weevil tells the story.

Every once in a while you run across a folk song that has so many entertaining variations you're tempted to try to put them all together. But that would be too much of a good thing and it would be difficult to keep an audience interested if you did. However, you can make use of all the possibilities by varying your performances from time to time. Immediately following the first version of "The Boll Weevil," I've listed some miscellaneous verses you may draw on from time to time to replace others. "The Boll Weevil Blues" provides an opportunity for a complete departure from the traditional ballad, in the blues idiom.

Recordings: Bill Bonyun (Folkways, FC 7402); Oscar Brand and Fred Hellerman (Tradition, TLP 1014); Erik Darling (Elektra, EKL 154); Cisco Houston (Folkways, FA 2346); Burl Ives (Decca, DL 8248); Huddie Ledbetter (Stinson, SLP 51); Hermes Nye (Folkways, FA 2128); Carl Sandburg (Lyrichord, LL 4); Josh White (ABC Paramount, ABC 124); The Weavers (Vanguard, VRS 9013).

Just a-look-in' for a home, Just a look-in' for a home, Just a-look-in' for a home. _____

2. The first time I seen the boll weevil,
   He was settin' on the square;
   The next time I seen the boll weevil,
   He had all his family there.

   Chorus: Just a-lookin' for a home.

3. And the farmer took the boll weevil,
   And buried him in hot sand;
   The boll weevil say to the farmer,
   "I'll stand it like a man."

   Chorus: This'll be my home.

4. Then the farmer took the boll weevil
   And left him on the ice;
   The boll weevil say to the farmer,
   "This is mighty cool and nice."

   Chorus: This'll be my home.

5. The farmer took the boll weevil
   And fed him on paris green;
   The boll weevil say to the farmer,
   "It's the best I ever seen."

   Chorus: This'll be my home.

6. The boll weevil say to the farmer,
   "You better let me alone;
   I et up all your cotton
   And now I'll start on the corn."

   Chorus: I'll have a home.

7. The merchant got half the cotton,
   The boll weevil got the rest;
   Didn't leave the poor old farmer
   But one old cotton dress.

   Chorus: And it's full of holes.

8. The farmer say to the merchant,
   "I ain't made but one bale,
   But before I'll give you that one,
   I'll fight and go to jail."

Chorus: I'll have a home.

9. If anyone should ask you
   Who was it made this song,
   Tell him 'twas a poor farmer
   With a pair of blue duckin's on.

   Chorus: Ain't got no home.

   Miscellaneous verses:

1. The first time I seen the boll weevil
   He was on the western plain.
   The next time I seen the boll weevil
   He was ridin' a Memphis train.

2. The first time I saw the boll weevil
   He was runnin' a spinnin' wheel.
   The next time I saw the boll weevil
   He was ridin' in an automobile.

3. The farmer took the boll weevil
   And sent him up in a balloon.
   The boll weevil say to the farmer,
   "I'll see you again next June."

4. The farmer took the boll weevil
   And throwed him in the sand.
   He put on the farmer's overcoat
   And stood up like a natural man.

BOLL WEEVIL BLUES

Well, the farm-er say to the wee-vil: "What you do-in' on the square?" That bug done say to the farm-er: "Got a nice big fam-'ly there. Gon-na make a home. Gon-na make a home. Gon-na make a home."

2. Boll Weevil say to the farmer:
   "Better ride your Ford machine;
   When I get through with your cotton
   You can't afford no gasoline.
   Gonna make a home, gonna make a home."

3. Boll Weevil say to the farmer:
   "Gonna swing down from your gate,
   Gonna gobble up all of your cotton;
   Make you sell your Cadillac eight.
   Gonna make a home, gonna make a home."

4. Then the farmer say to the weevil:
   "Weevil, I wish you well.
   Never wanted bad luck for no one,
   But I hope you burn in hell.
   'Cause you took my home, yes, I lost my home."

5. Well, the farmer took the boll weevil,
   And he covered him up with ice.
   Boll Weevil say to the farmer:
   "How come you treat me so nice?
   Makes a real fine home, makes a real fine home."

6. Then the farmer took the boll weevil,
   And he covered him up with sand.
   Boll Weevil say to the farmer:
   "You treatin' me like a man.
   It's a real good home, it's a real good home."

7. No use to fight the boll weevil.
   Gonna tear your farm house down.
   Gonna build hisself a mansion
   And run you out of town.
   He's done hit home. Boll Weevil's home.

BRENNAN ON THE MOOR

Willie Brennan was the Irish counterpart of England's Robin Hood and our Jesse James. Willie operated in the Kilworth Mountains of County Cork, Ireland, in the latter part of the eighteenth century and until he took a swing on the gallows in 1804. This long version of the ballad has been collected and collated from several versions. You may shorten it for performance by singing only those verses with asterisks.

Recordings: The Clancy Brothers with Tommy Makem (Tradition, TLP 1042); Burl Ives (Decca, DL 8444); Ed McCurdy (Riverside, RLP 12-601); Jeannie Robertson (Riverside, RLP 12-633).

'Tis— of a brave, young high-way man this stor-y I will tell, His name was Wil-lie Bren-nan and in Ire-land he did dwell, It was on the Kill-wood moun-tain— he com-menced his wild ca-reer, And man-y a weal— -thy nob-le-man be-fore him shook with fear. It was Bren-nan on the moor, Bren-nan on the moor, bold, brave and un-daunt-ed was young Bren-nan on the moor.

2. A brace of loaded pistols he carried night and day,
   He never robbed a poor man upon the King's highway;
   But what he'd taken from the rich, like Turpin and Black Bess,
   He always did divide it with the widow in distress.

3. One night he robbed a packman, his name was Pedlar Bawn;
   They traveled on together till day began to dawn.
   The pedlar seeing his money gone, likewise his watch and chain,
   He at once encountered Brennan and robbed him back again.

4. When Brennan saw the pedlar was as good a man as he,
   He took him on the highway his companion for to be.
   The pedlar threw away his pack without any more delay,
   And proved a faithful comrade until his dying day.

43

5. *One day upon the highway as Willie he went down,
   He met the mayor of Cashiell a mile outside of town.
   The mayor he knew his features and he said, "Young man," said he,
   "Your name is Willie Brennan, you must come along with me."

6. *Now Brennan's wife had gone to town, provisions for to buy.
   And when she saw her Willie she commenced to weep and cry.
   Said, "Hand to me that tenpenny." As soon as Willie spoke,
   She handed him a blunderbuss from underneath her cloak.

7. *Now with this loaded blunderbuss, the truth I will unfold,
   He made the mayor to tremble and he robbed him of his gold.
   One hundred pounds was offered for his apprehension there.
   So he, with horse and saddle, to the mountains did repair.

8. *Now Brennan being an outlaw upon the mountains high,
   With cavalry and infantry to take him they did try.
   He laughed at them with scorn until at last 'twas said,
   By a false-hearted woman he was cruelly betrayed.

9. In the county of Tipperary, in a place they called Clonmore,
   Willie Brennan and his comrade that day did suffer sore;
   He lay among the fern which was thick upon the field,
   And nine wounds he had received before that he did yield.

10. Then Brennan and his companion knowing they were betrayed,
    He with the mounted cavalry a noble battle made;
    He lost his foremost finger, which was shot off by a ball;
    So Brennan and his comrade they were taken after all.

11. So they were taken prisoners, in irons they were bound,
    And conveyed to Clonmore jail, strong walls did them surround.
    They were tried and found guilty, the judge made this reply:
    "For robbing on the King's highway you are both condemned to die."

12. Farewell unto my wife and to my children three,
    Likewise my aged father, he may shed tears for me,
    And to my loving mother, who tore her gray locks and cried,
    Saying, "I wish, Willie Brennan, in your cradle you had died."

BUFFALO BOY

Buffalo Boy had a simple formula for working his way out of a wedding proposal. But he wasn't the first one to come up with this clever ruse. I found an early ancestor with the same devious plan in John Ashton's *Modern Street Ballads*, published in 1888. Humphrey Duggins wooed and won the old Widow Warmpurse. The widow had a large house and no children. Humphrey had six children, none of them small, about whom he did not tell the widow. When she agreed with his hope that they would have a large family, he brought the six little Dugginses home the next day with this result:

> You wicked deceiver, quoth she, I am dish'd;
> Says he, for a great many children you wish'd,
> And, as no one is certain their wishes to have,
> I thought you might fancy a few ready made.

The obvious way to perform "Buffalo Boy" is to team up a boy and girl duo. However, many male performers feel it is more humorous, and certainly easier to organize, to forego a partner and sing the girl's part in falsetto.

Recordings: Marilyn Child and Glenn Yarbrough (Elektra, EKL 143); Bob and Louise Decormier (Stinson, SLP 68); Sam Hinton (Decca, DL 8108); Martha Schlamme (Vanguard, VRS 9019).

When are we gon-na get mar - ried, mar - ried, mar - ried? When are we gon-na get mar - ried, Dear old buf-fa-lo boy?

2. I guess we'll marry in a week, in a week, in a week,
   I guess we'll marry in a week, that is, if the weather be good.

3. How're you gonna come to the wedding, to the wedding, to the wedding?
   How're you gonna come to the wedding, dear old buffalo boy?

   Continue, as above:

4. I guess I'll come in my ox-cart,
   That is, if the weather be good.

5. Why don't you come in your buggy,
   Dear old buffalo boy?

6. My ox won't fit in the buggy,
   Not even if the weather be good.

7. Who're you gonna bring to the wedding,
   Dear old buffalo boy?

8. I guess I'll bring my children,
   That is, if the weather be good.

9. I didn't know you had no children,
   Dear old buffalo boy.

10. Oh, yes, I have five children,
    Six—if the weather be good.

11. There ain't gonna be no wedding,
    Not even if the weather be good.

BURY ME BENEATH THE WILLOW

This popular hillbilly song may have an ancestor in "The Willow Tree," which appeared in Percy's *Reliques of Ancient Poetry:*

> O take me to your arms, love,
> For keen the wind does blow,
> O take me to your arms, love,
> For bitter is my woe.
> She hears me not, she cares not,
> Nor will she list to me,
> Whilst here I lie alone to die
> Beneath the willow tree.

If this ancestry is correct, the song has changed—in form, if not in content—since the seventeenth century. Get out your bass runs and hammer-ons for a lively country-music rendition.

Recordings: Woody Guthrie and Cisco Houston (Stinson, SLP 53); Obray Ramsey (Riverside, RLP 12 649—under title "Weeping Willow").

Bur - y me be - neath the wil - low,
'Neath the weep-ing wil - low tree.
When he hears his — love is sleep-ing,
May - be then he'll think of me.

(The first verse may be sung as a chorus.)

2. My heart is sad and I am lonely,
   Thinking of the one I love.
   Will I see him never, never,
   Till we meet in Heaven above.

3. He told me that he dearly loved me,
   How could I believe him untrue.
   Then one day some neighbors told me,
   "He has proven untrue to you."

4. Tomorrow was to be our wedding.
   I pray: Oh, Lord, where can he be?
   He's gone, he's gone to love another.
   He no longer cares for me.

5. Place on my grave a snow-white lily
   To prove that I was true to him.
   And tell him that I died to save him
   When his love I could not win.

6. Then bury me beneath the willow,
   'Neath the weeping willow tree;
   And tell some brown-eyed boy I'm sleeping.
   Then perhaps he'll weep for me.

THE BUTCHER BOY

"The Butcher Boy" has a theme and floating verses that show up in many other songs and ballads. The same theme is developed in "There Is an Ale-house in Yonder Town" (from which the "pop" song "There Is a Tavern in the Town" was derived), Woody Guthrie's "Hard, Ain't It Hard," and John Allison's "In Tarrytown." If you care to look further, you'll also find it in "My True Love Once He Courted Me," "Sweet William," "The Foolish Young Girl," "The Squire's Daughter," "Died for Love," "The Cruel Father," and "A Brisk Young Sailor." This theme has inspired more variants, or different songs, than perhaps any other in folk music. As might be expected, it's a good story no matter how you tell it. You'll find the symbolic dove in many other songs (see, for example, "All the Good Times" and "In the Pines" in this book). The burial instructions also show up in many other songs—particularly the request for a grave that is "wide and deep."

Recordings: Buell H. Kazee (Folkways, FS 3810); Ewan MacColl (Riverside, RLP 12 612); Ed McCurdy (Riverside, RLP 12 601); Joan O'Bryant (Folkways, FA 2134); Jeannie Robertson (Riverside, RLP 12 633); Peggy Seeger (Folkways, FA 2049 and FP 49). Other songs or variants: "In Tarrytown," Pete Seeger (Folkways, FA 2412); The Weavers (Vanguard, VRS 9024); "Hard, Ain't It Hard," Robin Roberts (Stinson, SLP 77); Glenn Yarbrough (Elektra, EKL 135).

2. He stole from me my heart away,
   And with me now he will not stay.

3. There is a house in London town,
   Where my true love, he sits him down,

4. And takes a strange girl on his knee
   And tells her what he won't tell me.

5. It's grief to me; I'll tell you why,
   Because she has more gold than I.

6. But gold will melt and silver fly,
   True, constant love will never die.

7. Her father he came home from work,
   Saying: "Where is daughter, she seemed so hurt?"

8. He went upstairs to give her hope,
   And found her hanging by a rope.

9. He took his knife and cut her down,
   And on her bosom these lines he found:

10. "Must I go bound while he goes free?
    Must I love a man who don't love me?

11. "Oh, I have played a maiden's part
    And died for the man who broke my heart.

12. "Go dig my grave both long and deep,
    Place a marble stone at my head and feet,

13. "And over my grave place a snow-white dove,
    To show the world that I died for love."

*...wishing her lover
good speed*

And away, hey...

*She crossed the
broad prairies...*

...the leafy green dome

Can she bake a cherry pie...

As I was going to Derby...

THE CAMBRIC SHIRT

This second ballad in the monumental collection of ballads made by Francis James Child in the last century was a "proper . . . ballad entitled the Wind hath Blown my Plaid away, or, A Discourse betwixt a young Woman and the Elphin Knight." The elf tells a young maiden he will marry her if she'll make a shirt in an impossible way:

> For thou must shape a sark to me,
> Without any cut or heme, quoth he.
>
> Thou must shape it knife-and-sheerlesse,
> And also sue it needle-threadlesse.

The maiden matches his cunning by giving him a number of impossible tasks to perform, including:

> Thou must bring it over the sea,
> And thou must bring it dry home to me.

When he has completed these tasks, says she:

> Then come to me and get thy sark.

Needless to say, she sends the elf on his less than merry way. Since he evidently already had "seven bairns and a wife," he was probably not really interested in marriage in the first place. This ballad survives today in several versions, all of which follow the essential idea of assignments for suitors in a courtship situation. You may wish to replace "When it's marryin' time" in my version with the traditional line "Rose Marie and thyme."

Recordings: Ewan MacColl and Peggy Seeger (Riverside, RLP 12 637); Milt Okun and Ellen Stekert (Riverside, RLP 12 634); Jean Ritchie and Oscar Brand (Riverside, RLP 12 646). Variant: "The Elfin Knight," Ewan MacColl and Peggy Seeger (Tradition, TLP 1015).

2. Go tell her to make me a cambric shirt,
   When it's marryin' time,
   Without any seam or needle work,
   And she'll be a true lover of mine.

3. Go tell her to wash it in yonder well,
   When it's marryin' time,
   Where water never ran nor rain never fell,
   And she'll be a true lover of mine.

4. Go tell her to dry it on yonder thorn,
   When it's marryin' time,
   Where leaf never grew since Adam was born,
   And she'll be a true lover of mine.

5. If you go through the very next town,
   When it's marryin' time,
   That girl will turn the question around,
   "If he wants to be a lover of mine."

6. Go tell him to clear me an acre of land,
   When it's marryin' time,
   Between the sea and the sifting sand,
   And he'll be a true lover of mine.

   Continue, as above:

7. Go tell him to plow it with a muley cow's horn,
   And plant it all over with grains of corn.

8. Go tell him to reap it with an old stirrup-leather,
   And bind it all up in a peafowl's feather.

9. Go tell him to thresh it against a wall,
   And not let a single bit of it fall.

10. Go tell him to put it in a bottomless sack,
    And bring it home on a butterfly's back.

11. Go tell him that if his work's all done,
    To come to my house and the shirt'll be done.

CAN THE CIRCLE BE UNBROKEN

This old gospel favorite promises a return to the way things used to be: a future with friends and loved ones in the great by and by. It is very much in the "old-timey" tradition of sentimental songs, religious and otherwise, that have flourished in the southern mountain country for half a century. It is quite popular today with banjo-flailing city billies.

Recordings: The Carter Family (Harmony, HL 7280); George Pegram and Walter Parham (Riverside, RLP 12 650).

I was stand-ing____ by the win - dow____ On a cold and cloud - y day, When I saw the____ hearse come rol - ling____ For to car -ry my moth-er a-way.____ Can the cir - cle____ be un-brok - en____ By and by, Lord, by and by.____ There's a bet -ter____ home a - wait-ing____ in the sky, Lord, in the sky.____

2. For I followed close behind her;
   Tried to cheer up and be brave;
   But my sorrows, I could not hide them,
   When they laid her in the grave.

3. Went back home, Lord, my home was lonesome,
   Since my mother she was gone.
   All my brothers and sisters crying;
   What a home, so sad and lone.

CARELESS LOVE

This classic American lament song probably inspired several blues (e.g., "Every Night When the Sun Goes Down") including one by W. C. Handy, the famous blues impresario. The song has enjoyed a long-standing popularity with hillbilly bands and blues musicians. It has also been popular for a long time in college campus singing traditions. And several humorous verses have been contributed by the campus tradition. One provides an answer to what mother will say when the girl comes home in a family way (the first line is repeated three times):

> She'll tear her hair and bite her tongue,
> 'Cause she did the same when she was young.

Another comments on Daddy's position in the matter:

> What, oh what will Daddy say?
> He ain't my real pa anyway.

Obviously, it is difficult for student circles to take the song seriously. On our Cable Car Hoots in San Francisco we use a non-hillbilly, non-folk harmonization for the choruses, which I have included with the melody below. It's easy to learn, but you may wish to stick instead to traditional hillbilly harmony, mostly a third above the melody line.

Recordings: Clarence Cooper (Elektra, EKL 27); Ed McCurdy (Dawn, DLP 1127); Brownie McGhee (Folkways, FA 2030); Jean Ritchie (Collector Limited Edition, CLE 1201 – two versions); Bob Ross (Folkways, FA 2334); Carl Sandburg (Lyrichord, LL 4); Pete Seeger (Folkways, FA 2334); Josh White (Mercury, MG 20203).

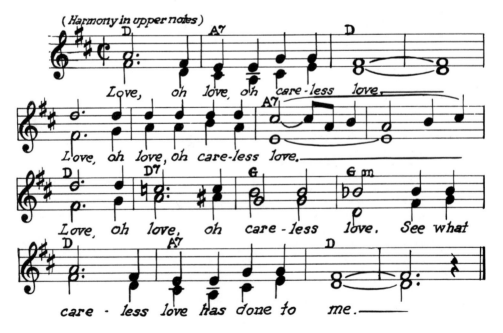

2. When my apron strings were long,
   When my apron strings were long,
   When my apron strings were long,
   You passed my window with a song.

3. Now my apron strings won't tie,
   Now my apron strings won't tie,
   Now my apron strings won't tie,
   You pass my cabin door right by.

4. I cried last night and the night before,
   I cried last night and the night before,
   I cried last night and the night before,
   Tonight I'll cry, then cry no more.

5. What, oh what will mother say?
   What, oh what will mother say?
   What, oh what will mother say?
   When I come home in a family way.

6. I love my mom and daddy, too,
   I love my mom and daddy, too,
   I love my mom and daddy, too,
   But I'd leave them both to go with you.

7. How I wish that train would come,
   How I wish that train would come,
   How I wish that train would come,
   And take me back where I come from.

8. It's on this railroad track I stand,
   It's on this railroad track I stand,
   It's on this railroad track I stand,
   All for the love of a railroad man.

There is a possibility that "Careless Love" was inspired by a floating verse that shows up in several variants of "The Butcher Boy":

When I wore my apron low
My love followed me through frost and snow.
When I wore it up to my chin
My love passed by and never looked in.

THE CAT CAME BACK

According to folklore, a cat has nine lives. The cat in this famous song will have a lot more than nine lives if verses continue to be created for the song at the present rate. A relatively recent verse has the cat surviving the human race:

The atom bomb fell just the other day.
The H bomb fell in the very same way.
Russia went, England went, and then the U.S.A.
The human race was finished without a chance to pray.

The adventures of this extraordinary cat began when its mentor, Harry S. Miller, composed this minstrel song just before the turn of the century. The song caught on when it was introduced by Billy Rice of Harvey's Minstrels. Earlier lives of another cat, however, probably provided the model for Miller. His song was preceded by a French song, "Le Chat de Mère Michel."

Recording: Josef and Miranda Marais (Decca, DL 9047); Cisco Houston (Vanguard, VRS 9084).

2. The man around the corner swore he'd kill the cat on sight.
   He loaded up his shotgun with nails and dynamite.
   He waited and he waited for the cat to come around.
   Ninety-seven pieces of the man is all they ever found.

3. He gave it to a little boy with a dollar note.
   Told him for to take it up the river in a boat.
   They tied a rope around its neck, it must have weighed a pound.
   Now they drag the river for the little boy that's drowned.

4. He gave it to a man going up in a balloon.
   He told him for to take it to the man in the moon.
   The balloon came down about ninety miles away.
   Where he is now, well, I dare not say.

5. He gave it to a man going way out west.
   Told him to take it to the one he loved best.
   First the train hit the curve; then it jumped the rail.
   Not a soul was left behind to tell the gruesome tale.

6. Away across the ocean they did send the cat at last.
   Vessel only out a day and taking water fast.
   People all began to pray, the boat began to toss.
   A great gust of wind came by, and every soul was lost.

7. On a telegraph wire, sparrows sitting in a bunch.
   The cat was feeling hungry; thought she'd like 'em for a lunch.
   Climbing softly up the pole, and when she'd reached the top,
   Put her foot upon the electric wire which tied her in a knot.

8. The cat was a possessor of a family of its own,
   With seven little kittens, till there was a cyclone.
   Blew the houses all apart and tossed the cat around.
   The air was full of kittens, and not a one was found.

THE CHERRY TREE CAROL

The story of this very old and popular carol (number 54 in the Francis James Child collection of ballads) is derived from the pseudo-Matthew's gospel, chapter twenty. My setting is based on a southern mountain version in the Aeolian mode with a spiritual-like quality. The Cherry Tree story has been widely circulated, both as a folk story and as a folk song, throughout Europe and America.

Recordings: Isla Cameron (Tradition, TLP 1001); Paul Clayton (Folkways, FA 2310); Cynthia Gooding (Elektra, EKL 107); Joseph and Miranda Marais (Decca, DL 9030); Peggy, Barbara, and Penny Seeger (Folkways, FC 7053).

2. Joseph and Mary walked through an orchard good,
   There were cherries and berries as red as your blood.

3. Oh, then up spoke Mary, so meek and so mild,
   "Pluck me one cherry, Joseph, for I am with child."

4. And then up spoke Joseph with words most unkind,
   "Let him pluck thee a cherry that brought thee with child."

5. Oh, then up spoke the babe within his mother's womb,
   "Bow down then tallest tree, for my mother to have some."

6. Then bowed down the tallest tree unto his mother's hand;
   Then she cried, "See, Joseph, I have cherries at my command."

7. Oh, then up spoke Joseph, "I have done Mary wrong;
   But cheer up my dearest, and be not cast down."

8. Then Mary plucked a cherry, as red as your blood,
   Then Mary went home with her heavy load.

9. Then Mary took her babe, and sat him on her knee,
   She said, "My dear son, tell me what with this world will be."

10. "Oh, I shall be as dead, mother, as the stones in the wall;
    And the people in the streets, mother, shall mourn for me all."

11. "Upon Easter day, mother, my uprising shall be;
    And the sun and the moon, mother, shall both rise with me."

CINDY

There was a time when fiddling and dancing were frowned upon by the more conservative members of communities. Some of the verses in "Cindy" reflect the conflict between the Saturday night crowd and the Sunday morning set. You can dress up "Cindy" appropriately by inserting some fancy fiddling and banjo playing between the verses. There are many more verses given here than anyone should ever need for one performance.

Recordings: Oscar Brand (Audio Fidelity, AFLP 1847); William Clauson (Capitol, TL 0158); Patrick Gainer (Folk Heritage, DB 2122-3); Sam Hinton (Decca, DL 8418); Milt Okun (Baton, BL 1203).

mouth. Get a-long home, Cin - dy, Cin - dy, Get a-long home, Cin - dy, Cin - dy, get a-long home, Cin - dy, Cin - dy, I'll mar - ry you some day.

2. The first I seen my Cindy,
   She was standing in the door,
   Her shoes and stockings in her hand,
   With her feet all over the floor.

3. She took me to the parlor,
   She cooled me with her fan,
   She swore I was the prettiest thing
   In the shape of mortal man.

4. She told me that she loved me,
   She called me sugar plum;
   She throwed her arms around me,
   I thought my time had come.

5. I wish I was an apple
   A-hangin' on a tree,
   And every time my Cindy passed
   She'd take a bite of me.

6. And if I was a sugar tree
   A-standin' in the town,
   Every time my Cindy passed
   I'd shake some sugar down.

7. And if I was a needle,
   As fine as I could sew,
   I'd sew myself to her coat tails
   And down the road I'd go.

8. Oh, Cindy is a pretty girl,
   Cindy is a peach.
   She throwed her arms around my neck
   And hung on like a leach.

9. Cindy got religion,
   I'll tell you what she done,
   She walked up to the preacher
   And chawed her chewing gum.

10. So full of her religion,
    She went preachin' 'round the town,
    She got so full of glory,
    She shook her stockings down.

11. Yes, Cindy got religion,
    She had it once before,
    But when she heard my old banjo
    She was the first one on the floor.

12. Cindy in the springtime,
    Cindy in the fall,
    If I can't have my Cindy
    I'll have no gal at all.

CLEMENTINE

Sigmund Spaeth says that "Clementine" was written by Percy Montrose in 1883. The tune may be older, but the words at least came along sometime after the big gold-rush days. Several verses have been added by campers and college students. Despite its age it remains a popular song for group singing.

Recordings: Logan English (Folkways, FH 5255); Will Holt (Coral, CRL 57114); Ed McCurdy (Riverside, RLP 12-807); The Weavers (Vanguard, VRS 9013).

Chorus:

Oh my darling, oh my darling,
Oh my darling Clementine,
You are lost and gone forever,
Dreadful sorry, Clementine.

2. Light she was, and like a fairy,
   And her shoes were number nine,
   Herring boxes without topses,
   Sandals were for Clementine.

3. Drove she ducklings to the water
   Every morning just at nine,
   Hit her foot against a splinter,
   Fell into the foaming brine.

4. Ruby lips above the water,
   Blowing bubbles soft and fine,
   But, alas! I was no swimmer,
   So I lost my Clementine.

5. In a churchyard near the canyon,
   Where the myrtle doth entwine,
   There grow roses and other posies,
   Fertilized by Clementine.

6. Then the miner, forty-niner,
   Soon began to peak and pine;
   Though in life I used to hug her,
   Now she's dead I draw the line.

7. In my dreams she still doth haunt me,
   Robed in garments soaked with brine;
   Though in life I used to hug her,
   Now she's dead I draw the line.

8. Listen Boy Scouts, heed the warning
   To this tragic tale of mine:
   Artificial respiration
   Could have saved my Clementine.

9. How I missed her, how I missed her,
   How I missed my Clementine,
   Till I kissed her little sister,
   And forgot my Clementine.

COCKLES AND MUSSELS

"Cockles and Mussels" or "Molly Malone" has been pretty much ignored by the scholars and collectors but not by the singers of folk songs. I assume the reason for its neglect by specialists is that it does not fit most definitions of folk song. Apparently it dates from the nineteenth century and has had little or no variation in form or content. The tune may have been written by James Yorkston.

Recordings: William Clauson (RCA Victor, LPM 1286); Cisco Houston (Disc, D 103); Burl Ives (Decca, DL 8444, 5490, and 8246); Susan Reed (Columbia Masterworks, ML 54368, and RCA Victor, LXA 3019); Josh White (Decca, DL 8665).

In Dub-lin's fair ci-ty where girls are so pret-ty, I first set my eyes on sweet Mol-lie Ma-lone. As she pushed her wheel bar-row Thro' streets broad and nar-row Cry-ing cock-les and mus-sels a-live, a-live oh, A-live, a-live, oh,— A-live, a-live, oh,— Cry-ing cock-les and mus-sels a-live a-live, oh.

2. She was a fishmonger, but sure 'twas no wonder,
   For so were her father and mother before,
   And they each pushed their wheelbarrow
   Through streets broad and narrow
   Crying cockles and mussels alive, alive, oh!

3. She died of a "faver," and no one could save her,
   And that was the end of sweet Mollie Malone;
   Her ghost wheels her barrow
   Through streets broad and narrow
   Crying cockles and mussels alive, alive, oh!

COPLAS

"Coplas" comes from Mexico's equivalent of our hillbilly music tradition. The verses are mostly fashioned out of proverbs of the Mexican people. According to an Italian saying, "Proverbs are the wisdom of the people." This may be an overstatement—proverbs frequently are—but, nevertheless, these popular sayings are an important part of the philosophical traditions of the folk and they reflect national or racial idioms, customs, and thinking. The making of proverbs is such an ancient folk art that examples have been found in some of the oldest languages known: Sanskrit, Chinese, Eyptian, and Akkadian. Many variations of these popular sayings appear in different languages. The muddy-water proverb used in the second verse *(Diles que no batan l'agua; Que al cabo lo han de beber)* shows up in Russian as "Don't defile the well; you may want to drink from it"; in French as "Don't spit in the air; it might fall back on you"; and in American English as "Don't bite the hand that feeds you." The English version given (Let them muddy up the water; when they drink it they will see) is based on my free translation of the Spanish.

Recordings: Trio de las Rancheras (Decca, DL 4520); Cynthia Gooding and Theodore Bikel (Elektra, EKL 109); Kingston Trio (Capitol, T 996).

2. Dicen que los de tu casa
   Ninguno me puede ver.
   Diles que no batan l'agua;
   Que al cabo lo han de beber. *Chorus.*

3. La mula que yo monté
   La monta hoy mi compadre;
   Eso a mí no me importa
   Pues yo la monté primero. *Chorus.*

4. La noche que me casé
   No pude dormirme un rato.
   Por estar toda la noche
   Corriendo detra de un gato. *Chorus.*

5. Me dijiste que fue un gato
   El que entró por tu balcón.
   Yo no he visto gato prieto
   Con sombrero y pantalón. *Chorus.*

English version *(with tongue in cheek, and poetic license in hand)*:

1. You ask me for a green pepper.
   I will tell you what I'll do.
   Let us go out in the garden
   To pick a pepper out for you. *Chorus.*

2. They have told me that your family
   Cannot stand the sight of me.
   Let them muddy up the water,
   When they drink it they will see. *Chorus.*

3. There's a mule that I have ridden.
   Now it's ridden by a friend.
   But to me it is no problem—
   I'm the one who broke it in. *Chorus.*

4. On the night that we were married,
   I could never go to sleep.
   All my time was spent in chasing
   A kitty running down the street. *Chorus.*

5. A kitten running from your bedroom.
   I can just imagine that.
   I have never seen a kitten
   Wearing trousers and a hat. *Chorus.*

COPPER KETTLE

An excellent tune makes this one of the best of the popular moonshine songs. I learned this particular version from Richard Jaqua, a Kentuckian who lives in Woodside, California. Dick, a talented singer and teacher, composed the last two verses* himself. It was a popular song with folksingers in Texas in the 1930s as well as with folk song revivalists later on.

Recordings: Oscar Brand (Riverside, RLP 12-630); Joan Baez (Vanguard, VRS 9112); Chet Atkins (Victor, LPM 2783); Bob Gibson (Elektra, EKL 197).

*New words by Richard Jaqua. Copyright © 1963 by James Leisy Music. Used by permission.

Get you a cop-per ket-tle,—— And get you a cop-per coil.—— Fill it with new mixed corn-mash.—— And nev-er more you'll toil.——

CHORUS

You just lay there by the jun-i-per—— while the fires burn bright.—— Lord, you just watch them jugs a-fil-lin'—— 'Neath the pale_ moon-light._

2. Fill your fire with hickory,
    Hickory, ash, and oak.
    Don't use no green or rotten wood;
    They'll catch you by the smoke.

3. My daddy, he made whiskey.
    My granddad, he did, too.
    We ain't paid no whiskey tax
    Since seventeen ninety-two.

4. I'd rather drink corn whiskey
    Than anything I know.

I'd rather be here on moonshine hill
Than down in the town below.

5. God bless you, copper kettle;
   May you never stop.
   Just let me hear that whiskey goin'
   Drop, drop, drop.

CORENA

"Corena" sings of the female counterpart to "Easy Rider" (see Index). Both songs have been commercial successes. While "Easy Rider" found its popularity with the jazz crowd, "Corena" has been a favorite of hillbilly singers. "Corena" probably originated as a Negro blues—or was adapted from one; but the trading of songs, ideas, and techniques that has taken place between southern Negro and hillbilly musicians makes it difficult to determine the original source. You may wish to repeat the first verse at the end of the song as many singers do. Or you may add this tough-minded verse, which shows up in some versions:

> Corena, Corena, oh fare you well.
> Corena, Corena, oh fare you well.
> If I don't meet you in heaven, I'll see you in hell.

Recording: "Spider" John Koerner (Elektra, EKL 290).

Co-ren-a, Co-ren-a, —— where you been so long?—— Co-ren-a, Co-ren-a, —— where you been so long?—— I ain't had no lov-in' —— since you been gone.——

2. Corena, Corena, where did you stay last night?
   Corena, Corena, where did you stay last night?
   Come in this morning, sun shining bright.
   (*Or:* Your shoes ain't buttoned, don't fit you right.)

3. I love Corena, tell the world I do.
   I love Corena, tell the world I do.

66

Just a little more lovin', let your love be true.
(*Or*: And I hope some day, Babe, you'll love me, too.)

4. I met Corena, far across the sea.
   I met Corena, far across the sea.
   Won't write me no letter; she don't care for me.

THE COWBOY'S LAMENT

An old British street ballad, "The Unfortunate Rake," provided a model for many popular songs and parodies. Two of the best known of these derivative songs in this country are "The Cowboy's Lament," also known as "The Streets of Laredo," and "The Saint James Infirmary." There have been sea-going versions ("Wrap Me Up in My Tarpaulin Jacket"), army versions ("The Trooper Cut Down in His Prime"), and parodies for every walk of life: "The Ballad of Bloody Thursday" commemorates a strike in San Francisco; "Streets of Hamtramck" relates the fate of a Detroit auto worker who is "too old to work and too young to die." There's one about a U.C.L.A. professor who used to go dashing, "first from the Co-op and then to the rest room." His dying request:

Oh read my books slowly and toll the chimes lowly,
And bring Lady I. and the Elf-Knight along;
And in the grave throw me and roll the sod o'er me,
For I'm a professor and I know I've done wrong.

There's another one for skiers:

When I was a-skiing the hills of Sun Valley,
As I was a-skiing old Baldy one day,
I spied a young skier all wrapped in alpaca,
All wrapped in alpaca and cold as der Schnee.

Although "The Cowboy's Lament" is usually sung to the tune of the Irish song "Bard of Armagh" today, the cowboys preferred the dirgelike melody in the second version given, as sung by Slim Critchlow of Berkeley, California.

Recordings: William Clauson (Capitol, T 10158); Cisco Houston (Folkways, FA 2022); Burl Ives (Decca, DL 5013); Alan Lomax (Tradition, TLP 1029); Ed McCurdy (Elektra, EKL 112); Brownie McNeil (Sonic, B 16847-8); Pete Seeger (Folkways, FA 2452). Variation: "The Unfortunate Rake": A. L. Lloyd (Riverside, RLP 12 614).

As I ___ walked out in the streets of La-
re-do, As I walked out in La-re-do one
day, I spied a young cow-boy wrapped up in white
lin-en, Wrapped up in white lin-en as cold as the clay.

2. "I see by your outfit that you are a cowboy"—
   These words he did say as I boldly stepped by,
   "Come sit down beside me and hear my sad story;
   I was shot in the breast and I know I must die.

3. "It was once in the saddle I used to go dashing,
   It was once in the saddle I used to go gay;
   First to the dram-house and then to the card-house;
   Got shot in the breast; I am dying today.

4. "Get six jolly cowboys to carry my coffin;
   Get six pretty maidens to carry my pall;
   Put bunches of roses all over my coffin,
   Roses to deaden the clods as they fall.

5. "Oh, beat the drum slowly and play the fife lowly,
   Play the dead march as you carry me along;
   Take me to the green valley and lay the sod o'er me,
   For I'm a young cowboy and I know I've done wrong.

6. "Go gather around you a crowd of young cowboys
   And tell them the story of this, my sad fate;
   Tell one and the other, before they go further,
   To stop their wild roving before it's too late.

7. "Go fetch me a cup, a cup of cold water,
   To cool my parched lips," the cowboy then said;
   Before I returned, the spirit had left him
   And gone to its Maker—The cowboy was dead.

8. We beat the drum slowly and played the fife lowly,
   And bitterly wept as we bore him along;

For we all loved our comrade, so brave, young, and handsome,
We all loved our comrade although he'd done wrong.

SECOND VERSION

So ear-ly one morn-ing I rode o'er the ranch-es, So
ear-ly one morn-ing I rode ov-er there I
spied a young cow-boy, So brave and so hand-some With
coal black eyes— and wav-y black hair.

2. His eyes were fast glazing and death was approaching,
   His white lips were curled and tortured with pain,
   As he spoke in a whisper of a scene far behind him,
   Of his home in Montana he'd ne'er see again.

3. "Oh, beat the drum slowly and play the fife lowly,
   Play the dead march as you carry me along;
   In the grave throw me and roll the sod o'er me,
   For I'm a young cowboy and I know I've done wrong.

4. "My home's in Montana; I wear a bandana,
   My spurs they are silver, my horse is a bay.
   I first took to drinking and then to card playing,
   Which brought me to trouble, I'm dying today.

5. "Let sixteen gamblers come and carry my coffin,
   Let sixteen cowboys come and sing me a song.
   In the grave throw me and roll the sod o'er me,
   For I'm a young cowboy and I know I've done wrong.

6. "Write me a letter for my gray-haired mother,
   And break the sad news to my sister so dear.
   But not one word of this shall you mention
   When a crowd gathers 'round you my story to hear.

7. "Oh, there is another, more dear than a sister;
   She's lovely and pure as the dew on a rose.
   Tell her to wait for her lover no longer,
   For he sleeps where the prairie wind smoothly blows.

8. "Tell her her image has always been with me,
   Carrying me up through the long, lonely days;
   And that I'm taking it down through the valley,
   Locked in my heart to be with me always.

9. "Then swing your rope slowly and rattle your spurs lowly,
   And give a wild whoop as you carry me on.
   Take me to the green valley and lay the sod o'er me,
   For I'm a young cowboy and I know I've done wrong.

10. "Oh, bring me a cup of pure, pure water,
    A cup of pure water," the poor fellow said.
    But when I'd returned his soul had departed
    And gone to the Giver; the cowboy was dead.

11. We beat the drum slowly and played the fife lowly,
    And bitterly wept as we bore him along;
    For we all loved our comrade, so brave, young, and handsome;
    We all loved our comrade although he'd done wrong.

THE CRAWDAD SONG

   This popular song appears to be an amalgamation of a play-party song and the blues from Negro folk music traditions. It would be difficult to include all of the verses—and parodies—that have been invented for the song. You'll find some typical ones included after the contemporary version shown below.

Recordings: Alan Arkin (Elektra, EKL 21); Big Bill Broonzy (EM Arcy, MG 26034); Folksay, Volume II (Stinson, SLP 6); Cisco Houston (Folkways, FC 7020); The Wagoners (Folkways, FC 7030).

Continue, as above:

2. Yonder is a man with a pack on his back,
   Totin' all the crawdads he can pack.

3. A-settin' on the ice till my feet got hot,
   A-watchin' that crawdad rack and trot.

4. Crawdad, crawdad, you'd better go to hole,
   If I don't catch you, damn my soul.

5. Whatcha gonna do when the lake runs dry?
   Sit on the bank and watch the crawdads die.

6. Whatcha gonna do when your man goes away?
   Get me a better one very next day.

Additional verses:

Get up old man you slept too late, honey,
Get up old man you slept too late, babe.
Get up old man you slept too late,
Last piece of crawdad's on your plate,
Honey, baby mine.

or

Get up now you slept too late, honey.
Get up now you slept too late, babe.
Get up now you slept too late,
Crawdad man done passed your gate,
Honey, baby mine.

I heard the duck say to the drake, honey,
I heard the duck say to the drake, babe.
I heard the duck say to the drake,
There ain't no crawdads in this lake,
Honey, baby mine.

I sell crawdads three for a dime, honey.
I sell crawdads three for a dime, babe.
I sell crawdads three for a dime,
Your crawdads ain't as good as mine,
Honey, baby mine.

CRIPPLE CREEK

"Cripple Creek" is part of the basic repertoire of almost every southern mountain instrumentalist. The words suggest, and most singers assume, that the inspiration for the song was some local creek and local custom. According to folk music specialist Kenneth S. Goldstein, there is reason to believe that the song is linked to the discovery of gold in Cripple Creek, Colorado, in 1891. The news of this discovery had a great impact on southern mountain people, and a town in North Carolina was named Cripple Creek, probably in honor of the event.

Recordings: American Banjo Songs Scruggs Style (Folkways, FA 2314); Josef and Miranda Marais (Decca, DL 9027); Obray Ramsey (Riverside, RLP 12-649); Pete Seeger (Folkways, FA 2003).

I got a girl and she loves me, She's as sweet as she can be. She's got eyes of ba-by blue, Makes my gun shoot straight and true. Go-in' down Cripple Creek, Go-in' in a run, Go-in' down Crip-ple Creek to have some fun.

2. I took a trip to Cripple Creek
To see what them girls had to eat.
Their corn likker was mighty good,
So I got drunk like I knowed I would.

3. Now that old creek is wide and deep,
And I got to cross it before I sleep,
So I roll my britches to my knees;
I'll wade that creek whenever I please.

*...wishing her lover
good speed*

And away, hey...

*She crossed the
broad prairies...*

D

...the leafy green dome

Can she bake a cherry pie...

As I was going to Derby...

THE DANVILLE GIRL

Danville is such a common place name in this country it might as well be called Anyplace, U.S.A. For that reason, it's a good name to use in a rambler's song like this one. The song was a particular favorite of the hoboes (see "The Big Rock Candy Mountain"). There are several versions in circulation, but this one is probably the best known. It is also popular in hillbilly, railroading, and campus singing traditions.

Recordings: Jack Elliott and Derroll Adams (Topic, 10 T 14); Pete Seeger (Folkways, FA 2003); Variation: "The Gambler": Cisco Houston (Folkways, FP 2013).

2. When I got off at Danville, got stuck on a Danville girl.
   You can bet your life she was out of sight, she wore those Danville curls.
   She took me into her kitchen, she treated me nice and fine,
   She got me in the notion of bummin' all the time.

3. She wore her hat on the back of her head, like high-tone people do,
   But the very next train come down the line, I bid that girl adieu.
   I pulled my cap down over my eyes, walked down to the railroad tracks;
   There I caught the next freight train, never to come back.

75

DARLIN' COREY

There isn't much romance left in moonshining nowadays. Like a good many other things, it's moved down out of the mountains into the foothills and the cities. Instead of a do-it-yourself, homespun operation, it's more likely to be in the hands of a syndicate. But though the moonshining mountaineers are disappearing, some of the grand songs they inspired remain with us: "Old Mountain Dew," "I've Been a Moonshiner," "Copper Kettle," and, of course, "Darlin' Corey." I've included two different sets of verses. You can pick the set you like or select some verses from each set to add to your own version.

Recordings: Logan English (Folkways, FA 2136); Burl Ives (Columbia, CL 6109); Buell H. Kazee (Folkways, FS 3810); Ed McCurdy (Elektra, EKP 108); Pete Seeger (Folkways, FA 2003); The Weavers (Decca, DL 5285); Variation: "Little Corey": Jean Ritchie (Elektra, EKLP 2).

Wake up, wake up, darlin' Corey, What makes you sleep so sound? The revenue officers are comin', Gonna tear your still house down.

2. The first time I saw darlin' Corey,
   She was standin' in the door,
   Her shoes and stockings in her hands
   And her feet all over the floor.

3. Go 'way from me, darlin' Corey,
   Quit hangin' around my bed,
   Pretty women run me distracted,
   Corn likker's killed me dead.

4. The next time I saw darlin' Corey,
   She was standin' on the banks of the sea,
   She had two pistols strapped around her body
   And a banjo on her knee.

5. Last night as I lay on my pillow,
   Last night as I lay on my bed,
   Last night as I lay on my pillow,
   I dreamed darlin' Corey was dead.

6. The last time I saw darlin' Corey,
   She had a wine glass in her hand,
   She was drinkin' that cold pizen likker
   With a low-down gamblin' man.

7. Go and dig me a hole in the meadow,
   A hole in the cold, cold ground,
   Go and dig me a hole in the meadow,
   Just to lay darlin' Corey down.

8. Don't you hear them blue-birds singin'?
   Don't you hear that mournful sound?
   They're preachin' Corey's funeral
   In the lonesome graveyard ground.

SECOND VERSION:

1. The first time I saw darling Corey,
   She was standing on the banks by the sea,
   With a forty-four buckled around her,
   And a banjo on her knee.

2. Go away, go away, darling Corey,
   And do the best you can.
   I will get me another woman,
   And you can get you another man.

3. The last time I saw darling Corey,
   She had a forty-four in her hand.
   Kill that revenue officer
   That took away her man.

4. Go away, go away, darling Corey,
   Quit your hanging around my bed.
   Whiskey has ruined my body,
   Pretty woman has killed me stone dead.

DEEP BLUE SEA

The origin of this song remains a mystery. It has some verses in common with "Old Blue," "Dig My Grave with a Silver Spade," and "Old Stormalong." It may well owe a debt to the West Indies and the spiritual tradition. The tune is simple, expressive, and majestic.

Recordings: Odetta (Tradition, TLP 1010); The Gateway Singers (Decca, DL 8671); Folk Singers (Elektra, EKL 157); Pete Seeger (Folkways, FA 2043, and Aravel, AB 1006).

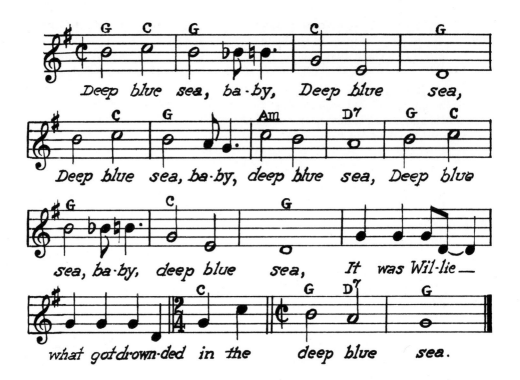

Deep blue sea, ba-by, Deep blue sea, Deep blue sea, ba-by, deep blue sea, Deep blue sea, ba-by, deep blue sea, It was Wil-lie— what got drown-ded in the deep blue sea.

2. Lower him down with a golden chain *(3 times)*
   It was Willie what got drownded in the deep blue sea.

3. Dig his grave with a silver spade *(3 times)*
   It was Willie what got drownded in the deep blue sea.

4. Wrap him up in a silken shroud *(3 times)*
   It was Willie what got drownded in the deep blue sea.

5. Golden sun, bring him back to me *(3 times)*
   It was Willie what got drownded in the deep blue sea.

DELIA'S GONE

I found two of my favorite Bahamian songs a long, long way from the Bahamas in the Newberry Library in Chicago. I first discovered "The John B. Sails" and "Delia's Gone" in the pages of a rare little book privately printed in 1927 by John and Evelyn McCutcheon and entitled (take a deep breath): THE ISLAND SONG BOOK Being a small COLLECTION of our favorite BALLADS, ANTHEMS, LULLABIES AND DIRGES Of *This Particular Section* of the BAHAMA ISLANDS And Also SUCH OTHER DITTIES As have seemed Befitting by Reason of their *Piratical, Nautical* or *Sentimental* Appeal Together with Several *Local* and *Topical Lays* Relating Only to TREASURE ISLAND To which is prefix'd An *Explanatory* and *Historical Introduction* To which is added A Number of SKETCHES and PHOTOGRAPHS Illustrative of Same.

The song has several things in common with "Frankie and Johnny": Both victims take a similar vehicle to the graveyard. Both songs are concerned with an old murder legend. Various conflicting claims have been made concerning the dramatis personae and the locale of both songs. One theory holds that Delia was murdered in Georgia around 1900 and that the ballad was carried to the West Indies by Negro sailors. Alan Lomax was told that the song is an account of a murder that took place in Dallas, Texas.

The first three verses presented here provide a short version as it is usually sung. The additional verses are from the McCutcheon book.

Recordings: Pete Seeger (Folkways, FA 2043); Josh White (Elektra, EKL 701 and EKL 123); Paul Clayton (Riverside, RLP 12-615); Harry Belafonte (RCA Victor, LPM 1022); Bob Gibson (Riverside, RLP 12 802); Will Holt (Coral, CRL 57114); Stan Wilson (Verve, MGV 2051).

Tony shot his Delia, 'Twas on one Christmas night.
First thing she did was hang her head and die. Delia's gone, one more round, Delia's gone, one more round. Delia's gone, one more round, Delia's gone, one more round.

2. Send for the doctor,
   The doctor came too late.
   Send for the minister
   To lay out Delia straight.

3. Delia, oh Delia,
   Where you been so long?
   Everybody's talkin' about
   Poor Delia's dead and gone.

4. Delia's mother dressed herself,
   Dressed herself in brown,
   Went to the cemetery
   To see her daughter layed down.

5. Rubber tired buggy,
   Double seated hack,

Take my Delia to the graveyard
An' never brought her back.

6. Tony asked the jailer,
   What is my time?
   Sixty-four years in prison,
   Sixty-four years is mine.

7. Sixty-four years,
   That ain't no time!
   Old Joe Bagstock
   Is servin' ninety an' nine!

8. All you gamblers
   That likes to bet,
   Come down to the courthouse
   And witness Delia's death.

The repetitious "one more round" of the chorus may call for another round of drink or song, or both. I prefer to drop the expression entirely, singing simply "Delia's gone" with sustained tones.

THE DERBY RAM

Folklorists have been collecting tall tales for a long time. "The Derby Ram" is a tall tale in song. (Derby is pronounced *Dar-by*.) According to Peggy Seeger it is part of an ancient winter ritual, "The Derby Tup," which is acted out, spoken, and sung in England at Christmas time by five or six mummers as they visit from house to house. She says that "similar rituals are still performed in rural England, with the central figure usually being a horse or bull, and the action full of crude humour and almost slapstick behaviour." The custom probably began in the town of Derby, where the oldest country fairs were held. Folk from the surrounding countryside brought things to sell. As the competition grew, the greater, no doubt, became the boasts of the competitors. One folklore theory holds that the custom bears a distant and comic relationship to primitive sacrificial rites. The years have contributed many verses to the song as well as several variants. I've included some of the miscellaneous verses for your selection.

Recordings: Oscar Brand (Riverside, RLP 12-825); Paul Clayton (Folkways, FA 2310); Billy Faier (Riverside, RLP 12-813); Cynthia Gooding (Elektra, EKL 107); The Kossoy Sisters (Tradition, TLP 1018); A. L. Lloyd (Riverside, RLP 12 618); Bascom Lamar Lunsford (Riverside, RLP 12 645); Alan Mills (Folkways, FC 7022); Peggy Seeger (Folkways, FC 7051, and Topic, TOP 18); The Greenbriar Boys (Vanguard, VRS 140). Peggy, Penny, and Barbara Seeger sing a sea-song variant, "It's a Lie," on another recording (Prestige, PR 13029).

As I was going to Derby upon a market day,— I saw the biggest ram, sir, That ever was fed on hay,— That ever was fed on hay. That ever was fed on hay.——

2. The ram was fat behind, sir,
   The ram was fat before,
   He measured ten yards 'round, sir,
   I think it was no more.

3. And he who knocked this ram down
   Was drown-ed in the blood,
   And he who held the dish, sir,
   Was carried away by the flood.

4. The wool grew on his back, sir,
   It reach-ed to the sky,
   And there the eagles nest, sir,
   I heard the young ones cry.

5. And all the boys in Derby, sir,
   Came begging for his eyes,
   To kick about the streets, sir,
   As any good football flies.

6. The wool grew on his belly, sir,
   It reach-ed to the ground.
   It was sold in Derby town, sir,
   For forty thousand pound.

7. The wool upon his tail, sir,
   Filled more than fifty bags.
   You'd better keep away, sir,
   When that tail shakes and wags.

Miscellaneous verses:

He had four eyes to see, sir,
And every eye it had,
Was looking straight at me, sir,
I never felt so bad.

He had four feet to walk, sir,
He had four feet to stand,
And each foot that he had, sir,
It covered an acre of land.

81

This ram he had two horns, sir,
They reach-ed to the moon,
Our preacher went up in January
And couldn't get back till June.

The man who owned this ram, sir,
He must've been very rich,
Or the man who wrote this song, sir,
Was a lying son of a bitch.

Perhaps you think it's a story,
Perhaps you think it's a lie,
But if you go to Derby
You'll see him as well as I.

DON'T YOU WEEP AFTER ME

In *Bahama Songs and Stories,* published in 1895 in the Memoirs of the American Folklore Society, Charles L. Edwards describes the "settin' up" custom for severely ailing friends in the Bahamas:

> The strangest of all their customs is the service of song held on the night when some friend is supposed to be dying. If the patient does not die, they come again the next night, and between the disease and the hymns the poor Negro is pretty sure to succumb. The singers, men, women, and children of all ages, sit about on the floor of the larger room of the hut and stand outside at the doors and windows, while the invalid lies upon the floor in the smaller room. Long into the night they sing their most mournful hymns and "anthems", and only in the light of dawn do those who are left as chief mourners silently disperse.

"Don't You Weep After Me" (in some versions, "grieve" replaces "weep"), a Bahamian hymn, might have been sung at a "settin' up" to *cheer up* the dying friend. The next to last verse might well have been volunteered by the dying man himself.

Recording: Peggy Seeger (Folkways, FA 2450).

me, Oh, I don't want you to weep af-ter me.——

2. Sailin' on the ocean,
   Don't you weep after me,
   Sailin' on the ocean,
   Don't you weep after me,
   Oh, I don't want you to weep after me.

   Continue, as above:

3. In the good old ship of Zion.

4. King Peter is the captain.

5. Bright angels are the sailors.

6. You poor distressed sinners.

7. Oh, look-a Mary.

8. She's lookin' over Jordan.

9. Oh, look-a Martha.

10. Oh, run along my friends.

11. Tell my Lord I'm coming.

DOWN IN THE VALLEY

"Down in the Valley" is part of the standard repertoire for group singing. It grew out of the melting pot of hillbilly and blues traditions in the southern mountain country. As Alan Lomax points out in *The Folk Songs of North America,* a mountain boy suffered greatly when he worked for an extended time, or was jailed, in the lowlands. The mountaineers loved their exhilarating atmosphere and were depressed by the valley country. A well-known version of this song is called "Birmingham Jail."

I've suggested several easy arrangements that might be used for group singing. The first melody below is the one commonly used in schools. You may add the echo effect in the fifth, sixth, eleventh, and twelfth measures as suggested. The second melody shown comes closer to the way the song is sung in the mountains, emphasizing the blues feeling more.

Recordings: Pete Seeger (Folkways, FA 2320); Richard Dyer-Bennet (Dyer-Bennet, RD-B1); Burl Ives (Decca, DL 5013); Bob Ross (Folkways, FA 2334).

FIRST MELODY

Down in the val-ley, the val-ley so low,_____
(val-ley so low,)

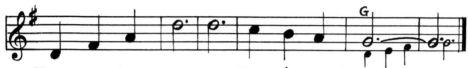

Hang your head o - ver, Hear the wind blow._____
(hear the wind blow.)

SECOND MELODY

Down in the val - ley,_____ the val-ley so
Hear the wind blow, love,_____ hear the wind

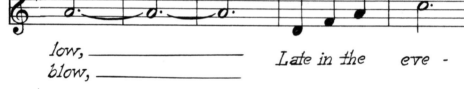

low,_____ Late in the eve -
blow,_____

ning,_____ hear the wind blow._____

2. If you don't love me, love whom you please,
Throw your arms 'round me, give my heart ease.
Throw your arms 'round me, before it's too late;
Throw your arms 'round me, feel my heart break.

3. Roses love sunshine, violets love dew;
Angels in heaven know I love you.
Know I love you, dear, know I love you,
Angels in heaven know I love you.

4. Build me a castle forty feet high,
So I can see him as he goes by.
As he goes by, dear, as he goes by,
So I can see him as he goes by.

5. Writing this letter, containing three lines,
   Answer my question, "Will you be mine?
   Will you be mine, dear, will you be mine?"
   Answer my question, "Will you be mine?"

Some singers like to add a wailing-wind effect at the end of each line (measures 6 through 8 and 14 through 16) in the second melody, using country harmony like this (one of various possibilities):

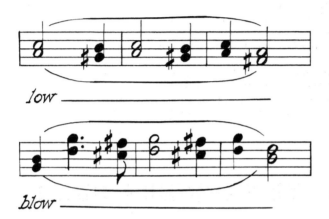

By changing from three to four beats a measure you may vary your interpretation rhythmically and melodically by improvising. Here's an example of what might be done:

Additional verses:

Bird in a cage, love, never been free;
Waiting for you, love, to come back to me.
Come back to me, love, come back to me.
Waiting for you, love, to come back to me.

Write me a letter, send it by mail,
Send it in care of the Birmingham Jail.
Birmingham Jail, love, Birmingham Jail,
Send it in care of the Birmingham Jail.

Write me a letter, send it by air.
Tell me you love me, tell me you care.
Tell me you care, love, tell me you care.
Tell me you love me, tell me you care.

Down by the levee, the levee so low,
Late in the evening hear the train blow.
Hear the train blow, love, hear the train blow,
Late in the evening hear the train blow.

DRILL, YE TARRIERS, DRILL

This tribute to, or protest in the name of, the Irish tarriers, who drilled and dynamited their way through the mountains for the railroads, was written by Thomas F. Casey and Charles Connelly, vaudeville entertainers with blasting-gang experience in the 1880s. In their performances, lines like the following were spoken at the end of each verse:

1. Stand out there with the flag, Sullivan. Stand back there! Blast! Fire! All over!

2. Stand out against the fence with the flag, McCarthy. Stand back! Blast! Fire! All over!

3. Where's the fuse, McGinty? What, he lit the pipe with it! Stop the belt car coming down! Stand back there! Blast! Fire! All over!

4. More oatmeal in the bucket, McCue! What's that you're reading, Duffy, the Staats Zeitung? Get out there with the flag! Stand back! Blast! Fire! All over!

Some specialists have attributed the nickname *tarriers* to the beards of the workers. However, it seems more likely that the nickname came from the boring instrument the men used or from an association between the digging habits of the terrier dog and those of the rock drillers.

Recordings: Bill Bonyun (Folkways, FC 7042); Richard Dyer-Bennet (Dyer-Bennet, RD-B4); Bob Gibson (Riverside, RLP 12-806); Cisco Houston (Folkways, FA 2346); Susan Reed (Elektra, EKL 116); The Weavers (Vanguard, VRS 9013). Variation: "Drill, Ye Heroes, Drill": Ken Peacock (Folkways, FG 3505).

Ear - ly in the mor - ning at sev - en o' - clock, There were

twen - ty tar - ri - ers a - work - in' on the rock, And the

boss comes a - long, And he says, "Kape still, and come down heav - y on the

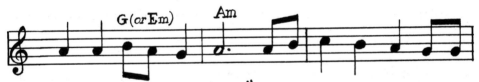

cast iron drill, And drill, ye tar - ri - ers, drill!

Drill, ye tar - ri - ers, drill!" And you work all day for the

sug - ar in your tay, down be - hind the rail - way, And

drill, ye tar - ri - ers, drill, and blast and fire.

2. The boss was a fine man down to the ground
   And he married a lady six feet 'round;
   She baked good bread, and she baked it well,
   But she baked it hard as the holes of hell!

3. Now the new foreman was Jean McCann;
   By God, he was a blamed mean man!
   Last week a premature blast went off,
   And a mile in the air went big Jim Goff.

4. The next time pay day came around,
   Jim Goff a dollar short was found.
   When he asked what for, came this reply:
   "You were docked for the time you were up in the sky."

THE DRUNKEN SAILOR

The tune of this *walk away* or *stamp and go* chantey was adapted from a traditional Irish dance and march tune. The chantey was usually sung while "walking" a light sail aloft, and often in a showy, man-o'-war fashion. The men would stamp loudly on the deck on the words "Way, Hey, up she rises." Although the tune is usually sung as a minor air (as shown here), some sailors preferred singing it in a major key. You can try it this way by changing the key signature to D major (two sharps) and using D major and A major chords instead of the minor chords. "Early" was and is always pronounced *earl-eye*.

Recordings: Richard Dyer-Bennet (Mercury, MG 20007); John Greenway (Riverside, RLP 12-607 — a parody); Burl Ives (Decca, DL 8245); Alan Mills (Folkways, FA 2312).

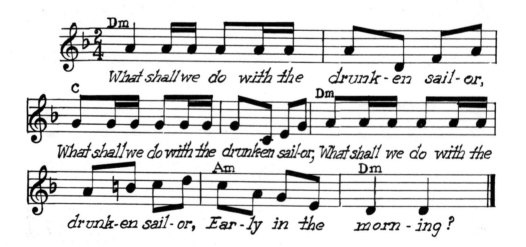

Chorus:
Way, Hey, up she rises,
Way, Hey, up she rises,
Way, Hey, up she rises,
Early in the morning.

2. Put him in the long boat till he's sober,
   Put him in the long boat till he's sober,
   Put him in the long boat till he's sober,
   Early in the morning.

   Continue, as above:

3. Pull out the plug and wet him all over.

4. Put him in the bilge and make him drink it.

5. Put him in a leaky boat and make him bale her.

6. Tie him to the scuppers with the hose pipe on him.

7. Shave his belly with a rusty razor.

8. Tie him to the topmast when she's yardarm under.

9. Heave him by the leg in a runnin' bowlin'!

10. Keel haul him until he's sober.

11. Temperance lectures will never help him.

12. Put him in the brig until he's sober.

13. Give him a hair of the dog that bit him.

14. Hoist him aboard with a running bowline.

15. Make him turn to at shining bright work.

16. Make him clear out the spit-kids.

   And, sometimes, referring to the captain himself:

17. Put him in his cabin and stop his likker.

   Any selection of verses usually ending with:

18. That's what we'll do with the drunken sailor.

E

...the leafy
green dome

Can she bake
a cherry pie...

As I was going
to Derby...

EARLY ONE MORNING

This beautiful English song is usually sung in the short form indicated first below. The additional verses help enlarge on the maiden's problem and extend the song to ballad form. The lack of modesty and the feigned innocence indicated in some of the verses may provide the answer to the question: "How could you use a poor maiden so?" It may also explain why the song is rarely performed by female singers.

Recordings: Richard Dyer-Bennet (Decca, DLP 5046); Milt Okun (Riverside, RLP 12 603); John Runge (Stinson, SLP 88); Andrew Rowan Summers (Folkways, FA 2041); Dylan Todd (Judson, J3010).

2. Oh, gay are the garlands and red are the roses
   I culled from the garden to bind on my brow.
   Oh, don't deceive me, *etc.*

3. Thus sang the maiden, her sorrow bewailing;
   Thus sang the poor maid in the valley below.
   Oh, don't deceive me, *etc.*

Long form:

2. Remember the vows that you made to me truly,
   Remember how tenderly you nestled close to me.
   Gay is the garland, fresh are the roses
   I've culled from the garden, to bind over thee.

3. Here I now wander alone as I wonder
   Why did you leave me to sigh and complain.
   I ask of the roses, why should I be forsaken,
   Why must I here in sorrow remain?

4. Through yonder grove by the spring that is running,
   There you and I have so merrily played,
   Kissing and courting and gently sporting,
   Oh, my innocent heart you've betrayed.

5. How could you slight so pretty a girl who loves you,
   A pretty girl who loves you so dearly and warm?
   Though love's folly is surely but a fancy,
   Still it should prove to me sweeter than your scorn.

6. Soon you will meet with another pretty maiden,
   Some pretty maiden, you'll court her for a while;
   Thus ever ranging, turning and changing,
   Always seeking for a girl that is new.

(Note: Last verse is the same as above in short version.)

EAST VIRGINIA

You really need banjo accompaniment to do this song effectively and appropriately. There are several melodies associated with this popular hillbilly song, but the one below is favored by banjo players. The "Greenback Dollar" (see Index) tune is also frequently used.

Recordings: Logan English (Folkways, FA 2136); Buell H. Kazee (Folkways, FS 3810); Pete Seeger (Folkways, FA 2003, and Aravel, AB 1006); Pete Steele (Folkways, FS 3828); Harry and Jeanie West (Stinson, SLP 74).

I was born and raised in East Vir-gin-ia; ___
It was there I met a fair young maid-en; ___
___ North Car-o-lin-a I___ did go. ___
___ Her name and age___ I did___ not know. ___

2. Well, her hair was dark of color,
   And her cheeks were rosy red;
   On her breast she wore white lilies
   Where I longed to lay my head.

3. I'd rather be in some dark holler,
   Where the sun refuses to shine,

Than for you to be another man's darlin',
And to know you'd never be mine.

4. For when I sleep I'm dreaming of you.
   When I'm awake I have no rest.
   Minutes seem to me like hours
   With aches and pains all through my breast.

5. In my heart you are my darlin',
   At my door you're welcome in.
   By my gate I'll always greet you.
   For you're the girl I've tried to win.

EASY RIDER

This blues classic is also known by the titles "C. C. Rider," "See See Rider," and "See See Mama." Evidently the initials C. C. are a corruption of the intended "See, See" ("See what you done done"). The easy rider is a man who latches on to a woman for what he can get out of her—but on a flexible basis: she gives all; he takes what he wants. The song has been a favorite of blues singers, folk singers, and both hot and cool jazz musicians. One of the coolest jazz performances was recorded by Ramsey Lewis a few years ago. Carl Sandburg and John Lomax were probably the first collectors to report the song after they heard it in the Silver King saloon in Austin, Texas. I've included several miscellaneous verses below from various versions of the song. Jerry Silverman presents three distinctive versions in his *Folk Blues*.

Recordings: Big Bill Broonzy (Columbia, WL 111, and Folkways, FG 3586); Variations: "Easy Rider": Will Holt (Coral, CRL 57114); Huddie Ledbetter (Folkways, FA 2024 and FA 2034); Odetta (Tradition, TLP 1010); "See See Mama": Tom Johnson and John Copeland (Folkways, FA 2654); "See See Rider": The Weavers (Decca, DL 5285).

2. You caused me, Rider, to hang my head and cry;
   You put me down, God knows I don't see why.
   You put me down, God knows I don't see why.
   You put me down, God knows I don't see why.

3. That Sunshine Special, comin' round the bend;
   It blowed just like it never blowed before.
   It blowed just like it never blowed before.
   It blowed just like it never blowed before.

4. If I had a headlight like on a passenger train,
   I'd shine my light on cool Colorado Springs,
   I'd shine my light on cool Colorado Springs,
   I'd shine my light on cool Colorado Springs.

5. Easy Rider, now see what you have done.
   You made me love you, now your sweetheart's come,
   You made me love you, now your sweetheart's come,
   You made me love you, now your sweetheart's come.

Miscellaneous verses (Adapt melody, as required):

See See Rider, see what you done done.
You made me love you, now your gal done come.
You made me love you, now your gal done come.
You made me love you, now your gal done come.

I'm goin' away, baby, I won't be back till fall.
Goin' away, baby, I won't be back till fall.
Goin' away, baby, I won't be back till fall.
If I find me a good man, I won't be back at all.

I'm gonna buy me a pistol just as long as I am tall.
Gonna kill my man and catch the Cannon Ball,
Gonna kill my man and catch the Cannon Ball.
If he won't have me, he won't have no gal at all.

See See Rider, where did you stay last night?
Your shoes ain't buttoned, clothes don't fit you right.
Your shoes ain't buttoned, clothes don't fit you right.
You didn't come home till the sun was shinin' bright.

If I was a catfish, swimmin' in the deep blue sea,
If I was a catfish, swimmin' in the deep blue sea,
If I was a catfish, swimmin' in the deep blue sea,
I'd have the pretty women divin' after me.

EGGS AND MARROWBONE

"Johnny Sands" and "Eggs and Marrowbone" are two related songs which appear to be founded on a folk tale common in England and Scotland. It suggests one way *not* to get rid of your man.

Recordings: Richard Dyer-Bennet (Decca, DLP 5046); Seamus Ennis (Tradition, TLP 1013); Tom Kines (Elektra, EKL 137); Dorothy Olsen (RCA Victor, LPM 1606).

There was an old woman an in our town In
our — town did dwell. She — loved her old man
dear-ly But a-noth-er man twice as well.

2. She went down to the doctor
   To see what she could find,
   To see what she could find, sir,
   To make her old man blind.

3. Eggs, eggs, and marrowbone,
   Feed them to him all;
   That will make him so gol-dern blind
   That he can't see you at all.

4. She fed him eggs and marrowbone,
   Fed them to him all;
   That did make him so gol-dern blind
   That he couldn't see her at all.

5. "Now that I am old and blind,
   And tired of my life,
   I will go and drown myself,
   And that will end my strife."

6. "To drown yourself, to drown yourself,
   Now that would be a sin,
   So I will go down to the water's edge
   And kindly push you in."

7. The old woman took a running jump
   For to push the old man in.
   The old man he stepped to one side
   And the old woman she fell in.

8. She cried for help, screamed for help,
   Loudly she did bawl.
   The old man said, "I'm so gol-dern blind
   I can't see you at all."

9. She swam along, she swam along,
   Till she came to the river's brim.

95

The old man got a great, long pole
And pushed her further in.

10. Now the old woman is dead and gone,
And the Devil's got her soul.
Wasn't she a blamed old fool
That she did not grab that pole?

11. Eggs, eggs and marrowbone
Won't make your old man blind,
So if you want to do him in,
You must sneak up from behind.

EVERY NIGHT
WHEN THE SUN GOES IN

This beautiful blues song is related to "Careless Love." The harmonic changes in this arrangement add a great deal of interest to the song. It may be chorded more simply, but less interestingly, by using only the chords in a standard blues progression.

Recordings: Harry Belafonte (RCA Victor, LPM 1150); Dan Isaacson (Cornell, CRS 10021); Milt Okun and Ellen Stekert (Riverside, RLP 12-634).

Chorus (same tune as verse):

True love, don't weep; true love, don't mourn, *(3 times)*
I'm goin' away to Marbletown.

2. I wish to the Lord that train would come, *(3 times)*
To take me back to where I come from. *Chorus.*

3. It's once my apron hung down low, *(3 times)*
He'd follow me through sleet and snow. *Chorus.*

4. It's now my apron's to my chin, *(3 times)*
He'll face my door and won't come in. *Chorus.*

5. I wish to the Lord my babe was born,
A 'sitting upon his papa's knee,
And me, poor girl, was dead and gone,
And the green grass growing over me.

F

...the leafy green dome

Can she bake a cherry pie...

As I was going to Derby...

THE FARMER
WHO WENT OUT FOR BEER*

When exchange students became the fashion on American campuses after World War II, it was inevitable that some of their folkways would rub off on American students. This Scandinavian song has been popular with students throughout Europe for a good many years. Several translations and versions are now widely known and sung on American campuses. This version is my translation† from the singing of Norwegian students at Stanford, Berkeley, and U. C. L. A. It's a grand song for mixing beer drinking with robust singing.

Recording: The Shanty Boys (Elektra, EKL 142).

There was a jol-ly old farm - er man who start-ed to go out for beer, ___ He start-ed to go out for beer, ___ He start-ed to go out for beer, af-ter Hup sa, sa, tra la, la, la, He start-ed to go out for beer. ___

*From *Hootenanny Tonight!* by James F. Leisy. Copyright © 1964 by Fawcett Publications, Inc., Greenwich, Conn.
†Translation by James Leisy. Copyright © 1963 by James Leisy Music. Used by permission.

2. A student then came to his sweet young wife
   When the old man had gone out for beer,
   When the old man had gone out for beer,
   The old man had gone out for beer, out for
   Hup sa, sa, tra la, la, la,
   The old man had gone out for beer.

Continue, as above:

3. Her rosy red lips the young student kissed
   And tenderly patted her cheek,
   While the old man was out after beer,
   While the old man was out after beer, after, *etc.*

4. But the farmer was hiding behind the door
   And saw all that happened within,
   While they thought he was out after beer,
   They thought he was out after beer, after, *etc.*

5. The farmer he took a dim view of this
   And booted them both out the door.
   And then he went out after beer,
   The farmer went out after beer, after, *etc.*

6. Now, farmers should profit from this advice:
   When out after beer take your wife.
   Take your wife when you're out after beer,
   Take your wife when you go out for beer, out for, *etc.*

7. The moral for students is plain to see:
   Behind the door take a look
   When the old man is out after beer,
   When you think that he's out after beer, after, *etc.*

FARTHER ALONG

George Bernard Shaw wrote, allegedly characterizing the inhabitants of hell, that these people are not kind, only sentimental. The same may be said of this hillbilly gospel song from the school of sentimentality and self-pity. Nevertheless, it's one of the best of its kind, and very singable. There are many commercial hillbilly recordings in addition to the ones listed below.

Recordings: John Greenway (Riverside, RLP 12 607); Hally Wood (Stinson, SLP 73); Hedy West (Vanguard, VRS 9162); The Black Ace (Arhoolie, F 1003).

Temp-ted and tried we're oft made to won-der, Why it should be thus all the day long. While there are oth-ers liv-ing a-bout us, Nev-er mo-lest-ed, though in the wrong.

Chorus (same tune as verse):

Farther along we'll know all about it;
Farther along we'll understand why.
Cheer up, my brothers, live in the sunshine,
We'll understand it all by and by.

2. When death has come and taken our loved ones,
Leaving our homes so lone and so drear;
Then do we wonder why others prosper,
Living as sinners year after year.
Chorus.

3. Often I wonder why I must journey
Over a road so rugged and steep;
While there are others living in comfort,
While with the lost I labor and weep.
Chorus.

4. "Faithful till death," saith our loving Master,
Only a while to labor and wait;
All of our toils will soon be forgotten
When we sweep thro' the beautiful gate.
Chorus.

5. Soon with the Lord, our wonderful Savior
We'll be at home beyond the blue sky;
There we shall meet the dear ones a-waiting,
We'll understand it all by and by.
Chorus.

FLORELLA
(The Jealous Lover)

This American murder ballad has a theme similar to "Omie Wise" and "Banks of the Ohio," also included in this book. In the many variations of the ballad, the name of the murdered girl varies considerably: Florilla, Floretta, Flo Ella, Lorella, Emily, Alice, Ellen, Lillie. The motive, jealousy, and the details of the crime are generally the same. Scholars have not traced the crime to a specific event.

Alan Lomax, in *The Folk Songs of North America*, attributes the song's popularity in the last century to the "extremes of repressiveness of the age" — an age in which men and women went their separate ways and "no respectable woman could speak to a stranger in the streets without a scandal falling upon her." For men, these songs provided "fantasy revenge upon the whole unsatisfactory, demanding feminine sex." The women "rejoiced in the demise of their less virtuous sisters, and wagged their heads devoutly over the warning prohibitions these ballads presented to their sex." But don't we see the same sort of morbid interest and attraction to sensation in the somewhat less repressed audiences of today? Hasn't there always been a willing audience for sex, sadism, and violence?

Woody Guthrie had among his many talents a knack for taking an old song and making a new and quite different one out of it. His melodramatic "Philadelphia Lawyer" is based on "Florella." The tune and many of the words are the same, but the end product is quite different. "Philadelphia Lawyer" is a humorous story of a western man who chased an eastern slikker off his private preserve and decreased Philadelphia's legal fraternity by one.

Recordings: Eugene Jemison (Folkways, FA 2023 – "Fair Forella"); Tom Paley (Elektra, EKL 12 – "The Jealous Lover"); Ellen Stekert (Folkways, FA 2354 – "The Jealous Lover"). Woody Guthrie and Cisco Houston sing "Philadelphia Lawyer" on a Stinson recording (Stinson, SLP 32).

Way down in love's green val-ley, ___ Where ros-es bloom and fade, ___ There was a jeal-ous lov-er ___ In love with a beau-ti-ful maid. ___

2. One night the moon shone brightly,
   The stars were shining, too.
   When to Florella's window
   The jealous lover drew.

3. "Come, love, and let us wander
   Down where the woods are gay.
   And strolling we will ponder
   Upon our wedding day."

4. So arm in arm they wandered;
   The night birds sang above;
   The jealous lover grew angry
   With the beautiful girl he loved.

5. The night grew dark and dreary.
   Florella was afraid to stay.
   "I am so tired and weary,
   I must retrace my way."

6. "Retrace your steps? No, never!
   For you have met your doom.
   Farewell to you forever,
   To parents, friends, and home."

7. Down on her knees before him,
   Florella pleaded for her life.
   And deep into her bosom,
   He plunged his fatal knife.

8. Down on his knees he bended,
   Saying, "Oh, God, what have I done?
   I murdered my own Florella,
   As true as the rising sun."

9. Now in that lonely valley
   Where the willows weep o'er her grave,
   Florella lies forgotten
   Where the merry sunbeams play.

THE FOGGY, FOGGY DEW

If you've ever wondered what this song is really all about, you're not the first one. Some say it's a dirty song. Others say it's not. Burl Ives once had a dispute on this question and ended up in jail in a little town called Mona in the western part of the United States. In all fairness to Mona, that was before Ives became a celebrity as a ballad singer.

In his book *The Idiom of the People*, James Reeves examines several versions of "The Foggy, Foggy Dew" in an attempt to understand the song better. Reeves shows how time and corruption in the folk process have robbed this song of meaning. He restores the meaning for us by a fascinating bit of scholarly detective work: He shows how "foggy dew" is probably symbolic, with "foggy" quite possibly meaning perpetual or, at least, protracted and "dew" meaning virginity or, more generally, chastity. If this symbolism is correct, the weaver in the ballad protects the girl from protracted chastity, which she fears—so that "the only thing I did that was wrong was to keep

103

her from the foggy, foggy dew." Or another way of looking at it would be to say that the girl found a method by which she could *persuade* a young bachelor to marry her. And, according to most versions of the song, it worked. In *The Idiom of the People* Reeves reconstructs the story in the ballad from fuller versions of it, as follows:

> The story is an unusual one in folk song literature. It is told in the first person, the teller being in some versions a weaver; in others no trade is mentioned, and in one he 'followed the roving trade.' He courts a girl, apparently with no immediate thought of seduction or marriage. The courtship may have begun on a midsummer morning expedition. The girl falls passionately in love with the young man and appears one night at his bedside in a state of frenzied agitation. She spends the night in bed with him 'for fear of the foggy dew'; in the morning she is afflicted with remorse, but her lover calms her by telling her that 'the foggy dew is gone'. Shortly afterwards ('the very next day', according to one version) the two are married, and either just before or soon after the marriage they discuss the probable arrival of children. Two babies would be, he tells her, a source of pleasure, but after the birth of two or three more they had better restrain themselves and 'think on the foggy dew'. The man concludes his narrative by admitting that the marriage turned out well despite its inauspicious beginning, and that the recollection of the 'foggy dew' is something of a joke between them.*

Reeves provides a composite version of "The Foggy, Foggy Dew" which tells the whole story:

> When I was young and in my prime
> I carried on the weaving trade
> And all the harm that ever I done
> Was courting a fair pretty maid.
>
> I courted her one midsummer day
> And part of the winter too
> Till I thought it my time to roll her in my arms
> Think no more on the foggy foggy dew.
>
> One night as I lay on my bed
> As I lay fast asleep
> Then up came this pretty fair maid
> And most bitterly did weep.
>
> She wept she moaned she tore her hair
> Crying Alas what shall I do,
> This night I'm resolved to stay with you
> For fear of the foggy dew.
>
> 'Twas in the first part of the night
> We passed our time away
> And in the later part of the night
> For she stayed with me till day.
>
> And when she rose and saw the light
> She cries I am undone
> I said fair maid be not afraid
> For the foggy dew is gone.

*From *The Idiom of the People* by James Reeves. Copyright © 1958 by James Reeves. Heinemann Ed. Books Ltd., London, and W. W. Norton and Company Inc., New York.

O when shall you come on my dear
O when shall you come on
When oaken leaves fall off the trees
And greener ones come on.

O that will be too long my dear
O that will be too long
My heart will burst, and die I must
That is if you don't come on.

The very next day I married her
I married her for life
And ever since I married her
I proved her for my wife.

When we have a child my dear
O that will make you smile
And when we have another
We will wait a little while.

And when we have another my dear
And have another too
Why we must leave off kissing
And think on the foggy dew.

And I never told her of her faults
And I never do intend so to do
But every time she smiles at me
I think of the foggy dew.

(Note: "O when shall you come on my dear" means "When will you marry me?")

With this background you may no longer be satisfied with the version below in the form it is usually sung today. If this is so, you can borrow from the version above and reconstruct the ballad along more meaningful lines.

Recordings: Oscar Brand (Audio Fidelity, AFLP 1806); Bob and Louise Decormier (Stinson, SLP 72); Richard Dyer-Bennet (Dyer-Bennet, RD-B4); Patrick Galvin (Stinson, SLP 85); Burl Ives (Decca, DL 5093); A. L. Lloyd (Riverside, RLP 12 618); Milt Okun and Ellen Stekert (Riverside, RLP 12 634); Susan Reed (Elektra, EKL 126); Robin Roberts (Stinson, SLP 63); Bob Ross (Folkways, FA 2334); John Runge (Riverside, RLP 12 814); Carl Sandburg (Lyrichord, LL 4); Tom Scott (Coral, CRL 56056); Paul Sykes (Crown, CLP 5057); Stan Wilson (Cavalier, CAV 5505); Josh White (London, LL 1147).

that was wrong Was to woo a fair young maid. I

wooed — her in — the winter time — And in the sum-mer,

too; And the on-ly, on-ly thing I did that was wrong Was to

keep her from the fog-gy, fog-gy dew.

2. One night she knelt close by my side,
   When I was fast asleep.
   She threw her arms around my neck,
   And then began to weep.
   She wept, she cried, she tore her hair—
   Ah me, what could I do?
   So all night long I held her in my arms,
   Just to keep her from the foggy, foggy dew.

3. Again I am a bachelor, I live with my son,
   We work at the weaver's trade;
   And every single time I look into his eyes
   He reminds me of the fair young maid.
   He reminds me of the wintertime
   And of the summer too;
   And the many, many times that I held her in my arms,
   Just to keep her from the foggy, foggy dew.

FOLLOW THE DRINKING GOURD

In the days before the Civil War, many Negroes, aided by Northerners who were opposed to slavery, escaped to freedom through an elaborate system known as the Underground Railroad. Although Negroes were occasionally shipped through in freight cars, the system was not a railroad and not underground. The name appears to have been derived from an earlier folk expression: When a hunter tracked his quarry on a warm trail that ultimately disappeared in thin air, he was likely to say, "He must've gone down an underground road."

The Underground Railroad provided "stations" for hiding and resting, "conductors" to escort the fugitives from one station to the next, and, of course, the "passengers" themselves.

Whether or not this slave song served any real function in the movement (and many specialists are convinced it did), it provides at least a symbolic timetable and map for the Underground Railroad. The drinking gourd refers to the Big Dipper, a convenient navigational guide. "Left foot, peg foot" refers to a man with a wooden leg, who helped out as a guide.

Recordings: Michael LaRue (Esoteric, ES 560); The Weavers (Decca, DL 5285).

When the sun comes back and the first quail calls,

Fol-low the drink - ing gourd, For the old man is a-wait-ing for to

car-ry you to free-dom, Fol - low the drink - ing gourd.

CHORUS

Fol-low_ the drink-ing gourd, Fol-low_ the drink-ing gourd, For the

old man is a - wait-ing for to car-ry you to free-dom,

Fol-low the drink - ing gourd.

107

2. The river bank'll make a mighty good road;
   The dead trees'll show you the way.
   Left foot, peg foot travelling on,
   Following the drinking gourd.

3. The river ends between two hills,
   Follow the drinking gourd.
   And there's another river on the other side,
   Follow the drinking gourd.

4. Where the great big river meets the little river,
   Follow the drinking gourd.
   The old man is waiting for to carry you to freedom,
   Follow the drinking gourd.

THE FOUR MARIES

This popular and beautiful Scottish ballad tells the story of a legendary scandal at the court of Mary Stuart — Mary, Queen of Scots. There are so many Marys in the song and in its historical scene that it is difficult to keep them all straight. Mary Stuart had four ladies in waiting: Mary Seaton, Mary Beaton, Mary Fleming, and Mary Livingston. The four Maries, as they were popularly known, were chosen to accompany her when she went to France as a little girl of five or six. These four girls, who were about her own age and who came from "honorable houses," remained with Mary Stuart while she was in France and returned to Scotland with her thirteen years later, in 1561. Despite the fact that they have been woven into the ballad, there is no record to indicate that any of these Marys was involved in a specific situation that would provide a basis for the story of this ballad. The Mary Carmichael and Mary Hamilton of the ballad appear from nowhere, although historians have located a Mary Hamilton who was a Scottish maid of honor at Peter the Great's court and was beheaded for infanticide (the crime in this ballad) in 1719. Surrounding Mary Stuart and her court there was considerable gossip, rumor, and criticism of romantic and political intrigues. This atmosphere in itself was sufficient to provide the basis for ballad and legend. Stories of illegitimate births occurring to members of her court and to the queen herself circulated widely at the time. Until research and scholarship turn up a better answer, if they ever do, we will have to assume the ballad emerged from this background of popular rumor and legend, with the customary confusions and distortions that accompany folk processes.

Ballad scholars have criticized the quality of this popular ballad because the story is told in the first person. In the opinion of these scholars, a proper ballad is rendered in a detached and objective manner by the balladeer. The "inferiority" of the ballad, however, does not seem to have affected its popularity with the folk, present or past.

The first version below is the short one commonly sung in this country. The whole story is spelled out in "Mary Hamilton," the longer, earlier version (from Scotland), which follows the short version.

Recordings: Joan Baez (Vanguard, VRS 9078); Cynthia Gooding (Elektra, EKL 131); John Jacob Niles (RCA Camden, CAL 330); Hermes Nye (Folkways, FA 2305);

Jeannie Robertson (Riverside, RLP 12 633); Andrew Rowan Summers (Folkways, FA 2044).

Last night there were_ four Mar - ies, To-night there'll be but three;___ There was Mar - y Beat-on and Mar - y Seat-on, and Mar-y Car-mich-ael and me.___

2. Oh, often have I dressed my queen
   And put on her braw silk gown;
   But all the thanks I've got tonight
   Is to be hanged in Edinburgh town.

3. Full often have I dressed my queen;
   Put gold upon her hair;
   But I have got for my reward
   The gallows to be my share.

4. They'll tie a kerchief around my eyes
   That I may not see to dee;
   And they'll never tell my father or mother,
   But that I'm across the sea.

5. Last night there were four Maries,
   Tonight there'll be but three;
   There was Mary Beaton and Mary Seaton,
   And Mary Carmichael and me.

Longer version:

1. **Word's gane to the kitchen,**
   And word's gane to the ha,
   That Marie Hamilton gangs wi bairn
   To the hichest Stewart of a'.

2. He's courted her in the kitchen,
   He's courted her in the ha,
   He's courted her in the laigh cellar,
   And that was warst of a'.

3. She's tyed it in her apron
   And she's thrown it in the sea;
   Says, Sink ye, swim ye, bonny wee babe!
   You'l neer get mair o me.

4. Down then cam the auld queen,
   Goud tassels tying her hair:
   "O Marie, where's the bonny wee babe
   That I heard greet sae sair?"

5. "There was never a babe intill my room,
   As little designs to be;
   It was but a touch o my sair side,
   Come oer my fair bodie."

6. "O Marie, put on your robes o black,
   Or else your robes o brown,
   For ye maun gang wi me the night,
   To see fair Edinbro town."

7. "I winna put on my robes o black,
   Nor yet my robes o brown;
   But I'll put on my robes o white,
   To shine through Edinbro town."

8. When she gaed up the Cannogate,
   She laughd loud laughters three;
   But whan she cam down the Cannogate
   The tear blinded her ee.

9. When she gaed up the Parliament stair,
   The heel cam aff her shee;
   And or she cam down again
   She was condemned to dee.

10. When she cam down the Cannogate,
    The Cannogate sae free,
    Many a ladie lookd oer her window,
    Weeping for this ladie.

11. "Ye need nae weep for me," she says,
    "Ye need nae weep for me;
    For had I not slain mine own sweet babe,
    This death I wadna dee.

12. "Bring me a bottle of wine," she says,
    "The best that eer ye hae,
    That I may drink to my we'il-wishers,
    And they may drink to me.

13. "Here's a health to the jolly sailors,
    That sail upon the sea;
    Let them never let on to my father and mother
    That I cam here to dee.

14. "Oh little did my mother think,
    The day she cradled me,
    What lands I was to travel through,
    What death I was to dee.

15. "Oh little did my father think,
    The day he held up me,
    What lands I was to travel through,
    What death I was to dee.

16. "Last night I washd the queen's feet,
    And gently laid her down;
    And a' the thanks I've gotten the nicht
    To be hanged in Edinbro town!

17. "Last nicht there was four Maries,
    The nicht there'l be but three;
    There was Marie Seton, and Marie Beton,
    And Marie Carmichael, and me."

FOUR NIGHTS DRUNK

This popular ballad is several hundred years old. Many different versions have been collected throughout Europe and America. As "Our Goodman," it is number 274 in the ballad collection of Francis James Child, the famous nineteenth-century ballad scholar. A German translation by Friedrich Wilhelm Meyer, published in 1790, contains a denouement, in which our goodman beats his wife and explains the blows as caresses sent to her by her mother. The Meyer version passed into oral circulation in Germany, Scandinavia, and Hungary. Contemporary re-composers of folk songs might wish to try their hands at developing the Meyer idea into a new version. Some of the contemporary versions have had a Thunderbird or its equivalent in the driveway when the drunk came home and have modernized the rest of his discoveries as well. The version presented here is probably the most widely used among folk song revivalists.

Recordings: Various versions under the "Four Nights Drunk" and the "Our Goodman" titles, or similar titles. Oscar Brand (Audio Fidelity, AFLP 1906); Sam Hinton (Decca, DL 8108); Ewan MacColl and A. L. Lloyd (Riverside, RLP 12-621); Ed McCurdy (Elektra, EKP 108). The song is also recorded on a Library of Congress Music Division record, *Anglo-American Songs and Ballads.* Cisco Houston's "The Intoxicated Rat" (Folkways, FP 42) uses one of the traditional melodies for "Four Nights Drunk."

I came home the oth-er night As drunk as I could

be. I saw a horse in the sta-ble Where my horse ought to

be. So I said to my wife, my pretty lit-tle wife, "Ex-plain this thing to

me. What's this horse do-in in the sta-ble Where my horse ought to

be?" "You darn fool, you drunk-en fool, Can't you nev-er see? It's

noth-ing but a milk cow that your moth-er gave to me." I've

trav-eled this wide world o-ver, Ten thou-sand miles or more, But a

sad-dle on a milk cow I nev-er did see be-fore.

2. I came home the second night,
   As drunk as I could be.
   I spied a hat on the hat rack
   Where my hat ought to be.
   So I said to my wife, my pretty little wife,

112

"Explain this thing to me.
What's this hat doing here on the hat rack
Where my hat ought to be?"
"You blind fool, you drunken old fool,
Can't you never see?
That's nothing but a chamber pot
My granny gave to me."
I've traveled this wide world over,
Ten thousand miles or more,
And a J. B. Stetson chamber pot
I never did see before.

3. I came home the third night
As drunk as I could be.
I spied some pants upon the chair
Where my pants ought to be.
So I said to my wife, my pretty little wife,
"Explain this thing to me.
What's these pants doing here on the chair
Where my pants ought to be?"
"You blind fool, you drunken old fool.
Can't you never see?
That's nothing but a dishrag
My granny gave to me."
I've traveled this wide world over,
Ten thousand miles or more,
And zippers on a dishrag
I never did see before.

4. I came home the fourth night
As drunk as I could be.
I spied a head on the pillow
Where my head ought to be.
So I said to my wife, my pretty little wife,
"Explain this thing to me.
What's this head doing here on the pillow
Where my head ought to be?"
"You blind fool, you drunken old fool,
Can't you plainly see?
That's nothing but a cabbage head
My granny gave to me."
I've traveled this wide world over,
Ten thousand miles or more,
And a mustache on a cabbage head
I never did see before.

THE FOX

"The Fox" appeared in a small collection of songs, *The Opera, or Cabinet of Song,* printed at Edinburgh for Joseph Skeafe in 1832, and believed to have been edited by the Scottish poet James Ballantyne. Whether or not it had its beginning there, it has delighted singers and audiences ever since. The tune is catchy and easy to sing, and the words are a pleasure to roll around in your mouth.

Recordings: Stan Wilson (Verve, MG V-2019); Woody Guthrie (Folkways, FC 7015);

113

Josef and Miranda Marais (Decca, DL 52680); Ellen Stekert (Folkways, FA 2354); Harry Belafonte (RCA Victor, LPM 1022); Pete Seeger (Folkways, FA 2321); Brownie McNeil (Sonic, B-16847-8); Odetta (Tradition, TLP 1025); Milt Okun (Baton, BL 1203).

2. He ran till he came to a great big pen
   Where the ducks and the geese were put therein,
   "A couple of you will grease my chin
   Before I leave this town-o,

   This town-o, this town-o,
   A couple of you will grease my chin
   Before I leave this town-o."

Similarly:

3. He grabbed the gray goose by the neck,
   Throwed a duck across his back;
   He didn't mind their quack, quack, quack,
   And their legs all dangling down-o *(etc.)*

4. The old mother Flipper-Flopper jumped out of bed,
   Out of the window she cocked her head,
   Crying, "John, John, the gray goose is gone,
   And the fox is on the town-o" *(etc.)*

5. Then John, he went to the top of the hill,
   Blowed his horn both loud and shrill;
   The fox, he said, "I better flee with my kill
   Or they'll soon be on my trail-o" *(etc.)*

6. He ran till he came to his cozy den;
   There were the little ones eight, nine, ten.
   They said, "Daddy, better go back again,
   For it must be a mighty fine town-o" *(etc.)*

7. Then the fox and his wife without any strife
   Cut up the goose with a fork and knife;
   They never had such a supper in their life,
   And the little ones chewed on the bones-o *(etc.)*

FRANKIE AND JOHNNY

There are almost as many theories about the origin of this favorite American blues ballad as there are verses and versions. Scholars have tried to trace it to an actual event, with little success. Frankie Silvers, who axed her husband in North Carolina in 1831, and Frankie Baker, who shot Allen Britt in St. Louis in 1899, are only two of the candidates who have been suggested as prototypes of the heroine. Most of the versions are cast in a ragtime-blues mold, as shown in the first version below. You may shorten your performance by singing only the verses marked with an asterisk in the composite version below.

Recordings: Big Bill Broonzy (Folkways, FA 2326); Sam Hinton (Decca, DL 8108); Cisco Houston (Disc, D 103); Burl Ives (Decca, DL 8080); Huddie Ledbetter (Stinson, SLP 51); Pete Seeger (Folkways, FA 2320); Stan Wilson (Cavalier, CAV 6002); Josh White (Decca, DL 8665).

FIRST VERSION

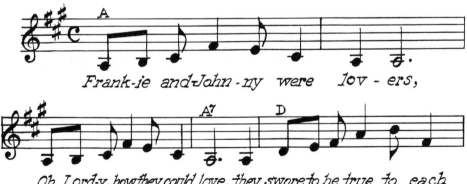

Frank-ie and John-ny were lov-ers,

Oh, Lord-y, how they could love. they swore to be true to each

115

oth-er, Just as true as the stars a-bove, He was her

man, but he done her wrong.——

2. *Frankie and Johnny went walking, John in his brand new suit.
   Then, "Oh, good Lawd," says Frankie, "don't my Johnny look real cute!"
   He was her man, but he done her wrong.

3. Frankie, she was a good woman, and Johnny was a good man,
   And every dollar that she made went right into Johnny's hand,
   He was her man, but he done her wrong.

4. *Frankie went down to the corner, just for a bucket of beer.
   She said to the fat bartender, "Has my lovin' man been here?"
   He was her man, but he done her wrong.

5. *"I don't want to cause you no trouble, I don't want to tell you no lie;
   But I saw your man an hour ago, with a gal named Nelly Bly,
   And if he's your man, he's a-doin' you wrong."

6. *Frankie looked over the transom, and found, to her great surprise,
   That there on the bed sat Johnny, a-lovin' up Nelly Bly.
   He was her man, but he done her wrong.

7. *Frankie drew back her kimono; she took out her little forty-four;
   Root-a-toot-toot, that gal did shoot right through that hardwood door,
   She shot her man, 'cause he done her wrong.

8. *"Roll me over easy, roll me over slow,
   Roll me on my right side, 'cause the bullet hurts me so.
   I was her man, but I done her wrong."

9. Johnny he was a gambler, he gambled for the gain.
   The very last words he ever said were, "High-low Jack and the game."
   He was her man, but he done her wrong.

10. Bring out your long black coffin, bring out your funeral clo'es;
    Bring back Johnny's mother; to the churchyard Johnny goes.
    He was her man, but he done her wrong.

11. Frankie went to his coffin, she looked down on his face.
    She said, "O Lawd, have mercy on me, I wish I could take his place,
    He was my man, and I done him wrong."

12. *Oh bring on your rubber-tired hearses, bring on your rubber-tired hacks,
    They're takin' Johnny to the buryin' groun' an' they won't bring a bit of him back;
    He was her man, but he done her wrong.

13. Frankie stood on the corner to watch the funeral go by;
    "Bring back my poor dead Johnny to me," to the undertaker she did say,
        "He was my man, but he done me wrong."

14. Frankie said to the warden, "What are they goin' to do?"
    The warden he said to Frankie, "It's the electric chair for you,
        You shot your man tho' he done you wrong."

15. The sheriff came around in the morning, said it was all for the best,
    He said her lover Johnny was nothin' but a doggone pest.
        He was her man, but he done her wrong.

16. The judge said to the jury, "It's as plain as plain can be;
    This woman shot her lover, it's murder in the second degree,
        He was her man, tho' he done her wrong."

17. Now it was not murder in the second degree, and was not murder in the third,
    The woman simply dropped her man, like a hunter drops a bird.
        He was her man, but he done her wrong.

18. *"Oh bring a thousand policemen, bring 'em around today,
    Oh lock me in that dungeon, and throw the keys away,
        I shot my man, 'cause he done me wrong.

19. "Yes, put me in that dungeon, oh put me in that cell,
    Put me where the northeast wind blows from the southeast corner of hell.
        I shot my man, 'cause he done me wrong."

20. Frankie mounted to the scaffold as calm as a girl can be,
    And turning her eyes to heaven, she said, "Good Lord, I am coming to Thee.
        He was my man, but he done me wrong."

21. *This story has no moral; this story has no end.
    This story only goes to show that there ain't no good in men.
        They'll do you wrong, just as sure as you're born.

SECOND VERSION

If you've worn out the standardized version of "Frankie and Johnny," you'll get a kick out of learning this hillbilly version. But watch out, it's like learning a whole new song. This is the version I used to play in hillbilly bands in Texas in the 1940s. If you have any doubts about this version's appeal, dispel them by listening to The New Lost City Ramblers recording for Folkways, or The Kingston Trio, or try to dig up an old recording by Charlie Poole and the North Carolina Ramblers.

Frank-ie and John-ny were sweet-hearts, They had a
quar-rel one day,— John-ny vowed to leave her,— Said he was
go-in' a-way, Goin'a-way from home,— Goin' a-way to
roam ———— Frank-ie begged and she plead-ed: "Oh, my
John-ny, please stay,— I know, hon-ey, I've done you wrong, But
please don't go a-way. And John-ny sighed,————
———— And Frank-ie cried. ————————

CHORUS
I'm go-in' a-way, I'm leav-in' to day, I'm never com-in' home.
———— You're gon-na miss me, hon-ey, In the days to come When the

118

winter winds be-gin to blow, The ground is cov-ered up with snow, You'll think of the way you're gonna wish me back your lov-in' man You're gonna miss me, hon-ey, In the days they say to come.

2. Frankie said to her Johnny:
 "Say, man, your time has come."
 Then from beneath her kimona
 She pulled her forty-four gun.
 These love affairs are hard to bear.

 Johnny ran down the stairway,
 Cryin', "Frankie, oh please don't shoot."
 Frankie aimed her forty-four
 And the gun went rooty toot toot.
 Old Johnny fell and Frankie yelled. *Chorus.*

3. Send for your rubber-tired hearse;
 Send for your rubber-tired hack,
 Take my Johnny to the graveyard,
 I done shot him in the back
 With my forty-four gun while he raced to run.

 Send for a big policeman
 To come take me away.
 Lock me up in a dungeon cell
 And throw the key away.
 My Johnny's dead because he said: *Chorus.*

G

*...the leafy
green dome*

*Can she bake
a cherry pie...*

*As I was going
to Derby...*

GENTLY, JOHNNY, MY JINGALO

Why should the devil have all the best tunes? It's a song like "Gently, Johnny, My Jingalo" that usually prompts this question, which has been asked over and over down through the ages. When the famous British folk song collector Cecil Sharp discovered the song, he decided the words were too coarse for publication; so he provided a new set of words to make the song respectable. These words, or variations thereof, are the ones that have survived in folk traditions to this day. The version censored by Sharp follows a traditional verse pattern found in various forms in many songs, including "A-Roving" and the contemporary collegiate bawdy song "Roll Me Over in the Clover." The first verse goes like this:

> I put my hand all on her toe,
> Fair maid is a lily O,
> She says to me, "Do you want to go?
> Come to me, quietly,
> Do not do me injury,
> Gently, Johnny, my jingalo."

In subsequent verses the singer is invited to put his hand on her knee, her thigh, her breast, her head, and so on. The rhyming lines generally go far beyond innuendo, with rather obvious "sporting" invitations. Several scholars have come to the conclusion that the song is a survival from medieval minstrelsy. It may be a corruption of the medieval lyric "Gentil Joli Jongleur." (Jugglers had a reputation for promiscuity in the Middle Ages.) This beautiful harmonization emphasizes the Mixolydian mode.

Recordings: Marilyn Child and Glenn Yarbrough (Elektra, EKL 143); Richard Dyer-Bennet (Stinson, SLP 35); Wallace House (Folkways, FW 6823); Terrea Lea (Hifirecord, R 404); Susan Reed (Columbia, ML 54368).

121

2. I held her hand and drew her near,
   Fair maid is a lily O.
   She whispered softly in my ear,
   Come to me, quietly,
   Do not do me injury,
   Gently, Johnny, my jingalo.

3. I placed my arms around her waist,
   Fair maid is a lily O.
   She laughed and turned away her face.
   Come to me, quietly,
   Do not do me injury,
   Gently, Johnny, my jingalo.

4. I kissed her lips like rubies red,
   Fair maid is a lily O.
   She blushed, then tenderly she said,
   Come to me, quietly,
   Do not do me injury,
   Gently, Johnny, my jingalo.

5. I took her to the church next day,
   Fair maid is a lily O.
   The birds did sing, and she did say,
   Come to me, quietly,
   Do not do me injury,
   Gently, Johnny, my jingalo.

GO DOWN, MOSES

Many musicians believe the Negro spiritual is America's greatest contribution to the music of the world. "Go Down, Moses" is certainly one of the classics of this great musical heritage. The long version presented below first appeared in *The Story of the Jubilee Singers,* by J. B. T. Marsh, published in the nineteenth century. Following a common practice, it includes some verses that seem to have been interpolated from other spirituals. You may wish to select your own verses to shorten the performance. A typical selection would include verses one, two, three, twelve, and fifteen. The phrase "Let my people go" appears three times in the song: in measures three and four and seven and eight of the verse and in the last two measures of the chorus. The phrase provides an opportunity for simple harmonization like this:

Recordings: Marian Anderson (RCA Victor, LRM 7006); Richard Dyer-Bennet (Dyer-Bennet, DYB 3000); Roland Hayes (Vanguard, VRS 494); Paul Robeson (Columbia, ML 4105).

When Is-rael was in E-gypt's land, Let my peo-ple go. Op-pressed so hard they could not stand, Let my peo-ple go.

CHORUS

Go down, Mos-es, 'Way down in E-gypt's land;— Tell— old Pha-raoh,— Let my peo-ple go.

2. Thus saith the Lord, bold Moses said,
   Let my people go;
   If not I'll smite your first-born dead,
   Let my people go.

3. No more shall they in bondage toil,
   Let my people go;
   Let them come out with Egypt's spoil,
   Let my people go.

4. When Israel out of Egypt came,
   Let my people go;
   And left the proud oppressive land,
   Let my people go.

5. O, 'twas a dark and dismal night,
   Let my people go;
   When Moses led the Israelites,
   Let my people go.

6. 'Twas good old Moses and Aaron, too,·
   Let my people go;
   'Twas they that led the armies through,
   Let my people go.

7. The Lord told Moses what to do,
   Let my people go;
   To lead the children of Israel through,
   Let my people go.

8. O come along, Moses, you'll not get lost,
   Let my people go;

Stretch out your rod and come across,
Let my people go.

9. As Israel stood by the water side,
Let my people go;
At the command of God it did divide,
Let my people go.

10. When they had reached the other shore,
Let my people go;
They sang a song of triumph o'er,
Let my people go.

11. Pharaoh said he would go across,
Let my people go;
But Pharaoh and his host were lost,
Let my people go.

12. O, Moses, the cloud shall cleave the way,
Let my people go;
A fire by night, a shade by day,
Let my people go.

13. You'll not get lost in the wilderness,
Let my people go;
With a lighted candle in your breast,
Let my people go.

14. Jordan shall stand up like a wall,
Let my people go;
And the walls of Jericho shall fall,
Let my people go.

15. Your foes shall not before you stand,
Let my people go;
And you'll possess fair Canaan's land,
Let my people go.

16. 'Twas just about in harvest time,
Let my people go;
When Joshua led his host divine,
Let my people go.

17. O let us all from bondage flee,
Let my people go;
And let us all in Christ be free,
Let my people go.

18. We need not always weep and moan,
Let my people go;
And wear these slavery chains forlorn,
Let my people go.

19. This world's a wilderness of woe,
Let my people go;
O, let us on to Canaan go,
Let my people go.

20. What a beautiful morning that will be,
Let my people go;

When time breaks up in eternity,
Let my people go.

21. O bretheren, bretheren, you'd better be engaged,
Let my people go;
For the devil he's out on a big rampage,
Let my people go.

22. The Devil he thought he had me fast,
Let my people go;
But I thought I'd break his chains at last,
Let my people go.

23. O take yer shoes from off yer feet,
Let my people go;
And walk into the golden street,
Let my people go.

24. I'll tell you what I likes de best,
Let my people go;
It is the shouting Methodist,
Let my people go.

25. I do believe without a doubt,
Let my people go;
That a Christian has the right to shout,
Let my people go.

GO TELL AUNT RHODY

You don't have to tell Aunt Rhody if you don't want to. Almost everybody's aunt, at one time or another, has been the recipient of the bad news about the old gray goose. If you wish to personalize this children's song, insert the name of your own favorite aunt. With a little experimentation you may introduce some interesting and dramatic effects by changing modes from major to minor, and back again, in your performance. Simply change all the D major chords to D minor chords. Try using the D minor chords in the third and the last verse only. Once you get the idea, work out an arrangement of your own.

Recordings: Marjorie Bennett (Judson, J 3028); Richard Dyer-Bennet (Dyer-Bennet, DYB 6000); Burl Ives (Decca, DL 5106); Terrea Lea (Hifirecord, R 404); Josef Marais (Decca, DL 5106); Susan Reed (Elektra, EKL 126); Pete Seeger (Folkways, FA 2321); Paul Sykes (Crown, CLP 5057); The Weavers (Vanguard, VRS 9024).

2. The one she's been savin',
   The one she's been savin',
   The one she's been savin'
   To make a feather bed.

   Continue, as above:

3. She died in the millpond, *(3 times)*
   Standin' on her head

4. The goslins are cryin', *(3 times)*
   Because their mommy's dead.

5. Go tell Aunt Rhody, *(3 times)*
   The old gray goose is dead.

GO TELL IT ON THE MOUNTAIN

A year-round popularity exists among both gospel singers and folk-style singers for this famous Christmas spiritual. In some versions the last verse is sung:

Down in a lowly manger
The humble Christ was born;
And God sent out salvation
That blessed Christmas morn.

Recordings: Roland Hayes (Vanguard, VRS 7016); The Weavers (Vanguard, VRS 9013); Howard University Choir (RCA Victor, LM 2126).

Go tell it on the mountain, Over the hills and ev-'ry-where, Go tell it on the mountain That Jes-us Christ is born. Oh, when I was a sin-ner, I prayed both night and day; I asked the Lord to help me, And he showed me the way.

2. When I was a seeker,
   I sought both night and day;
   I asked my Lord to help me,
   And he taught me to pray.

3. He made me a watchman
   Upon the city wall;
   And if I am a Christian,
   I am the least of all.

4. It was in a lowly manger
   That Jesus Christ was born;
   The Lord sent down an angel
   That bright and glorious morn.

GOIN' DOWN THE ROAD FEELIN' BAD

When Woody Guthrie migrated to California from the Dust Bowl of the Southwest, he sang "I'm blowin' down the road feelin' bad." And he passed along a Negro folk song that eventually earned a solid place in every folk song revivalist's repertoire. The song had long been popular with hoboes, and it became virtually a theme song for the Dust Bowl refugees in the 1930s. It has more verses than there would ever be time enough to sing, and new ones are being born every day.

Recordings: Woody Guthrie (Folkways, FA 2011); Clarence Cooper (Elektra, EKL 27); Elizabeth Cotton (Folkways, FG 3526); John Greenway (Riverside, RLP 12-619); Cisco Houston (Folkways, FA 2346); Burl Ives (Decca, DL 5093).

2. I'm goin' where the climate suits my clothes.
Lord, I'm goin' where the climate suits my clothes.
I'm goin' where the climate suits my clothes, Lord, Lord,
And I ain't gonna be treated this-a way.

Continue, as above:

3. I'm lookin' for a job with honest pay, *etc.*

4. These two-dollar shoes hurt my feet, *etc.*

5. Ten-dollar shoes suits me fine, *etc.*

6. I'm down in the jailhouse on my knees, *etc.*

7. Michigan water tastes like cherry wine, *etc.*

8. Prison water tastes like turpentine, *etc.*

9. I'm leavin' and I'm never comin' back, *etc.*

10. I'm goin' down the road feelin' bad, *etc.*

THE GOLDEN VANITY

"The Golden Vanity" probably has as many names as it does versions. Some of them include "The Sweet Trinity," "The Mary Golden Tree," "The Turkish Revelee," and "The Golden Willow Tree." Francis James Child traced it back to "The Sweet Trinity," a seventeenth-century British broadside ballad, in which Sir Walter Ralegh is the villain. Although the versions differ considerably in text and music, all of them deal with the same theme: an untrustworthy captain goes back on his promise to a heroic boy who rescues the captain's daughter. The first version provided below is the one usually sung today. The second version, a hillbilly version as sung by the Carter Family, has been recorded by Pete Seeger.

Recordings: Richard Dyer-Bennet (Dyer-Bennet, DYB 5000); Woody Guthrie (Stinson, SLP 53); Burl Ives (Decca, DL 8245); Bascom Lamar Lunsford (Riverside, RLP 12 645); Susan Reed (Elektra, EKL 126); Pete Seeger (Folkways, FA 2319); Ewan MacColl and Peggy Seeger (Riverside, RLP 12 637); Variation: "The Turkey Reveille": Brownie McNeil (Sonic, B-16847-8).

FIRST VERSION

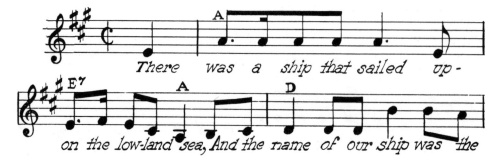

Gold-en Van-i-ty. And we feared she would be tak-en by the Span-ish en-e-my, As we sailed up-on the low-land, low-land, low-land, We sailed up-on the low-land sea.

2. Then up stepped our cabin boy, and boldly out spoke he,
   And he said to our captain, "What would you give to me,
   If I would swim up to the Spanish enemy
   And sink her in the lowland, lowland, low,
   And sink her in the lowland sea."

3. "Oh I would give you silver, and I would give you gold,
   And my own fairest daughter your bonny bride shall be,
   If you will swim alongside of the Spanish enemy
   And sink her in the lowland, lowland, low,
   And sink her in the lowland sea."

4. Then the boy he made him ready and overboard sprang he,
   And he swam alongside of the Spanish enemy,
   And with his brace and auger in her side he bored holes three,
   And he sunk her in the lowland, lowland, low,
   And he sunk her in the lowland sea.

5. Then quickly he swam back to the cheering of the crew,
   But the captain would not heed him, for his promise he did rue,
   And he scorned his poor entreatings when loudly he did sue,
   And he left him in the lowland, lowland, low
   And he left him in the lowland sea.

6. Then quickly he swam round to the port side,
   And up unto his messmates full bitterly he cried,
   "Oh, messmates, draw me up, for I'm drifting with the tide,
   And I'm sinking in the lowland, lowland, low,
   And I'm sinking in the lowland sea."

7. Then his messmates drew him up, but on the deck he died,
   And they stitched him in his hammock which was so fair and wide,
   And they lowered him overboard and he drifted with the tide,
   And he sank in the lowland, lowland, low,
   And he sank in the lowland sea.

There was a lof·ty ship, And— she put out to sea, And the name— of the ship was the Gold·en Van·i·ty, As she sailed up·on the low — and— lone·some low, — As she sailed up·on the lone·some sea. —

2. She had not been out but two weeks or three
   When she was overtaken by a Turkish Revelee
   As she sailed upon the low and lonesome low
   As she sailed upon the lonesome sea.

3. Then up spake our little cabin boy
   Saying "What will you give me if I will them destroy
   If I sink them in the low and lonesome low
   If I sink them in the lonesome sea?"

4. "O, the man that them destroys," our captain then replied
   "Five thousand pounds and my daughter for his bride
   If he sinks them in the low and lonesome low
   If he sinks them in the lonesome sea."

5. Then the boy smote his breast and down jumped he
   He swum till he came to the Turkish Revelee
   As she sailed upon the low and lonesome low
   As she sailed upon the lonesome sea.

6. He had a little tool that was made for the use
   He bored nine holes in her hull all at once
   And he sunk her in the low and lonesome low
   He sunk her in the lonesome sea.

7. He swum back to his ship and he beat upon the side
   Cried, "Captain pick me up for I'm wearied with the tide
   I am sinking in the low and lonesome low
   I am sinking in the lonesome sea."

8. "No! I will not pick you up," the captain then replied
"I will shoot you, I will drown you, I will sink you in the tide
I will sink you in the low and lonesome low
I will sink you in the lonesome sea."

9. "If it was not for the love that I bear for your men
I would do unto you as I did unto 'them'
I would sink you in the low and lonesome low
I would sink you in the lonesome sea."

10. Then the boy bowed his head and down sunk he
Farewell, farewell to the Golden Vanity
As she sails upon the low and lonesome low
As she sails upon the lonesome sea.

GOOD NEWS

This is one of the most popular of the good-news spirituals, particularly with gospel (which means "good news") singers. I've provided a simple three-part arrangement for group singing. If you want to sing it solo, you'll find the melody mostly in the bottom notes of the top staff. The melody moves around a little in the verses, but should be easy to locate.

Recordings: Lee Charles (Riverside, RLP 12 651); Bob Gibson (Riverside, RLP 12 816); The Howard University Choir (RCA Victor, LM 2126); The Wagoners (Folkways, FC 7030).

131

Char-i-ots a-com-in', And I don't want it to leave me be-hind.

Char-i-ots a-com-in', And I don't want it to leave me be-hind.

There's a long white robe in heav-en I know, _____

There's a long white robe in

There's a long white robe in heav-en I know, And I

heav-en I know, There's a long white robe in heav-en I know, And I

don't want it to leave me be - hind.

don't want it to leave me be - hind.

Continue, as above:

2. There's a pair of wings in heaven I know.

3. There's a starry crown in heaven I know.

4. There's a golden harp in heaven I know.

5. It's a better place than this world I know.

GOSPEL TRAIN

This familiar, lively spiritual is frequently sung without much imagination or variation. William C. Handy, whose early association with the blues earned him the title "father of the blues," tells us that in minstrel days "Gospel Train" was "ragged" with hand clapping, off-beat rhythm, syncopation, and gestures. In his demonstration the chorus included *all* the children (conventional versions limit the invitation to *little* children):

> Get on board, little children,
> Get on board, big children,
> Get on board, all the children,
> There's room for many a more.

In *Bahama Songs and Stories* I found a version that had a chorus like this:

> Get on board, you swearers,
> Get on board, rum drinkers,
> Get on board, backsliders,
> There's room for many a more.

With ideas like this, you should be able to loosen up and provide a lot of variation in your performance.

Recordings: Marian Anderson (RCA Victor, LM 110); Inez Matthews (Period Records, SLP 580); Paul Robeson (Vanguard, VRS 9037); Martha Schlamme (Vanguard, VRS 7012).

133

board, lit-tle chil-dren; Get on board, lit-tle chil-dren; Get on
board, lit-tle chil-dren; There's room for man-y a - more.

2. I hear the bell and whistle,
   A-comin' 'round the curve;
   She's playing all her steam and power
   And straining every nerve. *Chorus.*

3. No signal for another train
   To follow on the line;
   Oh, sinner, you're forever lost
   If once you're left behind. *Chorus.*

4. She's coming to the station,
   Oh, sinner, don't be vain;
   But come and get your ticket,
   And be ready for the train. *Chorus.*

5. The fare is cheap and all can go,
   The rich and poor are there;
   No second class on board the train,
   No difference in the fare. *Chorus.*

6. We soon shall reach the station,
   Oh, how we then will sing;
   With all the heavenly army,
   We'll make the welkin ring. *Chorus.*

GREAT SILKIE OF SULE SKERRY

In the folklore of the Hebrides and Orkney islanders, the silkies are seal-people. These "supernatural" creatures, legend has it, normally dwell at the bottom of the sea, but occasionally they appear as ordinary human beings on land. The earthly *nourris's* (woman's) story is filled with words that are better sung in the original than in translation, and they don't get in the way of understanding the story. The meanings of most of these words are clear in context. Sule (or Shule) Skerry is one of the Orkney Islands.

Recordings: Paul Clayton (Folkways, FA 2310); Cynthia Gooding (Elektra, EKL 107).

An earth-ly nou-ris sits and sings, And, aye, she sings, ba lil-ly wean.
"Lit-tle ken I my bairn-y's fath-er, Far less the land tha' he staps in."

2. Then in steps he to her bed fit,
   And a grumley guest I'm sure was he;
   Saying, "Here I am, thy bairny's father
   Although I be not comely.

3. "I am a man upon the land,
   And I am a silkie in the sea.
   And when I'm far and far from land
   My home it is in Sule Skerry."

4. "It was na' weel," quo' the maiden fair,
   "It was na' weel," indeed quo' she.
   "That the great silkie from Sule Skerry
   Should hae come and brought a bairn ta me."

5. Then he has taken a purse of gold,
   And he has pat it upon her knee;
   Saying, "Gie to me my little young son
   And take thee up thy nourris fee.

6. "It shall come to pass on a summer's day,
   When the sun shines hot on every stone,
   That I shall take my little young son
   And teach him for to swim the foam.

7. "And thou shalt marry a proud gunner,
   And a proud gunner I'm sure he'll be.
   And the very first shot that ever he'll shoot
   He'll kill both my young son and me."

8. "Alas, alas," the maiden cried,
   "This weary fate's been laid for me."
   And then she said, and then she said,
   "I'll bury me in Sule Skerry."

THE GREAT SPECKLED BIRD

Roy Acuff and his Smoky Mountain Boys made a hillbilly classic of this old gospel song from the mountain country. It was inspired by a Biblical passage (Jeremiah 12:9): "Mine heritage is unto me as a speckled bird, the birds round about are against her."

What a beau-ti-ful thought I am think-ing —
Con - cern - ing the great speck-led bird. —
Re - mem-ber her name is re - cord-ed —
On the pag - es of God's ho-ly word. —

2. All the other birds are flocking around her,
   And she is despised by the squad,
   But the great speckled bird in the Bible
   Is one with the great church of God.

3. All the other churches are against her.
   They envy her glory and fame,
   They hate her because she is chosen,
   And has not denied Jesus' name.

4. Desiring to lower her standard,
   They watch every move that she makes.
   They try to find fault with her teachings,
   But they can't find any mistakes.

5. She is spreading her wings for a journey,
   She's going to leave by and by.
   When the trumpet shall sound in the morning,
   She'll rise and go up in the sky.

6. In the presence of all her despisers,
   With a song never uttered before,
   She will rise and be gone in a moment,
   Till the great tribulation is o'er.

7. I am glad I have learned of her meekness.
   I am glad that my name's on the book,

136

And I want to be one never fearing
On the face of my Saviour to look.

8. When He cometh descending from Heaven
   On the cloud, as is wrote in the Word,
   I'll be joyfully carried up to meet Him,
   On the wings of the great speckled bird.

GREEN GROW THE LILACS

It has been suggested that "gringo," the Mexican word for foreigner or American (from the United States), may have originated with the frequent singing of "Green Grow the Lilacs" by Irish-American troops during the 1846 war with Mexico. But some scholars consider this only an interesting and romantic notion totally unrelated to the facts.

In other versions of this Irish song the first verse begins and ends with these lines:

> Oh, green grows the *laurel* and so does the *rue*;
> We'll change the green *laurel* for the *orange and blue.*

If we put together the thoughts of two folk song scholars on the use of the italicized words, we discover that the song may have hidden, symbolic meanings. Cox suggests that *orange and blue* (or *origin blue,* as it is sometimes sung) may be a corruption of *marjoram,* a blue plant. Blue symbolizes fidelity. Belden has shown that in old English street ballads *laurel* is a symbol of virginity, and *rue* means the opposite. With the blue flower representing fidelity, the symbolism suggests that a girl is giving up her maidenhood for a faithful love. Sam Hinton believes that marjoram stands for fertility rather than fidelity and that the fertility symbolism is even more appropriate to the subject. In any event, Irish immigrants apparently "changed the green laurel for the red, white, and blue" when they came to America, losing the folklore symbolism in the song as it is generally performed today. You may wish to restore the symbolism by including these lines in the first and last verses of the version below.

Folk singer Rosalie Sorrels has created still another version of this song by adapting the verses of "The Wagoner's Lad" to follow the first verse of "Green Grow the Lilacs."

Recordings: Sam Eskin (Cook Laboratories, 1020); Frank Luther (Decca, DL 5035); Ed McCurdy (Tradition, TLP 1003); Dylan Todd (Judson, J 3010).

137

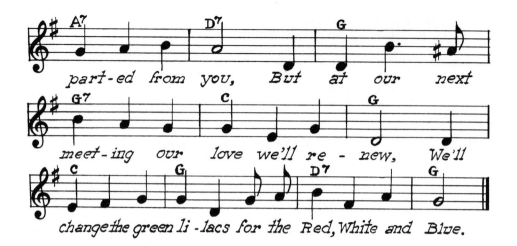

part-ed from you, But at our next
meet-ing our love we'll re - new, We'll
change the green li-lacs for the Red, White and Blue.

2. I once had a sweetheart but now I have none;
   He's gone off and left me to live here alone.
   He's gone off and left me contented to be;
   He must love another girl better than me.

3. I passed my love's window both early and late,
   The look that he gave me it made my heart ache.
   The look that he gave me was painful to see,
   For he loves another one better than me.

4. I wrote my love letters in red rosy lines,
   He sent me an answer all twisted in twines,
   Saying, "Keep your love letters and I will keep mine,
   Just you write to your love and I'll write to mine."

5. On top of the mountain where green lilacs grow,
   And over the valley where the still waters flow,
   I met my true love and he proved to be true.
   We changed the green lilac for the Red, White, and Blue.

GREEN GROW THE RUSHES

Folk song scholars have traced the theme of this popular cumulative folk song back to extremely antique antecedents coming from an original in Hebrew—specifically, from a chant in the service for the second night of the Passover:

Who knoweth thirteen?
I, saith Israel, know thirteen:
Thirteen divine attributes,
Twelve tribes,
Eleven stars,
Ten Commandments,
Nine months before childbirth,
Eight days before circumcision,
Seven days in the week,
Six books of the Mishnah,

Five books of the law,
Four matrons,
Three patriarchs,
Two tables of Covenant,
But one is God alone,
Which is over heaven and earth.

Other titles by which the song is known include "The Twelve Prophets," "The Carol of the Twelve Numbers," and "The Ten Commandments."

Recording: Tom Scott (Coral, CRL 56056—"The Story of Twelve").

Cloth-ed all in green O. One is one and all a-lone and ev-er-more shall be so.

④ I'll sing you four O, Green grow the rushes O. Four for the gos-pel makers,

Three, three the riv-als, Two for the lil-y white boys Cloth-ed all in green O.

One is one and all a-lone and ev-er-more shall be so.

⑤ I'll sing you five O, Green grow the rushes O. What is your five O?

Green grow the rush-es O. Five for the sym-bols at your door,

Four for the gos-pel mak-ers, Three, three the riv-als,

Two for the lil-y white boys Cloth-ed all in green O. One is one and all a-lone and

CONTINUE, AS ABOVE (6 and 10)

ev-er-more shall be so. ⑥ Six for the six proud walk-ers,
⑩ Ten for the ten com - mand-ments,

140

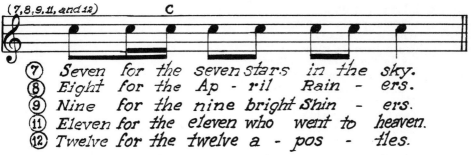

(7, 8, 9, 11, and 12) C

7 Seven for the seven stars in the sky.
8 Eight for the Ap - ril Rain - ers.
9 Nine for the nine bright Shin - ers.
11 Eleven for the eleven who went to heaven.
12 Twelve for the twelve a - pos - tles.

1. I'll sing you one O,
   Green grow the rushes O.
   What is your one O?
   Green grow the rushes O.
   One is one and all alone
   And evermore shall be so.

2. I'll sing you two O,
   Green grow the rushes O.
   What is your two O?
   Green grow the rushes O.
   Two for the lily white boys,
   Clothed all in green O.
   One is one and all alone
   And evermore shall be so.

3. I'll sing you three O,
   Green grow the rushes O.
   What is your three O?
   Green grow the rushes O.
   Three, three the rivals,
   Two for the lily white boys,
   Clothed all in green O.
   One is one and all alone
   And evermore shall be so.

4. I'll sing you four O,
   Green grow the rushes O.
   What is your four O?
   Green grow the rushes O.
   Four for the gospel makers,
   Three, three the rivals,
   Two for the lily white boys,
   Clothed all in green O.
   One is one and all alone
   And evermore shall be so.

5. I'll sing you five O,
   Green grow the rushes O.
   What is your five O?
   Green grow the rushes O.
   Five for the symbols at your door,
   Four for the gospel makers,
   Three, three the rivals,
   Two for the lily white boys,
   Clothed all in green O.
   One is one and all alone
   And evermore shall be so.

6. I'll sing you six O,
   Green grow the rushes O.
   What is your six O?
   Green grow the rushes O.
   Six for the six proud walkers,
   Five for the symbols at your door,
   Four for the gospel makers,
   Three, three the rivals,
   Two for the lily white boys,
   Clothed all in green O.
   One is one and all alone
   And evermore shall be so.

7. I'll sing you seven O,
   Green grow the rushes O.
   What is your seven O?
   Green grow the rushes O.
   Seven for the seven stars in the sky,
   Six for the six proud walkers,
   Five for the symbols at your door,
   Four for the gospel makers,
   Three, three the rivals,
   Two for the lily white boys,
   Clothed all in green O.
   One is one and all alone
   And evermore shall be so.

8. I'll sing you eight O,
   Green grow the rushes O.
   What is your eight O?
   Green grow the rushes O.
   Eight for the April Rainers,
   Seven for the seven stars in the sky,
   Six for the six proud walkers,
   Five for the symbols at your door,
   Four for the gospel makers,
   Three, three the rivals,
   Two for the lily white boys,
   Clothed all in green O.
   One is one and all alone
   And evermore shall be so.

9. I'll sing you nine O,
   Green grow the rushes O.
   What is your nine O?
   Green grow the rushes O.
   Nine for the nine bright shiners,
   Eight for the April Rainers,
   Seven for the seven stars in the sky,
   Six for the six proud walkers,
   Five for the symbols at your door,
   Four for the gospel makers,
   Three, three the rivals,
   Two for the lily white boys,
   Clothed all in green O.
   One is one and all alone
   And evermore shall be so.

10. I'll sing you ten O,
    Green grow the rushes O.

What is your ten O?
Green grow the rushes O.
Ten for the ten commandments,
Nine for the nine bright shiners,
Eight for the April Rainers,
Seven for the seven stars in the sky,
Six for the six proud walkers,
Five for the symbols at your door,
Four for the gospel makers,
Three, three the rivals,
Two for the lily white boys,
Clothed all in green O.
One is one and all alone
And evermore shall be so.

11. I'll sing you eleven O,
    Green grow the rushes O.
    What is your eleven O?
    Green grow the rushes O.
    Eleven for the eleven who went to heaven,
    Ten for the ten commandments,
    Nine for the nine bright shiners,
    Eight for the April Rainers,
    Seven for the seven stars in the sky,
    Six for six proud walkers,
    Five for the symbols at your door,
    Four for the gospel makers,
    Three, three the rivals,
    Two for the lily white boys,
    Clothed all in green O.
    One is one and all alone
    And evermore shall be so.

12. I'll sing you twelve O,
    Green grow the rushes O.
    What is your twelve O?
    Green grow the rushes O.
    Twelve for the twelve apostles,
    Eleven for the eleven who went to heaven,
    Ten for the ten commandments,
    Nine for the nine bright shiners,
    Eight for the April Rainers,
    Seven for the seven stars in the sky,
    Six for the six proud walkers,
    Five for the symbols at your door,
    Four for the gospel makers,
    Three, three the rivals,
    Two for the lily white boys,
    Clothed all in green O.
    One is one and all alone
    And evermore shall be so.

GREENBACK DOLLAR

Sometimes an expression or a phrase in a song has less meaning, in or out of context, to audiences of a later age than it did to those who first used the expression. The expression *greenback dollar* imparts some meaning in the context of this song: Don't try to buy me off, I wasn't after your money in the first place. But the meaning probably goes deeper than that. Something more than dollars is implied by the qualification *greenback.*

During the Civil War the federal government issued fiat paper money, or treasury notes, to finance war operations. These *greenback dollars,* as they were called popularly, were not backed by gold or silver deposits and were simply paper promises to pay. The value of these greenback dollars declined to a low of thirty cents on the dollar when the Union cause looked darkest, but improved as the tides of war changed. It was not until 1879 that these dollars were backed by gold again. In the meantime Confederate currency, on which appeared the promise "Fundable in eight per cent stocks or bonds of the Confederate States six months after the ratification of a treaty of peace between the Confederate States and the United States," became worthless when the Confederate government ceased to exist.

It is not surprising that many people were suspicious of greenback dollars for years to come, and insisted on *hard cash* instead of paper promises in any kind of exchange. Maybe the singer of this song would have taken hard cash—but no trinkets, and no *greenback* dollars!

I've never particularly liked the disjointed collection of verses usually put together by performers for this song. They lack a consistent story line. Also, many versions end violently, with verses like this one:

> I don't want your greenback dollar.
> I don't want your diamond ring.
> All I want is a thirty-eight special.
> I'll blow out your dirty brains.

I've used my own version,* for the reasons just mentioned, with lines and ideas from other songs, including "Fond Affection" and "Go Bring Me Back My Blue-Eyed Boy."

*Original words by James Leisy. Copyright © 1963 by James Leisy Music, Portola Valley, California. Used by permission.

2. Once you loved with fond affection,
   And your thoughts were just of me.
   Now you've left me for another
   And you care no more for me.

3. I don't want your greenback dollar,
   And those things you sent to me.
   If your conscience bothers you,
   Let it be, just let it be.

4. Oh, there's changes in the ocean;
   Yes, there's changes in the sea;
   And there's changes in the weather,
   But there'll be no change in me.

5. I don't want your greenback dollar,
   You can't buy your conscience free.
   I just want your arms around me.
   Darlin', please, come back to me.

GREENSLEEVES

"Greensleeves" has one of the most durable melodies in folk music (see the discussion under "Acres of Clams," indexed). During the almost four centuries of its known life, it has had texts fitted to it to please the man in the street, the drawing-room set, opera goers, the clergy, and twentieth-century teenagers. The texts have been bawdy, religious, political, social, literary, mundane, and temporal—but the melody has never failed to survive. The texts most frequently sung today are entitled "Greensleeves" and "What Child Is This?" The lyric to "Greensleeves" is tolerated by adults and ignored by children. In *The Ballad Mongers: Rise of the Modern Folk Song*, Oscar Brand suggests a method for communicating the text to children:

> . . . just tell the children that they are to raise their elbows on the word "greensleeves" as if they were wearing sleeves of that color. It'll be great fun. . . .
> You can tell them to put their right palms to their foreheads on the word "alas." On "you do me wrong," they must point an accusing finger at the head in front of theirs. On the phrase "to cast me off." they are to simulate throwing a bundle into the aisle. When they sing "For I," let them touch hand to breast sadly. This helps with the beat since it makes a wonderfully resounding "thwack." When they sing "you so long," the accusing finger is again indicated. And "delighting in your company" deserves a joyful throwing up of hands to the accompaniment of a wide-mouthed phony smile.
> The preceding exercise may forever sour the observing adults on "Greensleeves," but it will delight juvenile audiences.*

The text for "What Child Is This?" was written by William Chatterton Dix (1837–1898), the manager of a marine-insurance company in Glasgow. He had a talent for writing devotional poetry, of which he published several volumes. He contributed texts for many hymns and wrote *The Life of Chatterton, the Poet.*

*From *The Ballad Mongers: Rise of the Modern Folk Song* by Oscar Brand. Copyright 1962 by Oscar Brand, Funk and Wagnalls Company, Inc.

Recordings: William Clauson (Capitol, T 10158); Alfred Deller (Vanguard, VRS 479); Richard Dyer-Bennet (Decca, DLP 5046); Tom Glazer (Mercury, MG 20007); Odetta (Tradition, TLP 1025); Susan Reed (Elektra, EKL 116); Bob Ross (Folkways, FA 2334).

2. I have been ready at your hand,
   To grant whatever you would crave;
   I have both waged life and land,
   Your love and good-will for to have.

3. If you intend thus to disdain,
   It does the more enrapture me,
   And even so, I still remain
   A lover in captivity.

4. My men were clothed all in green,
   And they did ever wait on thee;
   All this was gallant to be seen;
   And yet thou wouldst not love me.

5. Thou couldst desire no earthly thing,
   But still thou hadst it readily.
   Thy music still to play and sing;
   And yet thou wouldst not love me.

6. Well, I will pray to God on high,
   That thou my constancy mayst see,
   And that yet once before I die,
   Thou wilt vouchsafe to love me.

7. Ah, Greensleeves, now farewell, adieu,
   To God I pray to prosper thee,
   For I am still thy lover true,
   Come once again and love me.

WHAT CHILD IS THIS?

1. **What Child is this, who, laid to rest,**
   On Mary's lap is sleeping?
   Whom angels greet with anthems sweet,
   While shepherds watch are keeping?
   This, this is Christ the King,
   Whom shepherds guard and angels sing:
   Haste, haste to bring Him laud,
   The Babe, the Son of Mary!

2. **Why lies He in such mean estate,**
   Where ox and ass are feeding?
   Good Christian, fear: for sinners here
   The silent Word is pleading.
   Nails, spear, shall pierce Him through,
   The cross be borne, for me for you:
   Hail, hail, the Word made flesh,
   The Babe, the Son of Mary!

3. **So bring Him incense, gold, and myrrh,**
   Come, peasant, king, to own Him;
   The King of Kings salvation brings,
   Let loving hearts enthrone Him.
   Raise, raise the song on high,
   The Virgin sings her lullaby:
   Joy, joy, for Christ is born,
   The Babe, the Son of Mary!

THE GYPSY LADDIE

"The Gypsy Laddie" is another one of the great ballads for which there are many versions and variants. I have included here the three most popular forms of the ballad in America: "Gypsy Davey," "The Wraggle-Taggle Gypsies," and "The Gypsy Rover." Some of the earliest-known versions are entitled "Johnny Faa, the Gypsy Laddie." This title is explained by Sargent and Kittredge, in *English and Scottish Popular Ballads* (one of the classic scholarly works, published in 1904), as follows:

Johnny Faa was a prominent and frequent name among the gypsies. Jonnë Faw's right and title as lord and earl of Little Egypt were recognized by James V in 1540. But in the next year Egyptians were ordered to quit the realm within thirty days on pain of death. The gypsies were formally expelled from Scotland by act of Parliament in 1609. Johnnë, alias Willie, Faa, with three others of the name, remained notwithstanding, and were sentenced to be hanged, 1611. In 1616, July 24, Johnnë Faa, Egyptian, his son, and two others were condemned to be hanged for contemptuous repairing to the country and abiding therein. Finally, in 1624, January 24, Captain Johnnë

Faa and seven others were sentenced to be hanged for the same offence. The execution of the notorious Egyptian and chieftain Johnny Faa must have made a considerable impression, and it is presumable that this ballad may have arisen not long after. Whether this were so or not, Johnny Faa acquired popular fame, and became a personage to whom any adventure might plausibly be imputed.

So the ballad properly belongs to another chapter in the history of man's inhumanity to man, despite the lightheartedness of the ballad itself.

Recordings: Ewan MacColl and Peggy Seeger (Riverside, RLP 12-637); John Jacob Niles (RCA Camden, CAL 245); Jeannie Robertson (Riverside, RLP 12 633). Variations: "Gypsy Davey": Woody Guthrie (Stinson, SLP 44); Cisco Houston (Folkways, FA 2013); Bascom Lamar Lunsford (Riverside, RLP 12 601); Milt Okun (Stinson, SLP 82); Jean Ritchie (Elektra, EKLP 2); Pete Seeger (Folkways, FA 2319). "The Wraggle-Taggle Gypsies": Alfred Deller (Vanguard, VRS 1001); Will Holt (Coral, CRL 57114); E. G. Huntington (Folkways, FA 2032); Burl Ives (Decca, DL 8245); Susan Reed (Elektra, EKL 126). "The Gypsy Rover": Tommy Makem at the Newport Folk Festival in 1960 (Vanguard, VRS 9083).

GYPSY DAVEY

It was late last night when the boss came home, A-ask-ing for his lad-y. The on-ly an-swer that he got: "She's gone with the Gyp-sy Dav-ey, She's gone with the Gyp-sy Dave."

2. Go saddle for me my buckskin horse
   And a hundred-dollar saddle,
   Point out to me their wagon tracks
   And after them I'll travel,
   After them I'll ride.

3. Well I had not rode to the midnight moon
   When I saw the campfire gleaming.

I heard the notes of the big guitar
And the voice of the Gypsies singing
That song of the Gypsy Dave.

4. There in the light of the camping fire,
   I saw her fair face beaming.
   Her heart in tune to the big guitar
   And the voice of the Gypsies singing
   That song of the Gypsy Dave.

5. Have you forsaken your house and home,
   Have you forsaken your baby?
   Have you forsaken your husband dear
   To go with the Gypsy Davey,
   And sing with the Gypsy Dave?

6. Yes I've forsaken my husband dear
   To go with the Gypsy Davey,
   And I've forsaken my mansion high
   But not my blue-eyed baby,
   Not my blue-eyed babe.

7. She smiled to leave her husband dear
   And go with the Gypsy Davey;
   But the tears come a-trickling down her cheeks
   To think of the blue-eyed baby,
   Pretty little blue-eyed babe.

8. Take off, take off your buckskin gloves
   Made of Spanish leather;
   Give to me your lily-white hand
   And we'll ride home together,
   We'll ride home again.

9. No, I won't take off my buckskin gloves,
   They're made of Spanish leather.
   I'll go my way from day to day
   And sing with the Gypsy Davey,
   That song of the Gypsy Dave.

THE WRAGGLE-TAGGLE GYPSIES

2. Then she pulled off her silk-finished gown,
   And put on hose of leather-o!
   The ragged, ragged rags about our door,
   And she's gone with the wraggle-taggle Gypsies, O!

3. It was late last night when my Lord came home,
   Inquiring for his a-lady, O!
   The servants said on ev'ry hand:
   She's gone with the wraggle-taggle Gypsies, O!

4. O saddle to me my milk-white steed,
   And go fetch me my pony, O!
   That I may ride and seek my bride,
   Who is gone with the wraggle-taggle Gypsies, O!

5. O he rode high, and he rode low,
   He rode through wood and copses too,
   Until he came to a wide open field,
   And there he espied his a-lady, O!

6. What makes you leave your house and land?
   What makes you leave your money, O!
   What makes you leave your new-wedded Lord?
   I'm off with the wraggle-taggle Gypsies, O!

7. What care I for my house and land?
   What care I for my money, O!
   What care I for my new-wedded Lord?
   I'm off with the wraggle-taggle Gypsies, O!

8. Last night you slept on a goose-feather bed,
   With the sheet turned down so bravely, O!
   Tonight you'll sleep in a cold, open field,
   Along with the wraggle-taggle Gypsies, O!

9. What care I for a goose-feather bed,
   With the sheet turned down so bravely, O!
   For tonight I shall sleep in a cold, open field,
   Along with the wraggle-taggle Gypsies, O!

THE GYPSY ROVER

The gyp-sy rov-er came ov-er the hill, And down thro' the val-ley so shad-y. He whis-tled and he sang till the

green woods rang And he won the heart of a la - dy.

Ah dee do, ah dee do da day, Ah dee do, ah dee

day dee. He whistled and he sang till the green woods rang, And he

won the heart of a la - dy.

2. She left her father's castle gate;
   She left her own true lover;
   She left her servants and her estate
   To follow the gypsy rover.

3. Her father saddled his fastest steed
   And roamed the valley all over.
   He sought his daughter at great speed,
   And the whistling gypsy rover.

4. He came at last to a mansion fine
   Down by the River Clayde;
   And there was music and there was wine
   For the gypsy and his lady.

5. "He's no gypsy, my father," said she,
   "He's lord of freelands all over;
   And I will stay till my dying day
   With my whistling gypsy rover."

H

*...the leafy
green dome*

*Can she bake
a cherry pie...*

*As I was going
to Derby...*

HANGMAN, HANGMAN

"Hangman, Hangman" is a popular contemporary American version of one of the more exciting old British ballads. As "The Maid Freed from the Gallows" it is number 95 in Child's ballad collection. The ballad has a long tradition with many variants, but the plot has remained pretty much intact throughout the years—only the sex of the central character and the melody and playing style seem to change very much. This particular version calls for a fast-paced and exciting rhythmic accompaniment.

Folk musicians sometimes refer to this kind of ballad as a *zipper* ballad. You have to learn a basic format for the song, and then you just "zip" a new word or a new line into this format for the rest of the song. Zipper songs and ballads are a boon to us all, since they cut down substantially on what we have to remember for performance. In "Hangman, Hangman" the zipper works like this: You begin by learning the first three verses; they provide the basic format for the ballad. Then you work the zipper by substituting *Mother* for *Sister* each time it appears. Repeat the three verses, using all of the same words except for this change. After mother has refused to save you from the gallows, you zip in brother and then father, repeating the process. You may zip in the relatives in whatever order pleases you most, but it would be going a little too far to get uncles and aunts into the act. In any event, you ultimately zip in sweetheart, by whatever name you choose, and the situation is saved.

Recordings: John Jacob Niles (RCA Camden, CAL 219); Jean Ritchie (Collector Limited Edition, CLE 1201); Andrew Rowan Summers (Folkways, FA 2041). Variations: "The Gallis Pole": Huddie Ledbetter (Stinson, SLP 51); Odetta (Tradition, TLP 1025); "Gallows Song": Carl Sandburg (Lyrichord, LL 66).

2. Sister, did you bring me silver?
   Sister, did you bring me gold?
   Did you bring me anything
   To keep me from the gallows pole?
   Lord, to keep me from the gallows pole?

3. I've brought you no silver;
   I've brought you no gold;
   I've come for to see you hangin',
   Hangin' from the gallows pole,
   Lord, hangin' from the gallows pole.

   Now zip in mother:

4. Hangman, hangman, slack your rope,
   Slack it for a while.
   I think I see my mother comin',
   Travelin' many a mile,
   Lord, travelin' many a mile.

5. Mother, did you bring me silver?
   Mother, did you bring me gold?
   Did you bring me anything
   To keep me from the gallows pole?
   Lord, to keep me from the gallows pole?

6. I've brought you no silver;
   I've brought you no gold;
   I've come for to see you hangin',
   Hangin' from the gallows pole,
   Lord, hangin' from the gallows pole.

   Continue, as above, zipping in brother and father and finally:

13. Hangman, hangman, slack your rope,
    Slack it for a while.
    I think I see my sweetheart comin',
    Travelin' many a mile,
    Lord, travelin' many a mile.

14. Laurie, did you bring me silver?
    Laurie, did you bring me gold?
    Did you bring me anything
    To keep me from the gallows pole,
    Lord, to keep me from the gallows pole?

15. I have brought the silver;
    I have brought the gold.
    I have brought you everything
    To keep you from the gallows pole,
    Lord, to keep you from the gallows pole.

HAUL AWAY, JOE

The short-haul or short-drag chantey is the simplest and one of the earliest forms of the chantey used. It probably grew out of the primitive "yo heave ho," or singing out of the sailors as they performed basic tasks aboard ship. Short-haul chanteys were used for work that called for a few short but strong pulls, as in boarding tacks and sheets or bunting up a sail in a furling. The humorous "Haul Away, Joe" was the favorite of sailors for sheeting home the foresail. The pull came on the last word of the chorus, and it was not at all unusual for the sailors to substitute the word *pull* for *Joe*. And, in any event, the word was actually grunted rather than sung while the men put all their effort into the pull itself. There is literally no end to the number of verses that might be included with the song. The chanteyman would simply draw them out of his memory as he went along or, if he was in the mood, make up one that was appropriate for the moment.

Recordings: Paul Clayton (Folkways, FA 2429); Cisco Houston (Disc, D 103); Burl Ives (Decca, DL 8245); Alan Mills (Folkways, FP 709); Tom Scott (Coral, CRL 56056).

2. King Louis was the King of France
   Before the revolution,
   Way, haul away, we'll haul away, Joe.
   When he got his head cut off
   It spoiled his constitution.
   Way, haul away, we'll haul away, Joe.

3. The cook is in the galley
   Making chow so handy.
   Way, haul away, we'll haul away, Joe.
   The captain's in his cabin
   Pulling on his brandy.
   Way, haul away, we'll haul away, Joe.

4. Once I was in Ireland
   Diggin' turf and 'taties.
   Way, haul away, we'll haul away, Joe.
   Now I'm on a lime-juice ship
   Hauling on the braces.
   Way, haul away, we'll haul away, Joe.

5. Once I had an Irish girl,
   But she was fat and lazy.
   Way, haul away, we'll haul away, Joe.
   Then I got a German girl

And she was fat and greasy.
Way, haul away, we'll haul away, Joe.

6. Then I got a yeller girl,
   She nearly drove me crazy.
   Way, haul away, we'll haul away, Joe.
   Now I've got a Yankee girl,
   And she is just a daisy.
   Way haul away, we'll haul away, Joe.

7. Way, haul away,
   We'll haul away together.
   Way, haul away, we'll haul away, Joe.
   Way, haul away,
   We'll haul for better weather.
   Way, haul away, we'll haul away, Joe.

HAUL ON THE BOWLINE

Able-bodied seamen don't call a forecastle a forecastle—it's a *foaksl*. A spritsail topgallant sail is a *sprisltiglnsl,* and, according to Walter Blair of the University of Chicago, nobody can say that "unless he's got some salt water running in his veins." All of which explains why, in seagoing lingo, a bowline is a *bo-lin'*—so don't sing this song like a landlubber!

In *On Board the Rocket,* Captain Robert C. Adams describes the action related to this chantey:

> . . . where a few strong pulls are needed, as in boarding a tack, hauling aft a sheet or tautening a weather brace . . . "Haul on the Bowline" is a favorite. . . . The *shanty man,* as the solo singer is called, standing up "beforehand," as high above the rest of the crew as he can reach, sings with as many quirks, variations and quavers as his ingenuity and ability can attempt, "Haul the bowline, Kitty is my darling"; then all hands join in the chorus, "Haul the bowline, the bowline haul!" shouting the last word with great energy, and suiting action to it by a combined pull, which must be witnessed by one who desires an exemplification of "a long pull, a strong pull and a pull altogether." This seldom fails to make the ropes "come home."
>
> Then the song is repeated with a slight change in words, "Haul the bowline, the clipper ship's a rolling," etc., and next time, perhaps, "haul the bowline, our bully mate is growling."
>
> Great latitude is allowed in the words, and the shanty man exercises his own discretion. If he be a man of little comprehension or versatility, he will say the same words over and over, but if he possesses some wit, he will insert a phrase alluding to some peculiarity of the ship, or event of the time, which will cause mouths to open wider and eyes to roll gleefully, while a lively pull follows that rouses the sheet home and elicits the mate's order, "Belay!" A good shanty man is highly prized both by officers and crew. His leadership saves many a dry pull, and his vocal effort is believed to secure so much physical force that he is sometimes allowed to spare his own exertions and reserve all his energies for the inspiring shanty.

The bowline was actually a minor rope on the square-rigged vessels in use after the sixteenth or early seventeenth century and was not big enough, therefore, to require a chantey. Joanna Colcord, author of *Songs of American Sailormen,* has suggested that this particular chantey must have been carried over from the carracks of Elizabethan times, when the bowline was the name for what was later called the fore-sheet.

Often an experienced chanteyman would use a verse to pass along a suggestion or word of advice to a young or inexperienced officer. You will see some of these verses in the collated version shown below. There were also many verses in the chanteyman's repertoire that were used whenever he felt like it in whatever chantey he was singing at the moment. The verses in "Haul Away, Joe" and "Haul on the Bowline" have frequently been crossed in this manner.

Recordings: Paul Clayton (Folkways, FA 2429); A. L. Lloyd and Ewan MacColl (Stinson, SLP 81).

2. Haul on the bowline,
Kitty lives in Liverpool.
Haul on the bowline,
The bowline haul.

3. Haul on the bowline,
Our bully ship's a rollin'.
Haul on the bowline,
The bowline haul.

4. Haul on the bowline,
The old man is a-growlin'.
Haul on the bowline,
The bowline haul.

5. Haul on the bowline,
So early in the morning.
Haul on the bowline,
The bowline haul.

Additional verses from which to select and sing as above:

It's a far cry to payday.

We'll surely make 'er render.

Me hearty lads, be handy.

Yankee Doodle Dandy.

157

The long-tailed bowline.

We'll either break or bend it.

We've men enough to mend it.

Another pull together.

And burst the chafin' leather.

She's makin' heavy weather.

We'll buckle off together.

We'll give her hell and blazes.

And fiddlestring her braces.

HENRY MARTIN

This famous British sea ballad may be based on the true story of Andrew Barton. Barton had obtained letters of reprisal from the king of Scotland against the Portuguese, who had seized a ship under his father's command. Barton evidently abused this privilege and became a pirate. In 1511, Sir Thomas and Sir Edward Howard, with the consent of Henry VIII, set out in two ships after Barton. In a hard fight Barton was killed and his ship was captured. In "Henry Martin" Martin (Barton?), the pirate, sails safely away with his mission accomplished. In other versions, Henry Martin is either fatally wounded or finally captured and taken to London, where he is hanged. The parenthetical Bb and F chords in the last phrase may be omitted and the Dm chord continued by less experienced guitarists.

Recordings: Joan Baez (Vanguard, VRS 9078); Burl Ives (Decca, DL 8080); Terrea Lea (ABC Paramount, ABC 161); Ewan MacColl and A. L. Lloyd (Riverside, RLP 12-627); Dick Wilder (Elektra, EKL 18).

158

go — For to turn rob-ber all on the salt sea. —

2. The lot it fell upon Henry Martin
   The youngest of all the three,
   That he should turn robber all on the salt sea,
       salt sea, salt sea,
   For to maintain his two brothers and he.

3. He had not been sailing but a long winter's night
   And part of a short winter's day,
     When he espi-ed a lofty stout ship,
       stout ship, stout ship,
   Come a-bibing down on him straightway.

4. "Hello, hello," cried Henry Martin,
   "What makes you sail so high?"
   "I'm a rich merchant ship bound for fair London Town,
       London Town, London Town,
   Will you please for to let me pass by?"

5. "O no, O no," cried Henry Martin,
   "That thing it never can be,
   For I have turned robber all on the salt sea,
       salt sea, salt sea,
   For to maintain my two brothers and me.

6. "So lower your topsail and brail up your mizzen,
   Bow yourselves under my lee,
   Or I shall give you a fast flowing ball,
       flowing ball, flowing ball,
   And your dear bodies drown in the salt sea."

7. With broadside and broadside and at it they went
   For fully two hours or three,
   Till Henry Martin gave to her the death shot,
       the death shot, the death shot,
   Heavily listing to starboard went she.

8. The rich merchant vessel was wounded full sore,
   Straight to the bottom went she,
   And Henry Martin sailed away on the sea,
       salt sea, salt sea,
   For to maintain his two brothers and he.

9. Bad news, bad news, to old England came,
   Bad news to fair London Town,
   There was a rich vessel and she's cast away,
       cast away, cast away,
   And all of her merry men drowned.

HE'S GOT THE WHOLE WORLD IN HIS HANDS

Sam Hinton told me this spiritual was introduced to folk-singing enthusiasts by Frank Warner, who had collected it from Sue Thomas at Nag's Head, North Carolina, in 1935. It became a favorite with concert audiences through the singing of Marian Anderson, and in the 1950s it became a hit with teenagers through a rock-and-roll record made in England. This universal success, along with a simple and repetitive structure, makes it particularly suitable for group singing. Look up the treatment for "Gospel Train" in this book for some ideas for variation in your performance. You don't have to stick to the hard line of repetition, for example. You could change the first verse to:

> He's got the little bitty children in His hands,
> He's got the grown-up children in His hands,
> He's got all the children in His hands,
> He's got the whole world in His hands.

Recordings: Marian Anderson (RCA Victor, LRM 7006); Odetta (Tradition, TLP 1025); Frank Warner (Elektra, EKLP 3).

1. He's got the little bitty babies in His hands,
   He's got the little bitty babies in His hands,
   He's got the little bitty babies in His hands,
   He's got the whole world in His hands.

2. He's got you and me, brother, in His hands,
   He's got you and me, sister, in His hands,
   He's got you and me, brother, in His hands,
   He's got the whole world in His hands.

3. He's got the gamblin' man in His hands,
   He's got the gamblin' man in His hands,
   He's got the gamblin' man in His hands,
   He's got the whole world in His hands.

For additional verses you may zip in: drinkin' man, worldly sinners, cheaters and the liars, two-bit hustlers, rich and the poor, meek and the humble, and others of your own invention.

HEY LIDEE

This is one of the two best songs I know for group composition and singing. The other one is Don Ho's beach-party song "E Lei Ka Lei Lei," which follows the same approach. "Hey Lidee", (or hey loddee, or hey lilee, or hey lollee—the words are there for sound rather than meaning, so it really doesn't matter what you use) originated in the calypso country of the Bahamas and then became a part of our folk tradition, particularly in collegiate circles. My version below explains how the song works in the first few verses. I use these to get people warmed up and thinking of some verses of their own. As soon as everyone is convinced you're going to keep the song going no matter who makes a fool of himself (or how), even the shyest person will join in with his own invented couplet. There are some pretty standard off-color lines that show up at campus parties:

> I know a girl who lives on a hill,
> Hey lidee, lidee lo,
> She won't fool around but her sister will,
> Hey lidee, lidee lo.

> I know a girl who lives in Greenwich Village,
> Hey lidee, lidee lo,
> She won't fool around but her brother will,
> Hey lidee, lidee lo.

> I know a girl named Buffalo Bill,
> Hey lidee, lidee lo,
> She won't fool around but her buffalo will,
> Hey lidee, lidee lo.

> I know a girl who's really stacked,
> Hey lidee, lidee lo,
> She makes her living on her back,
> Hey lidee, lidee lo.

Don't be surprised if some of these verses, and others like them, show up at a beach party. However, if you stick to my version* and amplify from it, the song is perfectly respectable for church, school, or home—and sure to be a hit.

Recordings: Pete Seeger (Folkways, FA 2043); The Limeliters (RCA Victor, LPM 2272). Variation: "E Lei Ka Lei Lei": Don Ho (Reprise, R 6161).

*Words by James Leisy, © 1966 by James Leisy Music. Used by permission.

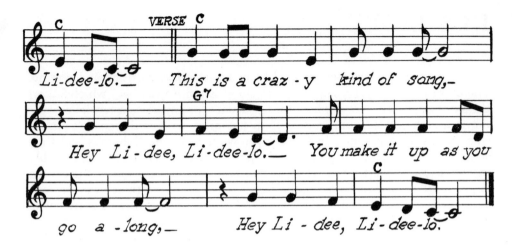

Li-dee-lo.__ This is a craz-y kind of song,—

Hey Li-dee, Li-dee-lo.__ You make it up as you

go a-long,__ Hey Li-dee, Li-dee-lo.

2. First you sing a simple line,
   Hey Lidee, Lidee-lo.
   Then you try to make it rhyme,
   Hey Lidee, Lidee-lo.

Continue, as above:

3. While you catch on I'll sing a verse,
   Then you do one that's even worse.

4. It doesn't matter what you say,
   If that rhyme comes out okay.

5. I guess it doesn't matter at all,
   Even if it doesn't rhyme.

Miscellaneous verses:

The singer you fast the getter it's tough,
To line up makes that you won't muff.

The deacon went down to the cellar to pray,
But he couldn't think of a thing to say.

My girl she had two eyes in her head,
One was green and the other was red.

She had two teeth in her mouth,
One went north and the other went south.

Let's put this song back on the shelf,
If you want any more you can sing it yourself.

THE HOLLY AND THE IVY

In the housecleaning that took place in the church during the Reformation, "The Holly and the Ivy" was among the first of the offending carols to be thrown out. The symbolization of the words and the customs associated with the song are of pagan origin, as are a number of our Christmas customs. The holly is a symbol for the male, and the ivy is a symbol for the female. According to the custom, if smooth holly was brought into the house before rough holly the wife would dominate the household.

The use of holly for Christmas had origins in both the Druidic practice of providing a protected winter home for the sylvan spirits, and the Roman Saturnalia of December 17-24. The Romans had long used holly wreaths or sprigs as a token of good will, and the extension of the custom to the Christian holiday was natural. The name "holly tree" is connected with a number of Christmas legends; the Germans believed that holly formed Christ's crown of thorns, and that the berries, originally yellow, had been stained with His blood. In many countries, a sprig of holly in the house was thought to repel lightning and to make animals docile. A large body of folklore grew up in Europe about the merits of holly, the proper time to cut it, bring it into the house, take it down, and dispose of it, and much of that tradition has been carried to the New World.

Recordings: Carols by the Bach Choir and Westminster Abbey Choir (London, LL 1095); Alfred Deller (Vanguard, VRS 499).

2. The holly bears a blossom,
   As white as the lily flower,
   And Mary bore sweet Jesus Christ
   To be our sweet saviour.

3. The holly bears a berry,
   As red as any blood,
   And Mary bore sweet Jesus Christ
   To do poor sinners good.

4. The holly bears a prickle,
   As sharp as any thorn,

163

And Mary bore sweet Jesus Christ
On Christmas Day in the morn.

5. The holly bears a bark,
   As bitter as any gall,
   And Mary bore sweet Jesus Christ
   For to redeem us all.

6. The holly and the ivy,
   When they are both full grown,
   Of all the trees that are in the wood
   The holly bears the crown.

HOME ON THE RANGE

Noted Composer Returns to Texas
By Ruth Eyre, Staff Writer

The man who took the cowboy to the Broadway stage has come back to Texas.

Distinguished American composer David W. Guion, whose West Texas background inspired such songs as "Home on the Range," moved back to Dallas this week.

But he left the cowboy and the big country from which he came in the memories of "The Yellow Rose of Texas" and nearly 200 other cowboy and Negro folk compositions which he had been writing for more than 60 years.

Mr. Guion grew up on a West Texas ranch near Ballinger where his father was a lawyer and rancher. The composer said he began playing the piano and picking out melodies at the age of 5 and by the time he was 16 he composed "Home on the Range."

He is credited with introducing cowboy music to the East and starting the cowboy's music career on the radio.

"In fact," he said jokingly, "hillbilly songs developed from my music. So if you don't like it, I guess you can throw something at me."

The life he lived in West Texas inspired "Home on The Range," the composer said, though it took a lot of hard work. "All creative work is inspirational. But after the inspiration comes hard work," the man who wrote hundreds of well-known tunes added.

His first published song was "Old Maid Blues" which he wrote for Nora Bayes for one of her Ziegfeld Follies productions in 1916. He then published Negro spirituals.

Some of his other more famous songs which followed are "Arkansas Traveler," "Carry Me Back to the Lone Prairie," "All Day on the Prairie," "Yellow Rose of Texas," "Turkey in the Straw" and "Lonesome Whistler."

1965, *The Dallas Times Herald*

The best known of all cowboy and western songs has been the subject of many suits and disputes concerning its authorship. The most widely held theory by folk song scholars and researchers is that it may have originated in a poem written by Dr. Brewster Higley when he lived in a cabin on the banks of Beaver Creek in Kansas in the 1870s. The tune probably was added by a neighbor, Dan Kelly. It was first popularized by David Guion and John A. Lomax, but according to Sigmund Spaeth "neither Guion nor Lomax can claim credit beyond that of a discoverer or arranger." "Home on the Range"

164

enjoyed great popularity in the 1930s through radio broadcasts and recordings during the cowboy-song fad. John Lomax called it "the cowboy's national anthem." It's an excellent song for group singing, especially around a camp fire, because the words and tune are universally known. It is rare, however, that anyone gets past the first verse. If a second verse is sung, it is usually the fourth one, "How often at night . . ." The lyric is hardly a folk lyric. It's too banal—it lacks what Oscar Brand calls that "special ring of truth which is germane to the folk song."

Recordings: Frank Luther (Decca, DL 5035); Pete Seeger (Folkways, FA 2320).

2. Where the air is so pure, the zephyrs so free,
   The breezes so balmy and light,
   That I would not exchange my home on the range
   For all of the cities so bright.

3. The red man was pressed from his part of the West,
   He's likely no more to return

To the banks of Red River where seldom if ever
Their flickering camp-fires burn.

4. How often at night when the heavens are bright
With the light from the glittering stars,
Have I stood there amazed and asked as I gazed
If their glory exceeds that of ours.

5. Oh, I love these wild flowers in this dear land of ours,
The curlew I love to hear scream,
And I love the white rocks and the antelope flocks
That graze on the mountain-tops green.

6. Oh, give me a land where the bright diamond sand
Flows leisurely down to the stream;
Where a graceful white swan goes gliding along
Like a maid in a heavenly dream.

7. Then I would not exchange my home on the range,
Where the deer and the antelope play;
Where seldom is heard a discouraging word
And the skies are not cloudy all day.

THE HOUSE CARPENTER

One of the earliest printed versions of this ballad appeared in *Pepys Ballads* in 1685 under this extensive title: "A Warning for Married Women, being an example of Mrs. Jane Reynolds (A West-country woman), born near Plymouth, who, having plighted her troth to a Seaman, was afterwards married to a Carpenter, and at last carried away by a Spirit, the manner how shall presently be recited To a West-country tune called 'The Fair Maid of Bristol', 'Bateman', or 'John True'".

"The House Carpenter" is another one of the great ballads in the Child collection (number 243) that has a strong tradition in Britain and America.

The broadside ballad reprinted by Pepys begins:

There dwelt a fair maid in the West,
Of worthy birth and fame,
Neer unto Plimouth, stately town,
Jane Reynolds was her name.

and then rambles through a long and drawn-out account of how "this damsel dearly was belovd by many a proper youth" but finally settled for a seaman brave, James Harris. They vowed "they would ever faithful be whilst Heaven afforded life" as husband and wife. But before they could get to the church on time "the young man he was prest to sea." Jane waited three years and then received word he was dead "within a forraign land." She "lamented many a day, and never was she known at all the wanton for to play." Then a carpenter living "hard by" wooed and won her, married her "with speed," and soon provided her with "three pritty children." One day, while he was away on a journey, James Harris returned in the form of a spirit and held a spirited discussion with Jane concerning the pros and cons of chucking the carpenter for a sea life (à la "The Gypsy Laddie"). Harris claimed he had passed up a king's daughter to return to Jane. She fretted about leaving the children and about Harris's ability to support her in the style to which she had become accustomed. Harris then bragged about his acquisitions and:

When he had told her these fair tales,
To love him she began,
Because he was in human shape,
Much like unto a man.

And, perhaps, she loved him a little, too, because of the financial shape he was in. Anyhow, off to sea she went with him "and since that time the woman kind was never seen no more." Her husband came home, found the babies alone, "beat his breast," "tore his hair," and "hangd himself for woe."

The children now are fatherless,
And left without a guide,
But yet no doubt the heavenly powers
Will for them well provide.

Contemporary Americans have tuned in late on this taut, suspense-filled drama of mystery and intrigue. They've made a house carpenter out of James Harris and brought him back as a real-life wife snatcher. As the commercial rises on the first scene the house carpenter greets the housewife, "Well met, well met . . ."

Recordings: Paul Clayton (Folkways, FA 2007); Richard Dyer-Bennet (Dyer-Bennet, DYB 3000); Joan O'Bryant (Folkways, FA 2338); Peggy Seeger (Folkways, FA 2049); Pete Seeger (Stinson, 57); Pete Steele (Folkways, FS 3828); Andrew Rowan Summers (Folkways, FA 2364).

2. "Oh, I could have married the king's daughter fair,
And she would have married me.
But I have refused the crown of gold,
And it's all for the sake of thee."

3. "If you could have married the king's daughter dear,
I'm sure you are to blame,

For I am married to the house carpenter
And he is a fine young man."

4. "If you'll forsake your house carpenter
And come away with me,
I'll take you to where the grass grows green
On the banks of Italy."

5. "If I forsake my house carpenter
And come away with thee,
What have you got to support me on
And keep me from slavery?"

6. "I have six ships on the salt, salt sea,
A-sailing for dry land,
And a hundred and twenty jolly young lads
Shall be at thy command."

7. She picked up her poor little babe;
Her kisses were one, two, three,
Saying, "Stay here with my house carpenter
And keep him company."

8. They had not been at sea two weeks,
I'm sure it was not three,
When this poor maid began to weep,
And she wept most bitterly.

9. "Oh, do you weep for your gold?" he said,
"Your houses, your land or your store?"
"No, I do weep for my poor little babe
That I shall see no more."

10. They had not been at sea three weeks,
I'm sure it was not four,
When in the ship there sprang a leak,
And she sank to rise no more.

11. "Farewell, farewell, my own true love,
Farewell, farewell," cried she,
"Oh, I have deserted my house carpenter
For a grave in the depths of the sea."

12. Oh, cursed be the sea-going train,
And all the sailors' lives,
For the robbing of the house carpenter,
And the taking away of his wife.

You may wish to vary the ending by using the following two verses instead of the last verse above:

"My house carpenter is still at home,
And living very well,
While my poor body is drowning in the sea
And my soul is bound for hell.

"A curse, a curse to all seamen;
A curse forever more.
They robbed me of my house carpenter
That I never shall see any more."

HUSH, LITTLE BABY

This is one of the most popular folk lullabies known in this country. Who can resist such an indulgent daddy? He's likely to come up with almost any gift imaginable, depending on the version presented. Jean Ritchie begins with:

> Hush, little baby, don't say a word,
> Papa's goin' to get you a talking bird;
> One to whistle; one to sing;
> One to holler hi-lo-ding!

Matthew Edel of Harvard University picked up another version from a seven-year-old while tracking down variants of "Glory Hallelujah, Teacher Hit Me with a Ruler":

> Mama, mama, have you heard,
> Daddy's gonna buy me a mockingbird;
> If that mockingbird don't sing,
> Daddy's gonna buy me a diamond ring.
>
> If that diamond ring don't pay,
> Daddy's gonna buy me a Chevrolet;
> If that Chevrolet won't run,
> Daddy's gonna buy me a B-B gun.
>
> If that B-B gun won't shoot,
> Daddy's gonna buy me a swimming suit;
> If that swimming suit don't fit,
> Daddy's gonna say, "Oh, gee, I quit!"

Recordings: Marjorie Bennett (Judson, J 3028); Tom Glazer (Mercury, MG 20007); Burl Ives (Decca, DL 5467); Ed McCurdy (Tradition, TLP 1003); Milt Okun (Baton, BL 1203); Jean Ritchie (Westminster, WP 6037); The Weavers (Decca, DL 5285).

2. And if that diamond ring turns brass,
   Daddy's gonna buy you a looking glass,
   And if that looking glass gets broke,
   Daddy's gonna buy you a billy goat.

3. And if that billy goat won't pull,
   Daddy's gonna buy you a cart and bull,
   And if that cart and bull turn over,
   Daddy's gonna buy you a dog named Rover.

4. And if that dog named Rover won't bark,
   Daddy's gonna buy you a horse and cart,
   And if that horse and cart fall down,
   You'll still be the sweetest little baby in town.

...wishing her lover good speed

And away, hey...

She crossed the broad prairies...

I

*...the leafy
green dome*

*Can she bake
a cherry pie...*

*As I was going
to Derby...*

I AM A PILGRIM

Many singers omit the blue notes in the fourth and twelfth measures of this popular hillbilly gospel song. Don't.

Recordings: The Kentucky Colonels (World Pacific Records, 1821); Obray Ramsay (Riverside, RLP 12 649); Merle Travis (Capitol, T 891).

I am a pil—grim,— and a stran—ger,— Trav-'ling through—— this wear-i-some land;— I got a home— in—— that yon— der city, Oh Lord, and it's not made, not made— by hand.——

2. I got a mother, a sister, and a brother,
   Who have gone to that sweet land.
   I'm determined to go and see them, good Lord,
   All over on that distant shore.

3. As I go down to that river of Jordan,
   Just to bathe my weary soul,
   If I could touch but the hem of His garment, good Lord,
   Well, I believe it would make me whole.

I KNOW WHERE I'M GOIN'

If the Johnny mentioned in this song is the Gypsy Laddie (see Index), and that's not a bad bet, then this Irish love song is an "Answer to the Gypsy Laddie" of sorts. The D chord in the last measure of this harmonization provides a natural transition into each succeeding verse and allows an ending which leaves the listener suspended—wondering whether he has heard the whole story. This interesting device (ending not on the tonic as would be conventional, but on the dominant) will add to the expressiveness of your performance. But if it jars you too much you can resolve the problem, and the song, by ending it conventionally with a G chord.

Recordings: Kathleen Ferrier (London, 5411); Patrick Galvin (Riverside, RLP 12 608); Lori Holland (Folkways, FG 3518); Burl Ives (Columbia, CL 6109); The Weavers (Decca, DL 5825).

I know where I'm go-in',— And I know who's go-in' with me; I know who I love,— And he knows who I'll mar-ry.

2. I'll give up silk stockings,
   And shoes of bright green leather,
   Combs to buckle my hair,
   And rings for every finger.

3. Feather beds are soft,
   And painted rooms are bonnie;
   But I would trade them all
   For my handsome, winsome Johnny.

4. Some say he's a bad one,
   But I say he is bonnie.
   Fairest of them all
   Is my handsome, winsome Johnny.

   Repeat first verse.

I NEVER WILL MARRY

This popular hillbilly lament may have been derived from a song that appeared in eighteenth-century broadsides under various titles, including "The Sorrowful Ladie's Complaint" and "The Damsel's Lament." I learned it from Tillman Hall of the University of Southern California, who learned it back in Tennessee in the 1920s. It was popularized by the Carter Family and Texas Gladden.

Recordings: The Kossoy Sisters (Tradition, TLP 1018); Herta Marshall (Folkways, FA 2333); Pete Seeger (Folkways, FN 2512); The Weavers (Vanguard, VRS 9042).

As I went a walk-ing _____ _____ Down by the sea-shore, _____ The wind it did whis-tle _____ And the wat-ers did roar. _____

2. I saw a young maiden,
   Sitting in the sand,
   And reading a letter
   That she held in her hand.

3. Crying, "My lover's gone,
   He's the one I adore,
   He's gone where I never
   Will see him any more."

4. I asked her would she marry
   Myself if she pleased.
   Her only answer:
   "My love lies fast asleep.

5. "I never will marry,
   I'll be no man's bride.
   I intend to stay single
   For the rest of my life.

6. "The shell in the ocean,
   Shall be my deathbed:
   And the fish in deep waters
   Shall swim over my head."

7. She threw her fair body
   In the water so deep;
   And closed up her dark eyes,
   Forever to sleep.

I RIDE AN OLD PAINT

This beautiful song was a favorite "last dance of the evening" tune at many a western get-together. Another popular variant is called "Goodbye, Old Paint." Ex-cowboy Slim Critchlow, of Berkeley, California, told me that the expression "throw the hoolihan" in this song always bothered him. In steer wrestling or roping, the steer or the horse (unfortunately for the rider) sometimes *turns a hoolihan,* a cartwheel, when the horse and the roped steer go in opposite directions. Thus, while you may *turn a hoolihan,* you don't *throw a hoolihan.* The suggestion in the chorus, on the other hand, makes a great deal of sense to Slim: "There were always some trouble makers in a herd that were ready to go—and when they went the whole herd went with them!"

Cowboy dances were not necessarily quiet affairs, as this passage from Andy Adams's *The Log of a Cowboy* indicates:

> I was at a dance once in Live Oak County, and there was a stuttering fellow there by the name of Lem Todhunter. The girls, it seems, didn't care to dance with him, and pretended they couldn't understand him. He had asked every girl at the party, and received the same answer from each—they couldn't understand him. "W-w-w-ell, g-g-g-go to hell, then. C-c-c-can y-y-you understand that?" he said to the last girl, and her brother threatened to mangle him horribly if he didn't apologize, to which he finally agreed. He went back into the house and said to the girl, "Y-y-you n-n-n-needn't g-g-g-go to hell; y-y-your b-b-b-brother and I have m-m-made other 'r-r-r-rangements."

Recordings: Richard Dyer-Bennet (Dyer-Bennet, DYB 5000); Cisco Houston (Folkways, FA 2022); Burl Ives (Columbia, CL 6144); Frank Luther (Decca, DL 5035); Ed McCurdy (Tradition, TLP 1003); Alan Mills (Folkways, FP 709); Carl Sandburg (Lyrichord, LL 66); Pete Seeger (Folkways, FA 2320); Paul Sykes (Crown, CLP 5057). Variation: "Goodbye, Old Paint": John A. Lomax, Jr. (Folkways, FG 3508).

2. Old Bill Jones had two daughters and a song.
   One went to Denver and the other went wrong.
   His wife she died in a poolroom fight,
   And still he keeps singin' from morning to night.

3. Oh when I die, take my saddle from the wall,
   Put it on my pony, lead him out of his stall;
   Tie my bones to his back, turn our faces to the west,
   And we'll ride the prairies that we love the best.

I WISH I WAS SINGLE AGAIN

The joys and sorrows of marriage have been a favorite topic of minstrels of all ages. Witness "The Joyful Maid and the Sorrowful Wife," which appeared in *The North Country Chorister; an unparalleled variety of excellent songs,* edited by Joseph Ritson of Durham, England, in 1792. In this song the joyful maid says:

And then I was a maid, a maid,
And joy came to me then;
Of meat and drink and rich clothing,
I'm sure I wanted none.

And the sorrowful wife says:

And then I was a wife, a wife,
And sorrow came to me then;
Of care and strife and weary life,
I'm sure I wanted none.

To avoid partisanship accusations and/or some kind of violation of the civil rights law, I've provided equal opportunity for both sides to be heard in the two songs that follow. I can assure you nothing prejudicial was intended by giving the ladies the last word.

Recordings: Paul Clayton (Elektra, EKL 147); Bob Gibson (Riverside, RLP 12-816); Burl Ives (Decca, DL 8125); Joan O'Bryant (Folkways, FA 2338); Milt Okun (Riverside, RLP 12-603); Peggy Seeger (Folkways, FA 2049); Pete Seeger (Folkways, FA 2176). Variation: "I Wish I Was a Single Girl": The Kossoy Sisters (Tradition, TLP 1018); Jean Ritchie (Westminster, WP 6037).

I WISH I WAS SINGLE AGAIN

when I was sin-gle my pock-ets did jin-gle, I
wish I was sin-gle a-gain.

2. I married a wife, oh then,
   I married a wife, oh then,
   I married a wife, she's the curse of my life,
   I wish I was single again.

3. My wife she died, oh then,
   My wife she died, oh then,
   My wife she died, and I laughed till I cried,
   To think I was single again.

4. I went to the funeral, oh then,
   I went to the funeral, oh then,
   I went to the funeral and danced Yankee Doodle,
   To think I was single again.

5. I married another, oh then,
   I married another, oh then,
   I married another, the devil's grandmother,
   I wish I was single again.

   Continue, as above:

6. She beat me, she banged me,
   She said she would hang me,
   I wish I was single again.

7. She went for the rope,
   When she got it, 'twas broke, (*etc.*)

8. Now listen, all you young men,
   Now listen, all you young men,
   Be good to the first, for the next will be worse,
   I wish I was single again.

I WISH I WAS A SINGLE GIRL

When I was sin - gle, mar-ry-ing was my
crave,— Now I am mar - ried and I'm troub-led to my

grave, And it's oh Lord, I — wish I was a sin-gle girl a - gain.

2. When I was single, I lived at my ease,
   Now I am married with a husband to please.

3. When I was single, I ate biscuits and pie,
   Now I am married, it's eat cornbread or die.

4. When I was single, my shoes, they were new,
   Now I am married and the water runs right through.

5. When I was single, I dressed up so fine,
   Now I am married, I go ragged all the time.

6. Dishes to wash and the spring to go to,
   No one to help me, I have it all to do.

7. A house full of children, and trouble they be,
   None of them big enough to do the work for me.

8. If you are single, hear what I say,
   Don't crave to be married, you'll regret the day.

I'M A RAMBLER

I'm partial to songs with an interlude quality that can be performed effectively without an obvious ending. This song and "I Know Where I'm Going" are my two favorites of this kind. You will notice that the melody ends on an E7 chord and that it cries out for resolution to the tonic chord (A) of the song. As you sing each verse, the tension is resolved when the melody returns to the tonic in the second measure. When you get to the last verse, you may be unable to resist the urge to follow the E7 chord with an A chord while you are holding the last tone of the song, but if you can you may find it intriguing to end there or taper off instrumentally by running through the chords of the song and still ending on the seventh. If you do, you will establish the effect of leaving the story "up in the air" with the implication that there is either more to follow, some day, or that not all of the story has been told.

The story here is from the same family of songs that has given us "On Top of Old Smoky," "The Wagoner's Lad," "The Cuckoo," "Jack of Diamonds," and "Rye Whiskey." You will notice the relationships in the verses.

Recordings: Odetta (Vanguard, VRS 9137); Peggy Seeger (Riverside, RLP 12 655, and Topic, TOP 72). Variation: "Rambler Gambler": Ian and Sylvia (Vanguard, VRS 9109).

Slowly

I'm a ram - bler, I'm a gam - bler; I'm a
long way from home, And if peo - ple don't
like me they can leave me a - lone.

2. It's dark and it's raining
   And the moon gives no light.
   My pony won't travel
   A dark road at night.

3. Oh, come feed your horses;
   Come feed them some hay;
   Come sit down beside me
   Just as long as you stay.

4. My horses aren't hungry;
   They won't eat your hay;
   I'm going to Wyoming;
   I'll graze on the way.

5. I once had a sweetheart;
   Her age was sixteen;
   She was the flower of Bolton
   And the belle of Saline.

6. Her parents were against me;
   Now she is the same;
   If I'm in your book, love,
   Please blot out my name.

7. There are changes in the ocean.
   There are changes in the sea.
   There are changes in my true love;
   But there's no change in me.

IN THE PINES (Black Girl)

This unique, moody, blues-style song from the southern mountain country
is like a bottomless treasure box of folk song elements. The deeper you dig, the
more you find. There appears to be no end to the verses that can be fitted into
its unique structure. And the rhythmic, melodic, and harmonic variations

make possible a limitless variety of presentations. With such an abundance of riches available, no singer should be in a hurry to select his method of presentation.

"In the Pines" may have been originally created out of a fragment from another song. Songs are sometimes born this way. A fragmentary lyrical phrase from a song catches and holds the conscious or unconscious attention of an inventive singer. It works its way around in his mind and one day emerges with a melodic strain to accompany it. The melody may have evolved from the original song or some other song or may simply be a free-wheeling tune dormant in the mind of the composer until its creation. The important thing is that the emerging song fits well, is appealing, and is worthy of repetition. Whether or not "In the Pines" started out this way, it has certainly grown by picking up floating verses, phrases, and ideas from other songs through the creative, loving attention of many an unknown folk lyricist.

Cecil Sharp, the British folk song collector, recorded a fragment of this song in Kentucky in 1917:

> Black girl, black girl, don't lie to me...
> Where did you stay last night?
> I stayed in the pines where the sun never shines,
> And shivered when the cold wind blows...

The simple, appealing melody for these words was built on a hexatonic scale and is essentially the melody most frequently used today (see the first version below).

Recordings: Paul Clayton (Folkways, FA 2110); The Kossoy Sisters (Tradition, TLP 1018). Variation: "Black Girl": Huddie Ledbetter (Stinson, SLP 48, and Folkways, FA 2014); Josh White (Elektra, EKL 123).

If you have three good harmonizers around, you might want to get them to back you up on the choruses, as follows:

181

slept in the pines where the sun nev-er shines And I shiv-ered when the cold wind blowed. To the pines, to the pines, where the sun nev-er shines, and you shiv-er when the cold wind blows.

2. You slighted me once; you slighted me twice;
   But you'll never slight me no more.
   You caused me to weep; you caused me to mourn;
   You caused me to leave my home.

3. Them long steel rails with short crossties
   Gonna carry me away from home.
   That lonesome track gonna take me back
   Where a man can call his soul his own.

4. The longest train I ever saw
   Was on the Georgia line.
   The engine passed at five o'clock;
   The caboose done passed at nine.

5. The longest day I ever saw,
   Ever since I started to roam,
   Was the day I left my own true love,
   The day I left my home.

6. Now, don't you hear those mournin' doves
   Flyin' from pine to pine,
   Mournin' for their own true love
   Just like I mourn for mine.

Miscellaneous verses:

The longest train I ever did ride
Was a hundred coaches long.
The only woman I ever did love,
She's on that train and gone.

It's the longest train in this whole wide world.
Comes down from the old coal mine.
Headlight comes 'round when the sun comes up,
The caboose when the sun goes down.

Look down, look down that lonesome road.
Hang down your head and cry.
The best of friends must part some time,
Then why not you and I?

I wish to the Lord I'd never been born,
Or died when I was young.
I never would've kissed your sweet, sweet lips,
Nor listened to your flattering tongue.

The prettiest girl I ever did see
Was sitting with her head bowed down.
Her hair was as curly as the waves at sea,
Her eyes was a Spanish brown.

Tell me where did you get them pretty little shoes?
And the dress you wear so fine?
I got my shoes from a railroad man.
Got my dress from a driver in the mine.

My husband he was a railroad man.
He was the best in this lonesome world.
The only thing he ever did that was wrong
Was to miss just-a one little curve.

Yes, my husband he was a railroad man.
He was killed just a mile out of town.
They found his head in an engine wheel.
But his body could never be found.

True love, true love, tell me where will you go?
I'm gonna go where the cold winds blow.
Gonna weep, gonna cry, gonna moan, gonna sigh,
Gonna dance in my good-time clothes.

If I had a-listened to what my daddy said
I wouldn't be here tonight.
I wouldn't be here in this rowdy crowd,
A-havin' such a rowdy time.

You can vary the mood, mode, tempo, and time with a little experimentation. The variant below may be used for a slow, strong-beat blues rendition or a fast-paced hillbilly-style delivery. The verses above may be adapted easily to whatever version you come up with.

J

...the leafy
green dome

Can she bake
a cherry pie...

As I was going
to Derby...

JACOB'S LADDER

Spirituals were created and sung by both Negroes and whites in the nineteenth century. Since many of the same spirituals were sung by both, it has been difficult for scholars to decide how some of them originated. "Jacob's Ladder" is one of those that are difficult to pin down, although it probably started out as a white hymn. Some singers prefer the ecumenical line "Brothers in our land" to "Soldiers of the cross." If you take this approach, you may wish to use the following lines and others of your own invention:

Every new man makes us stronger.

We have worked in dark and danger.

"Jacob's Ladder" has long been a favorite at church and camp meetings. It has also been adapted for union ("We Are Building a Strong Union") and political ("We Are Building a People's Party") singing.

Recordings: Paul Robeson (Monitor, MP 580, and Vanguard, VRS 9051); Pete Seeger (Folkways, FN 2512); Lucretia West (Westminster, WP 6063).

2. Every rung goes higher, higher,
   Every rung goes higher, higher,
   Every rung goes higher, higher,
   Soldiers of the cross.

3. Sinner, do you love my Jesus?
   Sinner, do you love my Jesus?
   Sinner, do you love my Jesus?
   Soldiers of the cross.

4. If you love Him, why not serve Him?
   If you love Him, why not serve Him?
   If you love Him, why not serve Him?
   Soldiers of the cross.

5. We are climbing higher, higher,
   We are climbing higher, higher,
   We are climbing higher, higher,
   Soldiers of the cross.

JESSE JAMES

Though Jesse James was neither the first nor the worst of our outlaws, he is the central figure in the most popular outlaw legend we have. It is not at all unusual for bad guys to become good guys in folk tradition, and this is the case with Jesse. James was shot in the back by Robert Ford—a member of his gang with a revenge motive and a secret deal with the governor of Missouri—while hiding out in St. Joseph under the alias of Howard. Ford was eventually assassinated himself in Colorado. No one knows who Billy Gashade was or whether he really wrote the ballad, but you've got to hand it to someone for getting his name cleverly, and permanently, placed in the last verse.

Recordings: Bill Bender (Stinson, SLP 18); Paul Clayton (Riverside, RLP 12-640); Woody Guthrie (Stinson, SLP 32); Bascom Lamar Lunsford (Riverside, RLP 12-645); Ed McCurdy (Elektra, EKL 112); Tom Scott and Will Rogers, Jr. (Judson, J 3013); Pete Seeger (Folkways, FA 2319).

Jes-se James was a lad who killed man-y a man; He robbed the Glen-dale train, And he stole from the rich and he gave to the poor, With a hand and a heart and a brain.

Poor Jes-se had a wife to mourn for his life, Three chil-dren they were brave, But that dirty lit-tle cow-ard who shot Mis-ter How-ard Has laid poor Jes-se in his grave.

2. It was Robert Ford, the dirty little coward,
   I wonder how he does feel,
   For he ate of Jesse's bread and he slept in Jesse's bed,
   Then he laid Jesse James in his grave.

3. It was his brother Frank that robbed the Gallatin bank,
   And carried the money from the town.
   It was in this very place that they had a little race,
   For they shot Captain Sheets to the ground.

4. They went to the crossing not very far from there,
   And there they did the same;
   And the agent on his knees he delivered up the keys
   To the outlaws Frank and Jesse James.

5. It was on a Saturday night, Jesse was at home
   Talking to his family brave,
   When the thief and the coward, little Robert Ford,
   Laid Jesse James in his grave.

6. How people held their breath when they heard of Jesse's death,
   And wondered how he ever came to die.
   'Twas one of the gang, dirty Robert Ford,
   That shot Jesse James on the sly.

7. Jesse went to his rest with his hand on his breast.
   The devil will be upon his knee.
   He was born one day in the county of Clay,
   And came from a solitary race.

8. This song was made by Billy Gashade,
   As soon as the news did arrive;
   He said there was no man with the law in his hand
   Who could take Jesse James when alive.

JOE BOWERS

The folk have a way of pinning a universal name on people of the same place or vocation. G. I. Joe was any dogface soldier in World War II. And Jack has always been every inch a sailor. They say you can take a boy out of Texas but you can't take Texas out of the boy; so when he's out of Texas, he'd better be prepared to answer to the name Tex. During the gold rush days in California any man arriving from Missouri had a name waiting for him, Joe Bowers. And Joe (along with his helpmate, sweet Betsy from Pike) was a Piker. So many people migrated from Missouri, particularly Pike County, intent on making their fortunes, that the Pikers became an object of derision, and the dictionary added a new word: formerly, a person from Pike County, Missouri, characterized by laziness and suspiciousness; a poor white; later, any Missourian.

"Joe Bowers" has been credited to John Woodward of Johnson's Minstrels of San Francisco. However, according to Alan Lomax, in *The Folk Songs of North America,* "Frank Swift, poet to a band of western Argonauts, is said to have composed it one night at a campfire on the prairie to tease one of the boys, whose name was Joe Bowers." In either event, the song was popularized throughout the country by the Johnson's Minstrels tours. And if the name-calling custom didn't make the song, the song made the custom. The custom received such widespread publicity that the Missouri legislature passed a resolution in 1897 to erect a monument to Joe Bowers (but that's as far as they got). Earlier, in the 1870s and 1880s, Bowers was indirectly involved in a bitter controversy between science and religion over the discovery of a fossilized skull found in a mine shaft in Calaveras County, California. Geologists believed that the skull was a million-year-old remnant of the Pliocene period. But the writer Bret Harte argued a Missouri source and thus left a "literary" monument commemorating Joe:

> Speak, thou awful vestige of the Earth's creation,
> Solitary fragment of remains organic!
> Tell the wondrous secret of thy past existence,
> Speak! thou oldest primate!
>
> Even as I gazed, a thrill of the maxilla,
> And a lateral movement of the condyloid process,
> With post-pliocene sounds of healthy mastication,
> Ground the teeth together.
>
> And, from that imperfect dental exhibition,
> Stained with expressed juices of the weed Nicotian,
> Came these hollow accents, blent with softer murmurs
> Of expectoration:
>
> "Which my name is Bowers, and my crust was busted
> Falling down a shaft in Calaveras County,
> But I'd take it kindly if you'd send the pieces
> Home to old Missouri!"

Many singers today miss the opportunities for pioneer punnery contained in the song. As you'll see in the words that follow, the second line in the second verse, for example, is frequently sung: "I *asked* her if she'd marry" instead of *axed,* which goes with the rest of the line: "she said it was a *whack.*"

Recordings: Loman Cansler (Folkways, FH 5324); Cisco Houston and Bill Bender (Stinson, SLP 37); Pete Seeger (Folkways, FA 2175).

My name it is Joe Bowers, I've got a brother Ike, I'm just here from Missouri and all the way from Pike; I'll tell you why I left there And why I came to roam And leave my aged parents, so far away from home.

2. I used to court a girl there, her name was Sally Black,
   I axed her if she'd marry, she said it was a whack;
   She says to me, "Joe Bowers, before we've hitched for life,
   You ought to get a little home to keep your little wife."

3. Says I, "My dearest Sally, Oh, Sally, for your sake,
   I'll go to California and try to raise a stake."
   Says she to me, "Joe Bowers, you're just the one to win."
   She gave me a kiss to seal the bargain and throwed a dozen in.

4. I'll never forget my feelings when I bid adieu to all.
   Sal she cotched me around the neck, and I began to bawl.
   When I began they all commenced, you never heard the like,
   How they took on and cried the day I left old Pike.

5. When I got to this country, I had nary a red;
   I had such wolfish feelings, I wished myself most dead.
   But the thoughts of my dear Sally soon made this feeling git,
   And whispered hopes to Bowers, Lord, I wish I had 'em yet.

6. At last I went to mining, put in my biggest licks,
   Came down upon the boulders just like a thousand bricks;
   I worked both late and early, in rain, in sun and snow,
   I was working for my Sally, 'twas all the same to Joe.

7. One day I got a letter from my dear brother Ike,
   It came from old Missouri all the way from Pike.
   It brought me the darndest news that ever you did hear,
   My heart it is a-breaking so please excuse this tear.

8. It said my Sal was false to me, that her love for me had fled,
   That she had got married to a butcher whose hair was red;
   It told me more than that; it's enough to make me swear,
   That Sal had had a baby and the baby had red hair.

9. Now I told you everything about this sad sad affair,
   About Sally marrying the butcher and the baby had red hair;
   But whether it was a boy or girl the letter never said,
   It only said the baby's hair was inclined to be red.

JOHN HENRY

John Henry is one of the greatest folk heroes of American legendry. The legend originated when steel drivers were drilling the Big Bend Tunnel on the Chesapeake and Ohio Railroad in West Virginia during the early 1870s. Since the beginning of industrialization, technological changes have constantly appeared to be a threat to the security of workers and have therefore been resisted. John Henry's battle with the steam drill symbolizes man's fight against automation and technological change. There are many other versions of the John Henry ballads and songs, and many stories in oral tradition. Howard Odum and Guy Johnson published eleven texts and four versions of the song, and Johnson wrote an entire book on his research, *John Henry: Tracking Down a Negro Legend.*

The blues setting of "John Henry" provides a natural and attractive opportunity for solo singing and improvisation. I've added a descant for group singing composed by Alice Snyder Knuth of San Francisco State College. The melody is in the top staff and the descant in the bottom staff. A *shaker* was an assistant who held the steam drill in place.

Recordings: Harry Belafonte (RCA Victor, LPM 1022); Richard Dyer-Bennet (Stinson, SLP 35); Sam Eskin (Cook Laboratories, 1020); Bob Gibson (Riverside, RLP 12-806); Woody Guthrie (Stinson, SLP 44); Buell H. Kazee (Folkways, FS 3810); Huddie Ledbetter (Stinson, SLP 17); John A. Lomax, Jr. (Folkways, FG 3508); Ed McCurdy (Riverside, RLP 12-601); Brownie McGhee (Folkways, FA 2327); John Jacob Niles (Tradition, TLP 1023); Odetta and Larry (Fantasy, 2352); Milt Okun (Baton, BL 1203); Paul Robeson (Columbia, ML 4105); Pete Seeger (Folkways, FA 2319); Stan Wilson (Cavalier, CAV 6002); Josh White (Decca, DL 8665, and the variation: "The Story of John Henry": Elektra, EKL 123).

me, oh Lord, This ham-mer'll be the death of me.

death, This ham-mer'll be the death, This ham-mer'll be the death of me.

2. Well, the captain said to John Henry,
   "I'm gonna bring that steam drill around,
   I'm gonna take that steam drill out on the job,
   I'm gonna whop that steel on down, oh Lord,
   Gonna whop that steel on down."

3. John Henry said to his captain:
   "A man ain't nothin' but a man,
   But before I'll let your steam drill beat me down,
   I'll die with the hammer in my hand, oh Lord,
   Die with the hammer in my hand!"

4. John Henry said to his shaker,
   "Now, shaker, why don't you sing?
   'Cause I'm throwing twelve pounds from my hips on down,
   Just listen to that cold steel ring, oh Lord,
   Just listen to that cold steel ring."

5. John Henry said to his shaker,
   "Shaker, you'd better pray,
   If I miss that little piece of steel,
   Tomorrow'll be your buryin' day, oh Lord,
   Tomorrow'll be your buryin' day."

6. The man that invented the steam drill;
   He thought he was mighty fine.
   But John Henry he made fourteen feet,
   While the steam drill only made nine, oh Lord,
   The steam drill only made nine.

7. John Henry hammered on the mountain,
   Till his hammer was striking fire.
   And he drove so hard he broke his poor heart,
   And he died with his hammer in his hand, oh Lord,
   He died with his hammer in his hand.

8. They carried John Henry to the graveyard,
   And they buried him in the sand,
   And every locomotive comes rolling by,
   Says, "There lies a steel drivin' man, oh Lord,
   There lies a steel drivin' man."

9. Now you've heard big John was born in Texas,
   And you've heard he was born in Maine.
   Well, I don't give a damn where that poor boy was born,
   He was a steel drivin' man, oh Lord,
   He was a steel drivin' man.

JOHNNY HAS GONE
FOR A SOLDIER (Buttermilk Hill)

After the Treaty of Limerick in 1691, many young Irish patriots enlisted in the "Wild Geese" of the Irish Brigade to serve in France. They hoped eventually to drive the English out of Ireland by fighting for the French king. The Irish song, "Shule Aroon," on which "Johnny" is based, apparently dates back to that period, although it may well have been based on an earlier song. A phonetic rendering of the Gaelic chorus goes like this:

> Shule, shule, shule aroon,
> Shule go succir agus, shule go kewn,
> Shule go dheen durrus oggus aylig lume,
> Iss guh day thoo avorneen slawn.

And translated:

> Come, come, come, oh love,
> Quickly come to me, softly move;
> Come to the door and away we'll flee;
> And safe for all may my darling be.

Most of the Gaelic verses are similar to those found with "Johnny Has Gone for a Soldier." One of them refers to a lover serving in France. Specifically:

> Now my love has gone to France
> To try his fortune to advance.
> And his return is but a chance
> Iss guh day thoo avorneen slawn.

The song, with the inevitable textual and melodic changes, has been popular in this country since the days of the American Revolution.

Recordings: Bill and Gene Bonyun (Heirloom, HL 500); Julie Felix (London, LL 3395); Sam Hinton (Decca, DL 8418); Wallace House (Folkways, FA 2163).

Here I sit on Buttermilk Hill, Who could blame me, cry my fill, And ev'ry tear would turn a mill, Johnny has gone for a soldier.

192

Me, oh my, I love him so;
It broke my heart to see him go;
And only time will heal my woe.
Johnny has gone for a soldier.

I'll sell my flax, I'll sell my wheel;
I'll make my love a sword of steel;
And this in battle he will wield.
Johnny has gone for a soldier.

I'll dye my dress; I'll dye it red;
And through the streets I'll beg for bread
Till he comes back and we are wed.
Johnny has gone for a soldier.

An optional chorus goes like this (to the same tune):

Shule, shule, shule, agrah,
Time can only heal my woe,
Since the lad of my heart from me did go,
Johnny has gone for a soldier.

Miscellaneous and variant verses:

Oh, Johnny dear has gone away,
He has gone far across the bay.
My heart is sad and weary today.
Johnny has gone for a soldier.

I'll sell my clock, I'll sell my reel,
I'll sell my flax and spinning wheel,
To buy my true love a sword of steel.
Johnny has gone for a soldier.

I'll dye my petticoats; I'll dye them red.
And 'round the world I'll beg my bread,
Until my parents shall wish me dead.
Johnny has gone for a soldier.

I wish, I wish, I wish in vain,
I wish I had him here again.
And never more would I complain.
Johnny has gone for a soldier.

JOHNNY, I HARDLY KNEW YE

While many of the folk have celebrated Johnny's return from the war with "When Johnny Comes Marching Home," others have greeted him with the Irish anti-war version, "Johnny, I Hardly Knew Ye." While the two songs share the same tune, and they're both concerned with a soldier's return from war, that's all they have in common. Not only is the spirit of each text opposed to the other, but the spirited supporters of each text frequently dispute which text had the tune first. It might be interesting to examine the thoughts of three folk music specialists on this question.

In *The Folk Songs of North America,* Alan Lomax states:

> When the Irish bandsman, Patrick Gilmore, arranged this best of all American marches ["When Johnny Comes Marching Home"] in the early days of the Civil War, he made use of an Anglo-Irish folk tune already firmly established in the States. The shape of the air indicates that it belongs to the Captain Kidd family, whose lineage has been traced back at least as far as the sixteenth century, but Johnny's immediate ancestor is probably the Irish anti-war song which runs . . .
> With yer guns and drums and drums and guns,
> Hurroo, hurroo . . .

In his *Irish Minstrelsy,* Spurling suggests that this song of soldier's protest dates back to 1802, when Irish regiments were recruited for a campaign in Ceylon.

Irwin Silber, the editor of *Sing Out* magazine, states in his book *Songs of the Civil War:*

> Unfortunately, none of those who claim the tune for the Irish can back up their assertion with demonstrable facts. I am willing to concede that the melody sounds like an Irish folk song, but subjective instinct is a poor substitute for evidence. The most frequently advanced argument is that the tune comes from the traditional Irish anti-war ballad, "Johnny I Hardly Knew Ye." Unfortunately for the proponents of this assertion, however, none can prove that the song was known and sung before the American Civil War. Some attribute "Johnny I Hardly Knew Ye" to the Crimean War, but we have already had some experience with this war, having been informed by various historians and singers that "Just Before the Battle, Mother" and "Battle Hymn of the Republic" were also products of the conflict which seems to have been best known heretofore for the typically senseless "Charge of the Light Brigade." With the experience of such unreliable musicology fresh in our minds, we will require more tangible proof than assertion before we consign "Johnny's" melody to the Crimean War.*

A disagreement like this provides us with an inviting opportunity to do a little scholarly detective work of our own. What can we find out about Patrick Gilmore and "When Johnny Comes Marching Home"? Gilmore was the bandmaster attached to General Butler's command in New Orleans during the Civil War. "When Johnny Comes Marching Home" was probably the most popular song to come out of the Civil War. It was introduced by Gilmore's Band as written by Louis Lambert, a pseudonym for Patrick S. Gilmore himself. Evidently Gilmore, like many musician-composers, used a pseudonym because he wanted to "keep his name out of it"—at least until the song had established itself. Later on, he was willing to acknowledge his authorship, but he admitted to having borrowed the tune from another source. Although, according to George P. Upton in *The Song,* Gilmore implied that "the melody is that of an old Negro song," it seems more likely that the tune is of Irish origin. Since Gilmore was an Irishman, and since he didn't put his name on the song to begin with and was willing to claim only the lyric as his own, let's concede that he was an honest man and look elsewhere for the source of the tune.

With a little sleuthing (and by checking the index of this book), you'll find this same melody embracing the words to "Billie Magee Magaw." Could that

*From *Songs of the Civil War* by Irwin Silber. Copyright © 1960 by Irwin Silber. Columbia University Press, New York.

be a clue? Of course, a folk song scholar would tell you, "Billie Magee Magaw" is a relatively contemporary version of a very old ballad, "The Three Ravens." That old ballad has hundreds of variants with many different melodies. Just because somebody sings "Billie Magee Magaw" today to that tune doesn't prove anything. Maybe somebody transferred the tune from "When Johnny Comes Marching Home" to that version of "The Three Ravens" instead of vice versa. Well, that might be true. Perhaps you'd like to look up old versions of "The Three Ravens" that pre-date the publication of "When Johnny Comes Marching Home" (1863) and see if you can find our melody? For myself, I'm reasonably satisfied with the discovery of the first three measures, quoted in *Old English Popular Music* by W. Chappell, from an 1825 source:

Evidently this much of the familiar strain was alive and kicking thirty-eight years before the publication of "When Johnny Comes Marching Home" and four years before Gilmore was born in Ballygar, Galway County, Ireland. Did Gilmore create the complete melody from this fragment? Or did somebody else (perhaps a writer of "Johnny, I Hardly Knew Ye") extend the fragment into the famous melody? Unless you can come up with the rest of the air from a source that pre-dates Gilmore's claim, we may have to concur with Irwin Silber, who came to this conclusion:

> Perhaps Gilmore, fresh from the Emerald Isles, reached back into his own portion of Irish folk memory to recall—and reconstruct—a tune. Who is to say that such a melody is not folk? And who is to say that Gilmore did not bring a creative effort to the air which justifies his individual stamp on it?
> Certainly, we must say that the burden of proof falls on Gilmore's detractors, and that in the absence of such tangible evidence, Gilmore's claim should be acknowledged.*

In any event, the song was soon firmly back in the hands of the folk as seen by the (cleaned-up) verses of the soldiers of the Civil War in "Johnny Fill Up the Bowl."

Recordings: Patrick Galvin (Riverside, RLP 12-613); Tom Makem (Vanguard, VRS 9083—at the Newport Folk Festival, 1960); Martha Schlamme (Vanguard, VRS 7012 and 9019); Glenn Yarbrough (Elektra, EKL 135).

*From *Songs of the Civil War* by Irwin Silber. Copyright © 1960 by Irwin Silber. Columbia University Press, New York.

roo,__ With your guns and drums and drums and guns, The en-e-my near-ly

slew you, Oh my dar - lin' dear, you

look so queer, Oh, John-ny, I hard-ly knew you.

2. Where are your eyes that were so mild, hooroo, hooroo,
   Where are your eyes that were so mild, hooroo, hooroo,
   Where are your eyes that were so mild
   When my heart you first beguiled;
   Oh, why did you run from me and the child?
   Johnny, I hardly knew you.

   Continue, as above:

3. Where are your legs that used to run, *etc.*
   When first you went to carry a gun?
   Indeed your dancing days are done.
   Oh, Johnny, I hardly knew you.

4. You haven't an arm you haven't a leg, *etc.*
   You're a hopeless shell of a man with a peg.
   And you'll have to be put with a bowl to beg.
   Oh, Johnny, I hardly knew you.

5. It's glad I am to see you home, *etc.*
   My darlin', you're so pale and wan.
   So low in flesh, so high in bone . . .
   Oh, Johnny, I hardly knew you.

6. They're rollin' out the drums again, *etc.*
   But they'll never take my sons again,
   No, they'll never take my sons again,
   Johnny, I'm swearin' to you.

WHEN JOHNNY COMES MARCHING HOME

1. When Johnny comes marching home again,
   Hurrah, hurrah!
   We'll give him a hearty welcome then,
   Hurrah, hurrah!
   The men will cheer, the boys will shout,
   The ladies they will all turn out,
   And we'll all feel gay when Johnny comes
     marching home.

2. The old church bell will peal with joy,
   Hurrah, hurrah!
   To welcome home our darling boy,
   Hurrah, hurrah!
   The village lads and lassies say,
   With roses they will strew the way,
   And we'll all feel gay when Johnny comes
        marching home.

3. Get ready for the Jubilee,
   Hurrah, hurrah!
   We'll give the hero three times three,
   Hurrah, hurrah!
   The laurel wreath is ready now
   To place upon his loyal brow,
   And we'll all feel gay when Johnny comes
        marching home.

4. Let love and friendship on that day,
   Hurrah, hurrah!
   Their choicest treasures then display,
   Hurrah, hurrah!
   And let each one perform some part,
   To fill with joy the warrior's heart,
   And we'll all feel gay when Johnny comes
        marching home.

JOHNNY, FILL UP THE BOWL

1. A soldier I'm just from the war,
   With bowls, with bowls!*
   A soldier I'm just from the war,
   With bowls, with bowls!
   A soldier I'm just from the war,
   Where thundering guns and cannons roar,
   And we'll all drink stone blind,
   Johnny, fill up the bowl.

   Continue, as above:

2. I was a man who went to war,
   The biggest fool you ever saw.

3. The ladies fell in love with me,
   My maiden name was Chivalry.

4. We are the boys of Potomac's ranks,
   We ran with McDowell, retreated with Banks.

5. We fought with McClellan, the Rebs, shakes and fever,
   But Mac joined the navy on reaching James River.

*Irwin Silber relates: "The 'Hurrah' refrain was also changed in most cases, with some variant of the word 'bowl' substituted—'for bales,' 'for bowls,' 'foot balls,' etc. Ellen Stekert, a young folklorist who has collected many Civil War songs in New York State, tells me that the song, as actually sung, has a decidedly less delicate and rather obvious earthy expression in the refrain." The contemporary versions recorded in my archives support this statement.

6. They gave us John Pope, our patience to tax,
   Who said that out West he'd seen naught but gray backs.

7. He said his headquarters were in the saddle,
   But Stonewall Jackson made him skedaddle.

8. Oh, Burnside, then he tried his luck,
   But in the mud so fast got stuck.

9. Then Hooker was taken to fill the bill,
   But he got a black eye at Chancellorsville.

10. Next came General Meade, a slow old plug,
    For he let them get away at Gettysburg.

JOSHUA FIT THE BATTLE OF JERICHO

It's a mistake to categorize Negro spirituals as *a* style. The styles are many and diversified, ranging from majestic, flowing tunes ("Deep River") to subdued, almost lullaby-like songs ("Steal Away") to spirited marches, like this one. The variety of styles is almost without limit. There is much variety in topics also. Many of the topics come from Biblical history. There are songs about Adam and Eve, Noah, David, Samson, Job, Jonah, and, of course, Joshua and the battle of Jericho. Some versions of this spiritual introduce the topic with two verses:

Good mornin' brother pilgrim,
Pray tell me where you bound.
Oh, tell me where you been travelin' to
On this enchanted ground.

My name it is Poor Pilgrim,
To Canaan I am bound,
Travelin' through this wilderness
On this enchanted ground.

Recordings: Lee Charles (Riverside, RLP 12-651); Odetta (Tradition, TLP 1010); Paul Robeson (Columbia, ML 4105, and Vanguard, VRS 9037); Pete Seeger (Folkways, FA 2452, and Disc, D 101); Josh White (Elektra, EKL 102).

walls came tumb-lin' down. You may talk a-bout your kings of

Gid-e-on, You may talk a-bout your men of Saul, But theres

none like good old Joshua, At the bat-tle of Jer-i-cho.

2. Well, the Lord done told old Joshua:
   "You must do just what I say,
   March 'round that city seven times
   And the walls will tumble away."

3. So up to the walls of Jericho,
   He marched with spear in hand,
   "Go blow them ram horns," Joshua cried,
   "Cause the battle am in my hand."

4. Then the lamb, ram, sheep horns began to blow,
   And the trumpet began to sound,
   Joshua told the children to shout that mornin'
   And the walls came tumblin' down.

THE JUG OF PUNCH

As the title implies, this is a drinking song, and it's one of the best in a long line of very good Irish drinking songs. The melody of the chorus repeats the melody of the verse, and the last two lines are changed each time to include the last two lines of the verse that has just been sung. One of the problems in writing down a song is what to do about the alternative lines found in different versions. This is the case with "The Jug of Punch," for which there is an attractive alternate line to the third line in the second verse, "Upon his knee is a pretty wench." The alternate is "A Kerry pippin and the crack and crunch." I hope you'll give each good line a chance from time to time.

Recordings: The Clancy Brothers (Tradition, TLP 1032); A. L. Lloyd (Riverside, RLP 12-618).

As I was sitting with a jug and spoon on one fine morn in the month of June, A bird-ie sang on an iv-y bunch And the song he sang was "The Jug of Punch."

CHORUS

Toora loo ra loo, too ra loo ra loo, too ra loo ra loo, too ra loo ra loo, A bird-ie sang on an iv-y bunch and the song he sang was "The Jug of Punch."

2. What more diversion can man desire?
Than to warm himself by an alehouse fire;
Upon his knee is a pretty wench,
Aye, and on the table a jug of punch.

3. All ye mortal lords drink your nectar wine
And the quality folks drink their claret fine;
I'll give them all the grapes in the bunch
For a jolly pull at the jug of punch.

4. Let the doctor come with all his art;
He'll make no impression on my heart.
Even the cripple forgets his hunch
When he's snug outside of a jug of punch.

5. If I get drunk, well, my money's my own,
And them as don't like me can leave me alone.
I'll tune my fiddle and rosin my bow;
Aye, and I'll be welcome where'er I go.

6. And when I'm dead and in my grave
No costly tombstone shall I crave.
Just lay me down in my bed of peat
With a jug of punch at my head and feet.

JUST A CLOSER WALK WITH THEE

Sustained notes against a rhythmic background and a forthright message to a highly personal God have made this song a strong favorite in the gospel-singing south. It provided country-music singer Red Foley with one of the best-selling records he ever made.

For group singing I've often had the girls singing a simple rhythmic chant while the men sing the melody. If you wish to try it, have the men sing the top line and the girls sing the bottom line; it takes only one quick run-through rehearsal to learn it—that is, if you settle for any harmony notes the girls are able to find within the chords. It will take more work to get the full harmonization I have shown below—but it's worth it.

Just a clos-er walk. Dail-y walk-ing close. Dail-y walk-ing close.

Just a clos-er walk. Just a clos-er walk. Let it be, Dear Lord,

Let it be, Dear Lord. Just a clos-er walk with Thee. ——

2. Through the days of toil that's near,
   If I fall, dear Lord, who cares?
   Who with me my burden shares?
   None but Thee, dear Lord, none but Thee.

3. When my feeble life is o'er,
   Time for me will be no more.
   Lead me gently, safely on,
   To Thy shore, dear Lord, to Thy shore.

*...wishing her lover
good speed*

And away, hey...

*She crossed the
broad prairies...*

K

*...the leafy
green dome*

*Can she bake
a cherry pie...*

*As I was going
to Derby...*

THE KEEPER OF
THE EDDYSTONE LIGHT

Here is a so-called "fake" folk song that has been a darling of folk-style singers. Richard Dyer-Bennet created the last verse, Sam Hinton told me, and in so doing earned the undying gratitude of us all. Although the song is almost a parody in itself, it has been frequently parodied. "The Keeper of the London Zoo" (by an anonymous author) has found favor with the college crowd; and "The Keeper of the Asteroid Light," by John Boardman (of Syracuse University at the time), is a space-age parody which I originally included in *Songs for Swingin' Housemothers*.

Recordings: Richard Dyer-Bennet (Stinson, SLP 2); Wallace House (Folkways, FW 6923); Burl Ives (Decca, DL 5080).

Oh, my fath-er was the keep-er of the Ed-dy-stone light, He slept with a mer-maid one fine night. From this un-ion there came three: A por-poise, a por-gy, and the other was me. Yo ho ho, the wind blows free, Oh, for a life on the rol-ling sea.

2. On nights when the winds and waves were high,
   Mother would sit on the rocks and sigh.
   Father would yell, "Come in from the gale,"
   But her only answer was the wiggle of her tail.

3. One night as I was a-trimmin' of the glim,
   A-singin' a verse of the evenin' hymn,
   A voice from the starboard shouted ahoy,
   And there was me mother a-sittin' on a buoy.

4. "Oh, what has become of my children three,"
   My mother then she asked of me.
   "One was exhibited as a talking fish,
   The other was served in a chafing dish."

5. The phosphorus flashed in her seaweed hair;
   I looked again and my mother wasn't there.
   A voice came echoin' out of the night:
   "To hell with the keeper of the Eddystone Light!"

THE KEEPER OF THE ASTEROID LIGHT

1. My father was the keeper of the Asteroid Light,
   He slept with a Martian one fine night.
   Out of this match came children three.
   Two were mutants and the other was me.

   Chorus:

   Yo, ho, ho, the jets run free;
   Oh, for the life at the speed of c!

2. When I was but a space cadet
   They put me in charge of a proton jet;
   I cleaned the tubes and filled them with fuel,
   And picked my teeth with an old slide rule.

3. One night as I was heading for the Moon
   And singing a well known spaceman's tune,
   I heard a voice cry out of the void,
   And there sat my mother on her asteroid.

4. "Oh, what has become of my children three?"
   My mother then she asked of me.
   "One is on exhibit in a zoo on Venus,
   And the other keeps a telepathic link between us."

5. The deuterons flashed in her hydrogen hair;
   I looked again, and my mother wasn't there.
   But she telepathed angrily out of the night,
   "Then to hell with the keeper of the Asteroid Light!"

THE KEEPER OF THE LONDON ZOO

1. My father was the keeper of the London Zoo,
   And he slept one night with a kangaroo.
   From this union there came three:
   A wallaby, a wombat, and the other was me.

   Chorus:

   The monkeys chatter the whole night through.
   Oh, for the life in the London Zoo.

2. I went to a carnival one fine night;
   Went into a tent to see a fight.
   And when the bell went ding dong ding
   I saw my mother standing in the ring.

3. "What has become of my children three?"
   My mother then she asked of me.
   "One was employed as a pogo stick
   And the other was given a bishopric."

4. Her chin connected with a smashing right;
   When I looked again she was out like a light.
   I heard her mumble as she came to:
   "To hell with the keeper of the London Zoo."

THE KEEPER
WOULD A-HUNTING GO

It is sometimes shocking to learn of the bawdy origins of some of our more innocent-seeming children's songs. You may be surprised to learn that "The Keeper" is a cleaned-up song based on an old English song with the theme of sexual pursuit as symbolized by a hunt. This idea was frequently used in medieval poetry, and it is quite likely that the song was passed down in oral tradition from the Middle Ages. In *The Idiom of the People* James Reeves provides an uncensored version:

> Oh, the keeper he a shooting goes,
> And all amongst his bucks and does.
> And, oh, for to shoot at the barren doe,
> She's amongst the leaves so green, O.
>
> The first doe he shot at he missed;
> The second doe he trimmed he kissed;
> The third ran away in a young man's heart;
> She's amongst the leaves so green, O.
>
> The fourth doe she did cross the plain;
> The keeper fetched her back again;
> Oh, and he tickled her in a merry vein;
> She's amongst the leaves so green, O.
>
> The fifth doe she did cross the brook.
> The keeper fetched her back with his long hook.
> What he done to her you must go and look,
> For she's amongst the leaves so green, O.

Recordings: Richard Dyer-Bennet (Dyer-Bennet, DYB 6000); Woody Guthrie (Folkways, FC 7015); Pete Seeger (Folkways, FA 2321).

mong the leaves so green, O. To my hey down, down. To me ho down, down. Hey down! Ho down! Der-ry, der-ry down, A-mong the leaves so green, O.

2. The first doe he shot at he missed;
   The second doe he trimmed he kissed;
   The third doe went where nobody wist
   Among the leaves so green, O.

3. The fourth doe she did cross the plain;
   The keeper fetched her back again;
   Where she is now she may remain
   Among the leaves so green, O.

4. The fifth doe she did cross the brook;
   The keeper fetched her back with his crook;
   Where she is now you must go and look
   Among the leaves so green, O.

5. The sixth doe she ran over the plain;
   But he with his hounds did turn her again,
   And it's there he did hunt in a merry, merry vein
   Among the leaves so green, O.

The most effective way to sing this old English song is to choose up sides and sing in two parts with answers to the appropriate lines.

KNAVES WILL BE KNAVES

"I Went to the Alehouse" is a broadside song from *Wit and Mirth, or Pills to Purge Melancholy* by Thomas D'Urfey. This six-volume collection of songs and poems, "Compleat, Pleasant and Divertive," from the eighteenth century is one of the monumental collections of its kind and is well known among folk song enthusiasts — though not generally held in very high esteem because of the large number of non-folk items included. History and song show that knaves haven't changed much since 1719. Oscar Brand's adaptation of the sea-going "A Gob Is a Slob" became a hit commercial song when Doris Day recorded it as "A Guy Is a Guy" almost two and a half centuries after it was written. You should recognize the familiar story in this interesting old version, for which I have provided harmonization only, the rest being entirely as it appeared in D'Urfey's *Pills*.

Recording: Alan Arkin (Elektra, EKL 21).

I went to the Ale-house as an hon-est woman should, And a knave fol-lowed af-ter, as you know knaves would, For Knaves will be Knaves in ev-'ry de-gree, I'll tell you by and by how this Knave served me.

2. I called for my pot as an honest woman should,
   And the knave drank it up, as you know knaves would.
   For knaves will be knaves in every degree,
   I'll tell you by and by how this knave served me.

3. I went to my house as an honest woman should,
   And the knave followed after, as you know knaves would,
   For knaves will be knaves in every degree,
   I'll tell you by and by how this knave served me.

4. I went into my bed as an honest woman should,
   And the knave followed suit, as you know knaves would,
   For knaves will be knaves in every degree,
   I'll tell you by and by how this knave served me.

5. I proved with child as an honest woman should,
   And the knave ran away, as you know knaves would,
   For knaves will be knaves in every degree,
   And thus I have told you how this knave served me.

KUM BA YA

There is a widely circulated theory that this song was based on the words "come by here" as Africans attempted to imitate these words as spoken by missionaries. In any event, this fragmentary song became traditional in Africa, where it was "found," and brought to America, to become part of our tradition. As the world gets smaller and cultures mix, more of this tradition swapping is bound to take place.

The words are pronounced *koom bah yah,* and the song is usually sung very slowly and with dignity. Many people use the English words "come by here" instead. New verses are constantly being coined. A few examples are shown here. The chorus may be repeated after each verse.

Recordings: Joan Baez (Vanguard, VRS 9112); Womenfolk (Victor, LPM 2821).

Kum ba ya, my Lord, kum ba ya. Kum ba ya, my Lord, kum ba ya. Kum ba ya, my Lord, kum ba ya.— Oh, Lord, kum ba ya.

Verses (same tune as chorus):

1. Someone's crying, Lord, kum ba ya,
   Someone's crying, Lord, kum ba ya,
   Someone's crying, Lord, kum ba ya,
   Oh, Lord, kum ba ya. *Chorus.*

Continue, as above:

2. Someone's singing, Lord, *etc.*
   Chorus.

3. Someone's praying, Lord, *etc.*
   Chorus.

4. Someone's hoping, Lord, *etc.*
   Chorus.

*...wishing her lover
good speed*

And away, hey...

*She crossed the
broad prairies...*

L

*...the leafy
green dome*

*Can she bake
a cherry pie...*

*As I was going
to Derby...*

LANDLORD, FILL
THE FLOWING BOWL
(Three Jolly Coachmen)

Here is one of the most popular of all drinking songs. Since the eighteenth century it has appeared in virtually every student song book from the British Isles and this country. The lyric grew out of Fletcher's "Drink To-day," which ends:

> Then let us swill, boys, for our health;
> Who drinks well, loves the commonwealth;.
> And he that will to bed go sober
> Falls with the leaf still in October.

In recent years singers often add the refrain:

> Three jolly coachmen stopped at an English tavern.
> Three jolly coachmen stopped at an English tavern.
> And they decided,
> And they decided,
> And they decided
> To have another flagon.

This refrain is derived from an earlier English verse (sung in the same manner as above):

> Three jolly post boys drinking at the Dragon,
> And they determined to finish out the flagon.

Skiers add verses like these:

> The man who skis with a mighty schuss and takes the trails wide open,
> Skis till he hits a tree and all his bones are broken.

> The man who skis with well-bent knees and plenty of vorlager,
> Skis as he ought to ski and lives to drink his lager.

Cynics among the college crowd frequently follow the next to last verse (below) with this one:

> The little girl who gets a kiss and goes back for another,
> Does a very foolish thing for she'll soon be a mother.

Recordings: Blazers (ABC Paramount 201); Oscar Brand (Riverside, RLP 12 630 – "Three Jolly Coachmen").

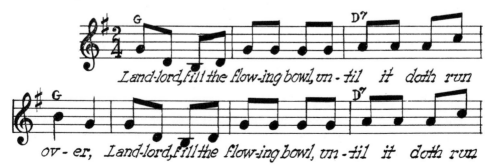

ov-er, For to-night we'll mer-rye be, For to-night we'll mer-rye be, For to-night we'll mer-rye be, To-mor-row we'll be sob-er.

Continue, as above:

2. The man who drinks cold water pure,
   And goes to bed quite sober,
   Falls as the leaves do fall,
   So early in October.

3. The man who drinks good whiskey clear,
   And goes to bed right mellow,
   Lives as he ought to live,
   And dies a jolly good fellow.

4. But he who drinks just what he likes,
   And getteth half seas over,
   Lives until he dies, perhaps,
   And then lies down in clover.

5. The little girl who gets a kiss,
   And runs and tells her mother,
   Does a very foolish thing,
   And seldom gets another.

6. The little boy who gets a kiss
   And runs and tells his brother,
   Does a very useful thing,
   And brother gets another.

LET MY LITTLE LIGHT SHINE

Pete Seeger probably did more than anyone to make this gospel song a favorite of folk song revivalists. It has been one of the "theme" songs of social-protest groups. During the days of sit-ins in the South, freedom singers added choruses like this:

> I've got the light of freedom, I'm gonna let it shine, *etc.*
> All over creation, I'm gonna let it shine, *etc.*
> Go tell everybody, I'm gonna let it shine, *etc.*

The name of a town or place is often substituted for *creation,* and a person for *everybody.* You may want to vary choruses by inventing lines of your own or borrowing from spiritual tradition verses like these:

Go tell the rich and poor, I'm gonna let it shine, *etc.*
Go tell the meek and humble, I'm gonna let it shine, *etc.*

You can find these ideas by looking around at the spirituals in this book.

If you sing this song in chorus-after-changing-chorus fashion you will probably want to omit the verse shown below—or use it only once as a bridge, or variation.

Recordings: The Gateway Singers (Decca, DL 8671); Bob Gibson and Bob Camp (Vanguard, VRS 9084), The Howard University Choir (RCA Victor, LM 2166); Odetta (Victor, LPM 2643); The Robert Shaw Chorale (RCA Victor, LM 2357); Pete Seeger (Folkways, FA 2451); Harry and Jeanie West (Folkways, FA 2357);

what to say.— On Sun-day gave me pow-er di-vine— just to let my lit-tle light shine.

THE LINCOLNSHIRE POACHER

This traditional English song very likely grew out of the protests of British shepherds and farmers in the late 1700s. They were driven from the extensive properties of wealthy landowners so that large game preserves could be established for hunting. Severe penalties were established for *poaching,* hunting in a private preserve without the permission of the owner. Many of these preserves, some of which were established as early as the Middle Ages, still exist today in Great Britain and throughout Europe. The Lincolnshire location is generally found in most versions of this song today, but other versions have been found with different locations, indicating that the song was probably adapted frequently to represent local feelings.

Recordings: Richard Dyer-Bennet (Stinson, SLP 61); John Runge (Stinson, SLP 88).

When I was bound ap-pren-tice in fam-ous Lin-coln-shire,— Full well I served my mas-ter for more than sev-en year,— Till I took up to poach-ing as you shall quick-ly hear: Oh, 'tis my de-light on a shin-ing night in the sea-son of the year—

2. As me and my comrades were setting of a snare,
   'Twas then we spied the gamekeeper, for him we did not care,
   For we can wrestle and fight, my boys, and jump o'er anywhere.

216

Oh, 'tis my delight on a shining night
In the season of the year.

3. As me and my comrades were setting four or five,
   And taking on 'em up again we caught a hare alive,
   We took the hare alive, my boys, and through the woods did steer.
   Oh, 'tis my delight on a shining night
   In the season of the year.

4. I threw him on my shoulder, and then we trudged home,
   We took him to a neighbor's house and sold him for a crown,
   We sold him for a crown, my boys, but I did not tell you where.
   Oh, 'tis my delight on a shining night
   In the season of the year.

5. Success to every gentleman that lives in Lincolnshire,
   Success to every poacher that wants to sell a hare,
   Bad luck to every gamekeeper that will not sell his deer.
   Oh, 'tis my delight on a shining night
   In the season of the year.

LITTLE MAGGIE

This modal mountain song is a great favorite with banjo players, of both
city and country variety. You'll often hear it played in company with songs
like "East Virginia" and "Darlin' Corey" (see Index).

Recordings: Tom Paley (Elektra, EKL 122); Obray Ramsay (Riverside, RLP 12 610).

2. Tell me how can I ever stand it,
   Just to see those two blue eyes.
   They're shining like a diamond,
   Like a diamond in the sky.

3. Sometimes I have a nickel,
   Sometimes I have a dime.
   And it's sometimes I have ten dollars,
   Just to buy Little Maggie some wine.

4. Pretty flowers were made for blooming,
   Pretty stars were meant to shine.
   Pretty girls were made for boys to love,
   And Little Maggie was made for mine.

5. The first time I seen Little Maggie,
   She was starin' straight at me
   With a forty-five strapped 'round her shoulder
   And a banjo on her knee.

6. Now, she's goin' down to the station
   With a suitcase in her hand.
   She's goin' away for to leave me.
   She's bound for a distant land.

LOLLY TOO DUM

Folk music literature abounds with variations on this theme. The mother has problems with her teenage daughter. But once the daughter leaves the nest the mother gets ideas of her own. Then it's daughter's turn to be concerned about mother. Next thing you know, mother steps out on her own, successfully.

Recordings: Gerald Campbell (London, LL 1714); Burl Ives (Decca, DL 5080); Robin Roberts (Stinson, SLP 77); Betty Vaiden Williams (Vanguard, VRS 9028).

As I went out one morn-ing to take the morn-ing air, Lol-ly-too-dum, too-dum, lol-ly-too-dum day. As I went out one morn-ing to take the morn-ing air, I ov-er-heard a moth-er A-scold-in' her daugh-ter fair, Lol-ly-too-dum, too-dum, lol-ly-too-dum day.

Continue, as above:

2. "You better go wash them dishes,
   And hush that clattering tongue,
   I know you want to get married
   And that you are too young."

3. "Oh, pity my condition
   As you would your own,
   For seventeen long years
   I've been sleeping all alone.

4. "Yes, I'm seventeen and over,
   And that you will allow —
   I must and I will get married
   For I'm in the notion now."

5. "Supposin' I was willin'.
   Where would you get your man?"
   "Why, Lordy mercy, Mammy,
   I'd marry handsome Sam."

6. "Supposin' he should slight you
   Like you done him before?"
   "Why, Lordy mercy, Mammy,
   I could marry forty more.

7. "There's peddlers and there's tinkers
   And boys from the plow,
   Oh Lordy mercy, Mammy,
   I'm gettin' that feeling now!"

8. "Now my daughter's married
   And well fer to do,
   Gather 'round young fellers,
   I'm on the market too."

9. "Lordy mercy, Mammy,
   And who would marry you?
   Ain't no man alive wants
   A wife as old as you."

10. "There's doctors and there's lawyers
    And men of high degree,
    And some of them will marry
    And one will marry me."

11. "Now we both are married
    And well fer to be.
    Ha ha ha, you pretty young girls,
    That feeling's off of me."

LORD LOVEL

Unless you're surrounded by scholars, you don't have to take all of the old ballads as seriously as they do. And there are some you don't have to take seriously even in their presence — because some songs are not *supposed* to be taken seriously. This is one of them. And it mocks all of them (the ballads). The schmaltzy little waltz melody is just that, and the words and syllables that call for repetition near the end of each verse are supposed to be ludicrously jammed in whether they are willing or not. Many singers prefer *Lord Lover* to *Lord Lovel*. And it is, perhaps, more appropriate under the circumstances. But either way, put a serious look on your face and give this a mock-ballad performance straight through to the sweet, neat little ending, with apologies to Barbara Allen.

Recordings: Alan Lomax (Tradition, TLP 1029); Peggy Seeger with Guy Carawan (E. M. I. Records, CLP 1174); Frank Warner (Elektra, EKLP 3).

2. "Oh, where are you going Lord Lovel?" she said;
   "Oh, where are you going?" said she.
   "I'm going, my dear Lady Nancy Bell,
   Strange countries to see, see, see,
   Strange countries to see."

3. "Oh, when will you be back?" she said;
   "When will you be back?" said she.
   "In a year or two, or three, three, three.
   Then I'll come back to thee, to thee,
   Then I'll come back to thee."

4. He had not been gone but a year and a day,
   Strange countries for to see,
   When ravishing thoughts came into his head.
   His lady he wanted to see, see, see,
   His lady he wanted to see.

5. He rode and he rode on his milk-white steed,
   Till he came to London town;
   And there he heard Saint Varnie's bell,

220

And the people all mourning around, round, round,
And the people all mourning around.

6. "Is somebody dead?" Lord Lovel he said.
   "Is somebody dead?" said he.
   "A lady is dead," the people all said,
   "They call her the Lady Nancy, cy, cy,
   They call her the Lady Nancy."

7. He ordered the grave to be opened forthwith,
   And the shroud to be folded down;
   And then he kissed her clay-cold lips,
   Till the tears came trickling down, down, down,
   Till the tears came trickling down.

8. Lady Nancy she died as it might be today,
   Lord Lovel he died on the morrow;
   And out of her bosom there grew a red rose,
   And out of Lord Lovel's a briar-riar-riar,
   And out of Lord Lovel's a briar.

9. They grew and they grew till they reached the church top,
   And they could not grow any higher.
   And there they entwined in a true lover's knot,
   Which true lovers always admire-mire-mire,
   Which true lovers always admire.

LORD RANDALL

Folk song scholars have traced this famous ballad all over Europe and America and have found many different melodic and textual variations. The nineteenth-century ballad scholar Francis James Child found that it had been popular in Italy for over three hundred years. The American version presented here is the most popular accompanied version in this country. A different melodic setting is favored for unaccompanied singing.

In some of the older British versions many more verses are used to get to the point of the poisoning. In the first verse Randall might simply say, "Make my bed soon, for I'm wearied with hunting and fain would lie down." Then the mother asks what Randall has eaten at his true-love's place and he answers, "Eels fried in a pan." The mother continues, Perry Mason style, by asking what happened to his leavings and he replies that he fed them to his hawks and hounds. It takes still another verse for her to learn what happened to the hounds: "They stretched their legs out and died." "Ah ha," says the mother triumphantly, finding her dark suspicions to be true: "I fear you are poisoned." And Randall answers simply, "Oh, yes, I am poisoned." Why didn't he say so in the first place? The mother immediately thinks of what this sinister turn of events means to her; in the very next verse she asks, "What d'ye leave to your mother?"

There is something to be said for the show-biz timing of this approach. However, most contemporary singers cut out all the poison rigamarole and get right down to the inheritance questions, although they usually give mother a slightly better image by letting her ask first what dad is getting.

Recordings: Isla Cameron (Tradition, TLP 1001); Paul Clayton (Folkways, FA 2110); Alfred Deller (Vanguard, VRS 1001); Richard Dyer-Bennet (Stinson, SLP 61); Burl Ives (Columbia, CL 6058); John Langstaff (Tradition, TLP 1009); Artus Moser (Folkways, FA 2112); John Jacob Niles (RCA Camden, CAL 330); Susan Reed (RCA Victor, LXA 3019); John Runge (Stinson, SLP 88); Pete Seeger (Folkways, FA 2439); Josh White (Decca, DL 8665).

2. Oh, what did you have for your supper, my son?
   What did you have, oh my pretty one?
   A cup of cold poison, mother.
   A cup of cold poison, mother.
   Make my bed soon for I'm sick to my heart
   And I fain would lie down.

   Continue, as above:

3. Oh, what will you leave your father, my son?
   My wagon and oxen, mother.

4. Oh, what will you leave your mother, my son?
   My house and my lands.

5. Oh, what will you leave your brother, my son?
   My horn and my hounds.

6. Oh, what will you leave your sister, my son?
   The rings on my fingers.

7. Oh, what will you leave your sweetheart, my son?
   A rope that will hang her.

*...wishing her lover
good speed*

And away, hey...

*She crossed the
broad prairies...*

M

*...the leafy
green dome*

*Can she bake
a cherry pie...*

*As I was going
to Derby...*

MAMA DON'T ALLOW

All we did was sing that old favorite "You've worked for us all of these years, Mother, now go out and work for yourself," and she got uppity and broke up the rehearsal. Born out of some real rehearsal problems, I'm sure, this country classic has been a favorite of just about every kind of group I've ever played with—from Dixieland to Hillbilly to Folk. And none of the groups I've played with ever did this number the same way twice. We never knew where we were going or how we would end until we got there. Plenty of the things mama wouldn't allow grew out of the situation at hand, and we rarely confined her prohibitions to the instruments in the group, though that is traditional and a good way to get started.

There are a lot of recordings around, but none of them quite come off. This is a jam-session piece that really doesn't mean a thing without the spontaneity, goofs, and horseplay of an off-the-record rendition. I've provided a few verse ideas to get you started. After that, you're on your own. You should be able to make up verses about bass bumpin', loud playin', soft playin', sad playin' (switch to A minor, using Am, E7, and Dm instead of the regular chords), foot stompin', mistakes (make 'em), hillbilly music, rock and roll, dixieland, or a hundred other things. It's customary to weave instrumental parts in and out of each verse as it is sung. For example, a fiddle player fiddles during his verse on the third and fourth, the seventh and eighth, and the last measures. He can also fiddle throughout measures nine through twelve—with or without those lines being sung, according to the preference of the group. Each verse is followed by an appropriate instrumental chorus.

2. Mama don't allow no guitar pickin' around here.
   Mama don't allow no guitar pickin' around here.
   We don't care what mama don't allow;
   Gonna pick that guitar anyhow.
   Mama don't allow no guitar pickin' around here.

3. Mama don't allow no banjo strummin' around here.
   Mama don't allow no banjo strummin' around here.
   We don't care what mama don't allow;
   Gonna flog that banjo anyhow.
   Mama don't allow no banjo strummin' around here.

MAN OF CONSTANT SORROW

The origin of this southern mountain song is typically obscure. It's missing from most of the large standard collections, and I've never seen any mention of it by earlier scholars. I have a hunch (and that's all it is) that it might have been derived from, or at least inspired by, the nineteenth-century hymn "I Am a Poor Pilgrim of Sorrow," which in turn seems to have been derived from a Negro spiritual. The poor pilgrim also left home and was bound to roam the world among strangers until he was reunited with his loved ones on God's golden shore.

Singers vary considerably in their performance of this song—the most obvious difference being between male and female performers. The latter sing, "I am a maid [or girl] of constant sorrow." A popular version, with verses written by Sarah Ogan, is sung by Peggy Seeger. Mike Seeger takes another tack with a modal version he derived from an old Columbia recording by Ralph Stanley and from earlier versions by Emry Arthur and Juanita Moore. You may hear all of these versions on the records listed below. The first one listed is similar to the version given here.

Recordings: Judy Collins (Elektra, EKL 209); Roscoe Holcomb (Folkways, FA 2363); Mike Seeger (Folkways, FA 2325); Peggy Seeger (Prestige International, 13058).

2. Each place I go I am a stranger.
   A friendly face I see no more.
   There's just one thought that keeps me goin':
   I'll sail on God's golden shore.

3. All through this world I'm bound to ramble,
   Through sun and wind and driving rain.

I'm bound to ride the western railway.
I guess I'll take the very next train.

4. Sometimes I'm tossed; sometimes I'm driven;
   Sometimes I know not where to roam.
   They'll bury me in some deep valley.
   Until then, I have no home.

5. I am a man of constant sorrow.
   I've seen trials all of my days.
   I said goodbye to old Kentucky,
   The place where I was born and raised.

MARYANNE

Popular songs today are promoted and sold to the public through an elaborate network of song writers, singers, arrangers, musicians, recording companies, publishers, performance societies, agents, publicity men, disk jockeys, trade magazines, distributors, record stores, and music stores. Usually a hit song results from a successful campaign of plugging the song on radio and television. In previous centuries (after the invention of the printing press made mass circulation possible) popular songs were promoted in the streets. A street singer sang the songs to create interest (or capitalize on previously generated interest) and sold them to the public on inexpensive printed sheets. The ballads and songs sold in this manner are called broadsides (named for the broad sheets on which they were printed), street songs or ballads, or stall ballads.

The approach to making these songs was journalistic. The writers either reworked existing songs or wrote up current events. Often ballad writers were sent out to cover events in the same way reporters do for newspapers today. The topics covered included murders, executions, scandals, rumors, fads, and a cross section of the public interests of the time.

"Maryanne," a popular street song of the nineteenth century, was worked and reworked by the popular-music industry of that time. Here is how it appeared on one broadside:

Fare-you-well my own Mary Ann,
Fare-you-well for a while,
For the ship is ready and the wind it is fair,
And I am bound for the sea, Mary Ann,
And I am bound for the sea, Mary Ann.

Don't you see that turtle dove
A sitting on yonder pile?
Lamenting the loss of her own true love,
And so am I for you, Mary Ann,
And so am I for you, Mary Ann.

A lobster in a lobster pot,
A blue fish wriggling on a hook,
May suffer some, but oh no! not
What I do feel for you, Mary Ann,
What I do feel for you, Mary Ann.

227

The pride of all our kitchen rare,
That in our kitchen garden grows,
Was pumpkins, but none could compare
In angel form to my Mary Ann,
In angel form to my Mary Ann.

The frequently stilted and forced lyrics of the professional broadside versi-
fier usually died out in the folk process of oral transmission, refinement, and
editing. But a surprising number of these awkwardly inspired phrases survive,
as they have in contemporary versions of "Maryanne" (see "Wildwood Flower"
for another prime example). The excellence of its melody may have something
to do with this survival. And, of course, the song had existed in oral tradition
before the broadside balladeers went to work on it:

Farewell my joy and heart's delight.
I must leave you for a while.
If I go away I will come again,
If I go ten thousand miles, my dear,
If I go ten thousand miles.

Ten thousand miles it is too far
To leave me here alone.
Here I may lie, lament, and cry.
And you cannot hear my moan, my dear,
And you cannot hear my moan.

Suppose my friends will never be pleased
And look with an angry eye.
O then I will love thee more and more,
Until the day I die, my dear,
Until the day I die.

O don't you see that milk white dove
Sitting on yonder green tree?
Lamenting for her own true love
As I lament for thee, my dear,
As I lament for thee.

You call me where you see me not;
And speak by me as you find;
And don't be like the weather cock
That changes with the wind, my dear,
That changes with the wind.

The crow that is so black, my dear,
Shall change his color white
If ever I prove false to thee;
And the day shall turn to night, my dear,
The day shall turn to night.

With a little adaptation you may borrow from this traditional version for
your own version of the song.

The widespread popularity of the song has been demonstrated by its discovery in folk traditions of the southern mountains as well as in Canada. A
delightful verse from a Canadian version goes like this:

Oh, had I but a flask of gin
With sugar here for two,

And a great big bowl for to mix it in,
I'd pour a drink for you, Mary Ann,
I'd pour a drink for you, Mary Ann.

Fare thee well, my own true love. Fare thee well for a-
while. My ship is wait-ing, the wind blows free. I'm
bound a-way to the sea, my dear Mar-y-Anne. I'm
bound a-way to the sea, my dear Mar-y-Anne.

2. Ten thousand miles away from home,
   Ten thousand miles or more.
   The sea may freeze and the earth may burn
   If I never no more return to you, Maryanne.

3. Do you see the crow flying high?
   She will surely turn to white;
   If I ever prove false to you, my love,
   Bright morning will turn to night, my dear Maryanne.

4. See the grass growing under your feet,
   Arise and stand on end.
   Love it is a killing thing,
   Did you ever feel the pain, my dear Maryanne?

5. I wish my breast was made of glass,
   Wherein you might behold
   The secret of my love so true
   In letters writ of gold, my dear Maryanne.

MICHAEL, ROW THE BOAT ASHORE

Folk song revivalists found "Michael, Row the Boat Ashore" in the Georgia
Sea islands and circulated the song widely and fervently. As it is usually
performed today, the song is a melding of spiritual, calypso, and sea-song
styles (see page XIV). It seems to have originated in the United States as a
spiritual sung by the slave crews on plantation riverboats. You can find it in

the earliest-known source of the folk songs created by American Negroes, *Slave Songs of the United States* by William Francis Allen, Charles Pickard Ware, and Lucy McKim Garrison, published in 1867. Charles Ware notes that "Michael" was one of the rowing songs used when the load was heavy or the boat was going against the tide. The name Michael refers to the Archangel Michael. Although many folk music specialists like to classify work songs and spirituals separately, Afro-American folk song scholar Henry Edward Krehbiel has demonstrated that many spirituals were in fact working songs, as was "Michael." So the song is a spiritual, but it's also a chantey; and since the forms are essentially the same, there's no classification problem.

2. Michael's boat's a music boat, Alleluia,
   Michael's boat's a music boat, Alleluia.

3. Sister, help to trim the sail, Alleluia,
   Sister, help to trim the sail, Alleluia.

4. Jordan's River is chilly and cold, Alleluia,
   Kills the body but not the soul, Alleluia.

5. Jordan's River is deep and wide, Alleluia,
   Meet my mother on the other side, Alleluia.

6. Gabriel, blow the trumpet horn, Alleluia,
   Blow the trumpet loud and long, Alleluia.

7. Brother, lend a helping hand, Alleluia,
   Brother, lend a helping hand, Alleluia.

8. Michael's boat's a gospel boat, Alleluia,
   Michael's boat's a gospel boat, Alleluia.

9. Michael, row the boat ashore, Alleluia,
   Michael, row the boat ashore, Alleluia.

MIDNIGHT SPECIAL

The Lomaxes found prisons to be a gold mine for folk song collecting. "Midnight Special" is probably one of the most popular of the songs to come from this source. This swingy blues-style song is based on a prison legend that a man would go free if the headlight of this train would shine through the bars on him. The song is closely associated with Huddie "Leadbelly" Ledbetter (see page 265).

Recordings: Cisco Houston (Folkways, FA 2346, and Disc, D 103); Huddie Ledbetter (Folkways, FA 2942); John A. Lomax, Jr. (Folkways, FG 3508); Odetta (Tradition, TLP 1025); Pete Seeger (Folkways, FA 2321); The Weavers (Vanguard, VRS 9024); Josh White (Elektra, EKL 114).

Let the mid-night spec-ial — shine its light on me. —

— Let the mid-night spec-ial — Shine its ev-er-lov-in' light on me. —

— Well, you wake up in the morn-ing, — hear the ding dong ring. —

— You go march-in' to the tab-le — see the same — old —

thing. Well, it's on-a the tab-le, — Knife, a fork, and a pan. —

— If you say a thing a-bout it — You're in troub-le with the man.

2. If you ever go to Houston, you better walk right,
   You better not stagger, and you better not fight.
   Sheriff Benson will arrest you, and he'll carry you down,
   You can bet your bottom dollar, you're sugarland bound.

3. Yonder come Doc Melton, tell me how do you know?
   He gave me a tablet just the day before.
   There never was a doctor travelin' over the land
   That could cure the fever of a convict man.

4. Yonder comes Miss Rosy, tell me how do you know?
   I know her by her apron, and the dress that she wore,
   Umbrella on her shoulder, piece of paper in her hand,
   She says to the captain, "I want my lifetime man!"

MISS BAILEY

"Isn't a good tune like a well-constructed building which, over a period of time, is used for various purposes? It may be used as a dwelling house and, later, a storehouse, a workshop, a meeting hall, a church, a school, or a barn. Similarly, there are melodies which were once used for ancient British murder ballads, and later served as vehicles for Christian hymns, and later yet for union songs or peace songs." (Pete Seeger, in his "Johnny Appleseed, Jr." column in *Sing Out,* Vol. 15, No. 2, May 1965).

This particular song, though popular with singers of folk songs, doesn't measure up to a lot of scholarly definitions of folk song. It was written by George Colman, an English playwright who died in 1794. Colman borrowed the tune from other sources, and it has been borrowed for other songs since — Andrew Jackson's campaign song, "The Hunters of Kentucky," being perhaps the most famous.

Vengeful ghosts have been popular with the folk and may be found haunting many an old ballad. This song, though, is just a spook spoof. The word *ratafee* mentioned is a cordial flavored with fruit kernels.

Recordings: Shep Ginandes (Elektra, EKL 133); Dean Gitter (Riverside, RLP 12 636); Will Holt (Stinson, SLP 64); Josef and Miranda Marais (Decca, DL 9047); Milt Okun (Riverside, RLP 12 603); Susan Reed (Elektra, EKL 116). Variation: "The Hunters of Kentucky": Oscar Brand (Folkways, FH 5280).

2. One night betimes he went to bed, for he had caught a fever,
Said he, "I am a handsome man and I'm a gay deceiver."
His candle just at twelve o'clock began to burn quite palely,
A ghost stepped up to his bedside and said, "Behold! Miss Bailey!"

3. "Avaunt, Miss Bailey," then he cried, "you can't affright me, really."
   "Dear Captain Smith," the ghost replied, "you've used me ungenteelly,
   The coroner's quest was hard with me because I've acted frailly,
   And Parson Biggs won't bury me though I'm a dead Miss Bailey."

4. "Miss Bailey, then, since you and I accounts must once for all close,
   I've got a five-pound note in my regimental small-clothes.
   'Twill bribe the sexton for your grave." The ghost then vanished gaily,
   Crying, "Bless you, wicked Captain Smith, remember poor Miss Bailey."

THE HUNTERS OF KENTUCKY

1. Ye gentlemen and ladies fair who grace this famous city,
   Just listen if you've time to spare while I rehearse a ditty,
   And for the opportunity conceive yourself quite lucky,
   For 'tis not often that you see a hunter from Kentucky.

Chorus:

Oh, Kentucky,
The hunters of Kentucky,
Oh, Kentucky,
The hunters of Kentucky.

2. We are a hardy free-born race, each man to fear a stranger,
   Whate'er the game, we join in chase, despoiling time and danger;
   And if a daring foe annoys, whate'er his strength and forces,
   We'll show him that Kentucky boys are alligator horses.

3. I s'pose you've read it in the prints, how Packenham attempted
   To make old Hickory Jackson wince, but soon his scheme repented;
   For we, with rifles ready cocked, thought such occasion lucky,
   And soon around the gen'ral flocked the hunters of Kentucky.

4. You've heard, I s'pose, how New Orleans is famed for wealth and beauty;
   There's girls of ev'ry hue it seems from snowy white to sooty;
   So Packenham he made his brags, if he in fight was lucky,
   He'd have their girls and cotton bags in spite of old Kentucky.

5. But Jackson, he was wide awake, and was not scared of trifles;
   For well he knew what aim we take with our Kentucky rifles;
   He led us down to Cypress Swamp, the ground was low and mucky;
   There stood John Bull in pomp, and here was old Kentucky.

6. A bank was raised to hide our breasts, not that we thought of dying.
   But that we always like to rest unless the game is flying;
   Behind it stood our little force, none wished it to be greater;
   For every man was half a horse and half an alligator.

7. They did not let our patience tire before they showed their faces.
   We did not choose to waste our fire, so snugly kept our places.
   But when so near we saw them wink, we thought it time to stop 'em,
   And 'twould have done you good, I think, to see Kentuckians drop 'em.

8. They found at last 'twas vain to fight where lead was all the booty.
   And so they wisely took to flight and left us all our beauty.
   And now if danger e'er annoys, remember what our trade is.
   Just send for us Kentucky boys and we'll protect the ladies.

MISTER FROGGIE WENT A-COURTIN'

This ballad for children of all ages has been popular for several centuries in hundreds of variations. In *Old English Popular Music,* W. Chappell relates:

> In Wedderburn's *Complaint of Scotland,* 1549, one of the songs sung by the shepherds is *The frog cam to the myl dur* (mill door). In 1580 a ballad of 'A most strange Wedding of the Frog and the Mouse,' probably the same as the above, was licensed to Edward White, at Stationers' Hall. It is the progenitor of several others. . . .

The version shown below is one of the most popular ones today.

Recordings: Marjorie Bennett (Judson, J 3028); William Clauson (Capitol, T 10158); Alfred Deller (Vanguard, VRS 1001); Richard Dyer-Bennet (Dyer-Bennet, DYB 6000); Shep Ginandes (Elektra, EKL 7); Burl Ives (Decca, DL 8080); Ewan MacColl and Peggy Seeger (Riverside, RLP 12 637); Ed McCurdy (Tradition, TLP 1027); Alan Mills (Folkways, FC 7021); John Jacob Niles (RCA Camden, CAL 219); Jean Ritchie (Collector Limited Edition, CLE 1201—two versions; and Westminster, WP 6037); Pete Seeger (Folkways, FC 7001 and FC 7010).

2. So off he went with his opera hat, mm mm,
   So off he went with his opera hat,
   And on the way he met a rat, mm mm.

Continue, as above:

3. But he went on to Missy Mouse's door,
   Where he had been many times before.

4. He took Missy Mousy on his knee,
   And asked her, "Will you marry me?"

5. "Without my Uncle Rat's consent,
   I wouldn't marry the President."

6. So, Uncle Rat gave his consent,
   And the Weasel wrote the publishment.

7. The Owl did hoot and the birds they sang,
   All through the woods the music rang.

8. What will the wedding breakfast be?
   Two green beans and a black-eyed pea.

9. They all went sailing across the brook,
   And a big white duck came and gobbled them up.

10. There's bread and cheese upon the shelf,
    If you want any more, you can sing it yourself.

MUST I GO BOUND

There must have been at least twelve million five hundred and sixty-five thousand two hundred and thirty-eight or nine commercial country music ballads written on the formula laid down by this hillbilly song over the last twenty years or so. It's got everything the formula calls for: a constant lover who'll never be cured, and a fickle lady whose love had seemed to be the Rock of Gibraltar until the lady showed her true colors. This delightful song is related to, and derived from, "Waly, Waly," an old Scottish song.

O waly, waly, up the bank,
And waly, waly, doon the brae.
And waly, waly, yon burnside,
Where I and my love wont to gae.

I lean'd my back unto an aik,
I thocht it was a trusty tree.
But first it bow'd and syne it brak;
And sae did my fause love tae me.

O waly, waly, but love be bonnie
A little time while it is new;
But when it's auld it waxes cauld,
And fades away like the morning dew.

O wherefore should I busk my heid,
Or wherefore should I kame my hair?
For my true love has me forsook,
And says he'll never love me mair.

See Index listing "The Water Is Wide" for another relative.

Recordings: Milt Okun and Ellen Stekert (Riverside, RLP 12 634); Dorothy Olsen (RCA Victor, LPM 1606); Susan Reed (Elektra, EKL 126); Buffy Sainte-Marie (Vanguard, VRS 9171).

Must I go bound while you go free?__Must I love a girl who won't love me?__Must I then act the child-ish part__ __and love a girl who'd break my heart?__

2. I put my finger to the bush
   To pluck a rose of fairest kind.
   The thorn it pricks me at a touch;
   And, oh, I left that rose behind.

3. I leaned my back against an oak,
   Thinking that it was a mighty tree.
   But first it bent and then it broke,
   Just as my love proved false to me.

4. So I'll go bound while you go free.
   And I'll love a girl who won't love me.
   And I will act the childish part;
   And love a girl who'd break my heart.

...wishing her lover good speed

And away, hey...

She crossed the broad prairies...

N

*...the leafy
green dome*

*Can she bake
a cherry pie...*

*As I was going
to Derby...*

NEW RIVER TRAIN*

This group-sing counting song has long been popular with backwoods buffs and campus-based city billies. It is a natural for harmonizing by ear, and the verses are easy to remember once you've learned the system. All you have to do is know how to count, and appropriately zip in the third line for each verse. The best versions come out of a spontaneous session, with everyone taking turns making up his own verses. You won't find the version given here in school songbooks. Maybe it will stimulate you to some fresh ideas of your own. The New River Train mentioned is any train you want it to be.

Recordings: Laurel River Valley Boys (Judson, J 3031); Alan Mills (Folkways, FP 709); *Mountain Music, Bluegrass Style,* recorded by Mike Seeger (Folkways, FA 2318).

I'm riding on that New River Train; I'm riding on that New River Train; Same old train that brought me here, gonna carry me home again.

2. Oh, baby, remember what you said;
   Oh, baby, remember what you said;
   Remember what you said: You would rather see me dead
   Than ridin' on that New River Train.

3. Oh, darlin', you can't love one,
   Oh, darlin', you can't love one;
   You can't love one and have any fun,
   Oh, darlin', you can't love one.

Continue, as above:

4. You can't love two—and your little heart be true.
5. You can't love three—and still love me.
6. You can't love four—and love me any more.
7. You can't love five—and still stay alive.
8. You can't love six—and not get in a fix.
9. You can't love seven—if you want to go to heaven.
10. You can't love eight—'cause you'll make somebody wait.
11. You can't love nine—and keep 'em all in line.
12. You can't love ten—and stay out of the county pen.
13. You can't love eleven—you should've stopped at seven.

NINE HUNDRED MILES

The railroad is a popular subject in blues, spirituals, and hillbilly songs. There is a theory that the railroad symbolized escape for the oppressed Negro and therefore found a natural place in his song. Another way of looking at it is to realize that, for a while at least, the railroad was where a good deal of the action was taking place.

This popular blues song grew out of the same Negro tradition that gave us "In the Pines." A composite version of "In the Pines" appears in the Frank C. Brown Collection of North Carolina Folklore, published by Duke University Press in the 1950s and 1960s. That version contains elements of "Nine Hundred Miles" and of "The Lonesome Road," "Darling Little Pink," and "The Turtle Dove." Another version of this same song, "The Railroader's Lament" by Hedy West, also is very popular under the title "Five Hundred Miles."

So, just pick out how far you want to go and get on board. For interesting parallels see "In the Pines."

Recordings: Sam Hinton (Decca, DL 8108); Cisco Houston (Folkways, FA 2013); Dan Isaacson (Cornell, CRS 10021).

2. I will pawn you my watch;
   I will pawn you my chain;
   Pawn you my gold diamond ring. *Chorus.*

3. If my woman tells me so,
   I will railroad no more;
   I'll hang around her shanty all the time. *Chorus.*

4. Now this train I ride on
   Is a hundred coaches long;
   Travels back a hundred miles or more. *Chorus.*

NINE-POUND HAMMER

Here is one of the staple items for Bluegrass repertoires. It even catalogues a couple of tough, wide-open Kentucky towns, Hazard and Harlan. When I was rambling around the Saturday-night jamborees in Kentucky in 1949, Harlan had a new sheriff about every other week. "Nine-Pound Hammer" comes from the mixed gangs of whites and Negroes who built the railroads in the southern Appalachians.

Recordings: Lester Flatt and Earl Scruggs (Columbia, CL 1830); Smiley Hobbs (Folkways, FA 2318); The Kentucky Colonels (World-Pacific Records, 1821); Laurel River Valley Boys (Judson, J 3031); Merle Travis (Capitol, T 891).

2. Ain't nobody's hammer in this mountain
   That rings like mine, that rings like mine.

3. Well, I went up on the mountain just to see my baby;
   And I ain't a-comin' back, Lord, I ain't a-comin' back.

4. When I'm long gone you can make my tombstone
   Out of number nine coal, out of number nine coal.

5. It's a long way to Hazard; it's a long way to Harlan,
   Just to get a little booze, just to get a little booze.

Alternate chorus:

So, roll on, buddy,
Don't you roll so slow.
When the sun goes down
You'll roll no more.

Miscellaneous verses:

Now one of these days, and it won't be long,
You're gonna call my name and I'll be gone.

I asked my captain just to give me my time;
"Go on, buddy, you're time behind."

I asked my captain just to give me a dime;
"Roll on, buddy, you're a dime behind."

I told my captain my feet was cold;
"God damn your feet, boy, let the wheelin' roll."

I wish I was a rich man's son;
I'd stand on the bank and see the work gets done.

But the good Lord knows I'm a poor man's son;
I'll wait in the cut till the pay train comes.

NOBODY KNOWS
THE TROUBLE I'VE SEEN

This is the most popular version of a Negro hymn of tribulation which has several versions with widely differing melodies. In the book *Religious Folk-Songs of the Negro as Sung at Hampton Institute,* the following is related:

> This song was a favorite in the Sea Islands. Once when there had been a good deal of ill feeling excited, and trouble was apprehended, owing to the uncertain action of the Government in regard to the confiscated lands on the Sea Islands, Gen. Howard was called upon to address the colored people earnestly. To prepare them to listen, he asked them to sing. Immediately an old woman on the outskirts of the meeting began "Nobody knows the trouble I've seen," and the whole audience joined in. The General was so affected by the plaintive melody that he found it difficult to maintain his official dignity.

The parallel third harmony may be used to sing the verses in two parts, with all voices contributing to the response, "Oh, yes, Lord," and to the chorus.

Recordings: Marian Anderson (RCA Victor, LM 110); Lee Charles (Riverside, RLP 12-651); Howard University Choir (RCA Victor, LM 2126); Paul Robeson (Columbia, ML 4105); Lucretia West (Westminster, WP 6063).

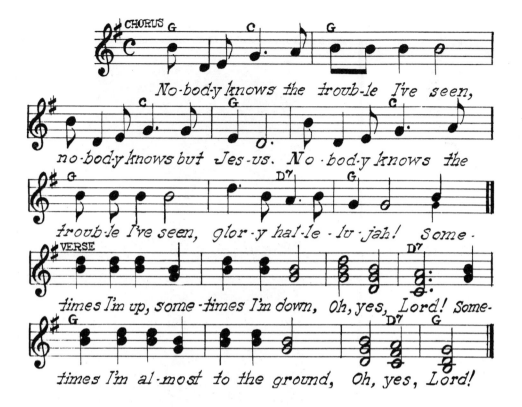

Continue, as above:

2. Now, you may think that I don't know,
   But I've had my troubles here below.

3. One day when I was walkin' along,
   The sky opened up and love came down.

4. What makes old Satan hate me so?
   He had me once and had to let me go.

5. I never shall forget that day,
   When Jesus washed my sins away.

O

*…the leafy
green dome*

*Can she bake
a cherry pie…*

*As I was going
to Derby…*

OH MARY, DON'T YOU WEEP

In addition to its popularity as a spiritual, "Oh Mary, Don't You Weep" has appealed to union singers and campus humorists. As a protest song it provides a certain note of satisfaction in the drowning of Pharaoh's army, which makes a good symbol for any oppressor. The version shown below is a collation of contemporary verses from various sources.

Recording: Pete Seeger (Folkways, FA 2320).

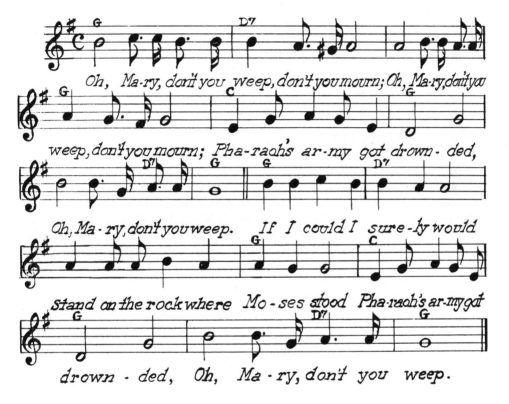

Oh, Mary, don't you weep, don't you mourn; Oh, Mary, don't you weep, don't you mourn; Pharaoh's army got drown-ded, Oh, Mary, don't you weep. If I could I sure-ly would stand on the rock where Mo-ses stood Pharaoh's ar-my got drown-ded, Oh, Ma-ry, don't you weep.

2. Wonder what Satan's grumblin' 'bout,
   Chained in Hell an' he can't git out.
   Pharaoh's army got drownded,
   Oh, Mary, don't you weep.

   Continue, as above:

3. Ol' Satan's mad an' I am glad,
   He missed a soul he thought he had.

4. Brother, better mind how you walk on the cross,
   Foot might slip and your soul get lost.

5. One of these nights about twelve o'clock,
   This old world's goin' to reel and rock.

6. I went down in the valley to pray,
   My soul got joy and I stayed all day.

7. Now don't you believe the Bible ain't true,
   'Cause you'll be sorry if you do.

8. That primrose path is wide and fair,
   Many a soul's done perished there.

Additional verses:

One of these mornings bright and fair,
I'll take my wings and cleave the air.

When I get to Heaven goin' to sing and shout;
Nobody there for to turn me out.

When I get to Heaven goin' to put on my shoes,
Run about glory and tell all the news.

See that sister dressed so fine.
She ain't got religion on her mind.

OH, NO, JOHN

Cecil Sharp applied his editorial censorship to an old English (at least seventeenth-century) song about a seduction. His courtship version, or those derived from it, continues to be a favorite in homes, schools, and concert halls. Most of the versions follow the form shown below, although some end with the man's giving up his wooing and telling the girl she can be an old maid for all he cares. The song Sharp adapted from had earthier verses, like this one:

Madam in your face is beauty,
In your bosom flowers grow.
In your bedroom there is pleasure.
Shall I view it, yes or no?

Whether the young man is seducing or courting his lady, he has an obstacle to overcome. The lady's father wisely told her always to say no to any kind of proposition. When the suitor sees that compliments and gifts won't do the trick, he cleverly comes up with a way of turning the *no* into *yes* — thus making everyone happy: the father, the girl, and the suitor.

Recordings: Richard Dyer-Bennet (Stinson, SLP 61); Milt Okun and Ellen Stekert (Riverside, RLP 12-634); Jean Ritchie and Oscar Brand (Elektra, EKL 22); Pete Seeger (Folkways, FA 2453); Andrew Rowan Summers (Folkways, FA 2021).

On yon-der hill there stands a creat-ure, Who she is I do not know. I'll go and court her for her beau-ty. She must ans-wer

yes or no. Oh, no, John, no, John, no, — John, no.

2. My father was a Spanish captain,
   Went to sea a month ago;
   First he kissed me, then he left me;
   Told me always answer no. *Chorus.*

3. Oh, madam, in your face is beauty,
   On your lips red roses glow,
   Will you take me for your lover?
   Madam, answer yes or no. *Chorus.*

4. Oh, madam, I will give you jewels,
   I will make you rich and free,
   I will give you silken dresses;
   Madam, will you marry me? *Chorus.*

5. Oh, madam, since you are so cruel,
   And since you do scorn me so,
   If I may not be your lover,
   Madam, will you let me go? *Chorus.*

6. Then I will stay with you forever,
   If you will not be unkind;
   Madam, I have vowed to love you,
   Would you have me change my mind? *Chorus.*

7. Oh, hark, I hear the church bells ringing,
   Will you come and be my wife?
   Or, dear madam, have you settled
   To live single all your life? *Chorus.*

THE OLD ARK'S A-MOVERIN'

It is not unusual for words to get reshaped in folk music — sometimes probably from lack of understanding of their meanings; sometimes (as in "The Old Ark's a-Moverin'") to fit the rhythmic needs of the song. In any event, the presence of *a-moverin'* makes this hard-driving spiritual a rhythmic success. The first version shown here is the one commonly sung at camps and campuses around the country today. The second set of words is in the spiritual tradition.

The old ark's a-mov-e-rin', a-mov-e-rin', a-mov-e-rin', the old ark's a-mov-in' by the spir-it of God. The old ark's a-mov-e-rin'a-mov-e-rin', a-mov-e-rin', the old ark's a-mov-in' and I thank God.

How man-y days did the wat-er fall?____

For-ty days and nights in all. Old ark she reel, old ark she rock, Old ark she land-ed on a moun-tain top.

2. Ham, Shem, and Japheth was settin' one day,
   Talkin' on the upper deck and lookin' at the bay;
   While they was disputin' 'bout this and that,
   The ark done bump on Ararat.

3. See that sister dressed so fine?
   She ain't got religion on her mind.
   See that brother dressed so gay?
   Devil's gonna come and carry him away.

SECOND VERSION

Chorus:

Oh, the ol' ark's a moverin', a-moverin', a-moverin',
The ol' ark's a-moverin' an' I'm goin' home.
The ol' ark's a-moverin', a-moverin', a-moverin',
The ol' ark's a-moverin' an' I'm goin' home.

Verses:

2. **See that sister all dressed so fine.**
   She ain't got Jesus on her min'.
   See that brother all dressed so gay?
   Death's gonna come for to carry him away.

3. **See that sister there comin' so slow?**
   She wants to go to heaven 'fore the heaven door close.
   Ain't but one-a thing on my min',
   My sister's gone to heaven an'-a lef'-a me behin'.

248

THE OLD CHISHOLM TRAIL

The Chisholm Trail was the most famous of the cattle trails used to drive herds to the railroads in Kansas. It was named for Jesse Chisholm, a half-breed Cherokee Indian trader, who drove a wagon through Indian Territory to his trading post in Kansas in 1866. The trail extended from San Antonio, Texas, to Abilene and Dodge City, Kansas, where some cattle were shipped east; it then branched northward to Idaho, Montana, and the Dakotas, where other cattle were fattened on the rich pastures there. Between 1868 and 1871, when the railroads moved further west, over a million and a half cattle were moved over the trail. "The Old Chisholm Trail" is said to have as many verses, many of them unprintable, as the trail had miles.

Recordings: Bill Bonyun (Folkways, FC 7402); Woody Guthrie (Stinson, SLP 32); Cisco Houston (Folkways, FA 2022); Merrick Jarrett (Riverside, RLP 12 631); Frank Luther (Decca, DL 5035).

Come a-long boys, and lis-ten to my tale, I'll tell you 'bout my troub-les on the old Chis-holm Trail. Com a ti yi yip-py, yip-py yay, yip-py yay, Com a ti yi yip-py yip-py yay.

2. I woke one morning on the old Chisholm trail,
   Rope in my hand and a cow by the tail.

3. Two-dollar horse and a forty-dollar saddle,
   I could see I was ready to go punch cattle.

4. I jumped in the saddle and grabbed the horn,
   Best durn cowboy that ever was born.

5. Up in the morning before daylight,
   And before I sleep the moon shines bright.

6. Oh, it's bacon and beans most every day,
   I'd just as soon eat a pile of prairie hay.

7. It's cloudy in the west and it looks like rain,
   And my damned old slicker's in the wagon again.

8. It's raining like hell and it's getting mighty cold,
   And these long-horned so-and-sos are gettin' hard to hold.

9. I herded and I hollered and I done right well,
   Till the boss he says just to let 'em go to hell.

10. So, I went to the boss to draw my roll,
    He figured me out nine dollars in the hole.

11. I didn't like that so we had a little chat;
    I slapped him in the face with my big slouch hat.

12. So I sold my rope and I sold my saddle,
    'Cause I'm gettin' tired of punchin' these here cattle.

13. Goin' back to town to draw my money,
    Goin' back home to see my honey.

14. I'll ride my horse to the top of the hill,
    I'll kiss my gal, goldurn, I will.

15. My seat is in the saddle, and my saddle's in the sky;
    And I'll quit punchin' cows in the sweet by and by.

THE OLD MAID'S SONG

As might be expected, old maids have provided a popular theme for folk songs. There are many songs on the subject, but none of them caught the fancy of twentieth-century folk song revivalists more than this delightful one. It comes from our British heritage and is popular in both England and America.

Recordings: Julie Felix (London, LL 3395); Peggy Seeger (Folkways, FA 2049).

*The reference to pinsman in the first line of the chorus, above, has me stumped. Does it refer to a pin setter in bowling? Or some other obscure trade or craft involving pinning of any kind? Or is it a fictional craft invented by a folk lyricist to cover a memory lapse?

sai-lor Gen-tle-man, a poor man, a fool or a
wit-ty, Don't you let me die an old__ maid, But
take me out of pi - ty._____

Verses (same tune as chorus):

1. Oh, I had a sister Sally, was younger than I am,
   She had so many sweethearts, she had to deny them;
   As for my own part, I never had many,
   If you all knew my heart, I'd be thankful for any.
   Come a landsman, *etc.*

2. Oh, I had a sister Susan, was ugly and misshapen,
   Before she was sixteen years old she was taken,
   Before she was eighteen, a son and a daughter,
   Here am I six and forty and nary an offer.
   Come a landsman, *etc.*

3. Oh, I never will be scolding, I never will be jealous,
   My husband shall have money to go to the alehouse,
   While he's there a-spending, well I'll be home a-saving,
   And I'll leave it to the world if I am worth having.
   Come a landsman, *etc.*

OLD MOUNTAIN DEW

If you'd been one of the early settlers of the Appalachians, if you'd found yourself with a lot of corn on your hands that was difficult to move out of the mountains, and if you knew how to sprout the corn, grind it, and then let it ferment, you might easily have decided to set up your own still and start making home brew. This popular hillbilly song is a tribute to the art — and the product.

Recordings: Oscar Brand (Riverside, RLP 12 630); Grandpa Jones (King, 554); Laurel River Valley Boys (Judson, J 3031); Ed McCurdy (Elektra, EKL 24); Eric Weissberg and Marshall Brickman (Elektra, EKS 7238).

I know a place 'bout a mile down the road Where you
lay down a dol-lar or two; — If you hush up your
mug they will slip you a jug of that good old
moun-tain dew. — They call it that old moun-tain
dew, — And them that re-fuse it are
few. — You may go 'round the bend, but you'll
come back a-gain For that good old moun-tain dew. —

2. When its fragrance so rare starts to fill up the air
   You know that they're just about through;
   So you pucker up your lips, and you take a few sips
   Of that good old mountain dew. *Chorus.*

3. Up on the hill there's an old whiskey still
   Run by a hard-working crew.
   You can tell by the whiffle when you sniffle a smell,
   That they're makin' that good old mountain dew. *Chorus.*

4. My brother Nort, he is sawed off and short;
   He measures about four foot two;
   But he thinks he's a gi'nt when they give him a pint
   Of that good old mountain dew. *Chorus.*

5. The preacher came by with a tear in his eye,
   He said that his wife had the flu;
   We told him he ought to give her a quart
   Of that good old mountain dew. *Chorus.*

6. My Uncle Bill's got a still on the hill
   Where he runs off a gallon or two;
   And the birds in the sky get so drunk they can't fly
   On that good old mountain dew. *Chorus.*

7. My Aunty June tried a brand new perfume,
   It had such a sweet-smelling pu.
   She was surprised when she had it analyzed,
   It was good old mountain dew. *Chorus.*

OLD STORMALONG

Captain Alfred Bulltop Stormalong was one of America's first great legendary heroes. Legend places his birthplace at Kennebunkport, Kittery, or Nantucket—but it may have been nowhere at all. According to legend he signed on for the first time as a rather large cabin boy at the age of twelve, going on thirteen. Among other things he helped John Paul Jones win the Revolutionary War on the sea, changed the black cliffs of Dover to white by soaping the sides of his clipper so he could get through the English Channel, and learned to fling a harpoon twenty-five fathoms to break the record of five fathoms set by some ordinary man. His famous clipper ship, the *Albatross,* had masts so high it took five men to see the top of any of them and they were hinged so they could be bent down to let the moon and sun go by. Ten mates, a thousand hands, and three hundred and four white horses were required to sail the *Albatross,* and it took thirty-three able-bodied seamen to manage the wheel old Stormy twirled with ease in one hand while he fanned off a school of flying fish with the other. It is no coincidence that his initials also stand for *able-bodied seaman.*

Walter Blair retells the legend of Stormalong in his *Tall Tale America, A Legendary History of Our Humorous Heroes,* published in 1944. Blair readily admits that two-thirds of the tales told about Stormy aren't true at all.

There are many versions, with much melodic variation, of the Stormalong chanteys. A convenient source for several versions is the beautifully illustrated *Chanteying Aboard American Ships* by Frederick Pease Harlow, published in 1962 by the *Barre Gazette* of Barre, Massachusetts.

Recordings: Paul Clayton (Tradition, TLP 1005); Burl Ives (Decca, DL 8245); A. L. Lloyd and Ewan MacColl (Stinson, SLP 81); Tom Scott and Will Rogers, Jr. (Judson, J 3013).

253

was— a good old man, Hur-rah, my boys,— we're home-ward bound.

Last verse only

home-ward bound.

2. I wish I was old Stormy's son,
   O goodbye, fare you well,
   Goodbye, fare you well.
   I wish I was old Stormy's son.
   Hurrah, my boys, we're homeward bound.

Continue, as above:

3. I'd buy me a bark of a thousand ton,
   I'd buy me a bark of a thousand ton.

4. I'd fill her up with New England rum,
   I'd fill her up with New England rum.

5. And my old shell-backs* they'd have some,
   And my old shell-backs they'd have some.

6. Now if ever again I get ashore,
   I'll wed that gal that I adore.

7. And if ever children we should have
   I'll bring him up as a sailor lad.

In some of the verses that follow (collected from here, there, and everywhere) you will note similarities to verses in "Deep Blue Sea" and "Old Blue":

Old Stormy heard the bugle call,
We sang his dirge, then, one and all.

We dug his grave with a silver spade,
Of the finest silk his shroud we made.

We rolled him up in his silvery shroud,
We rolled him up in his silvery shroud.

We lowered him down with a golden chain,
Our eyes were dim, but not from rain.

Although he's gone, he left a son;
Oh, how I wish I was old Stormy's son.

I'd buy me a ship of a thousand ton,
And load her down with New England rum.

I'd pour out drinks for every man,
And a double cup for the chanteyman.

*Old seamen.

He was a sailor bold and true;
A good old skipper to his crew.

OMIE WISE

Naomi Wise, a nineteen-year-old orphan, loved Jonathan Lewis. Jonathan loved the beautiful Naomi and promised to marry her—but that was before he saw he had a chance to marry Hattie Elliott and move up in society. Naomi insisted and Jonathan resisted, while Hattie became suspicious. Then the unpredictable Mr. Lewis, on the pretext of elopement, took Naomi up the river and drowned her by pulling her skirt up over her head, tying it like a sack, and throwing her into the water. Jonathan was caught later—with still another girl, Martha, on his lap—and jailed. He escaped from jail and by the time he was found again the whole affair was so dim in everyone's mind that he was acquitted of the murder charge. It is said that he finally confessed to the murder on his deathbed. So goes the account of the murder that took place in 1808 near Asheboro, North Carolina, and that has lived on in the legend, story, and song of "Omie Wise."

Recordings: Paul Clayton (Riverside, RLP 12 615, and Folkways, FA 2310); Cynthia Gooding (Elektra, EKL 107); Ed McCurdy (Riverside, RLP 12 601); Doc Watson (Vanguard, VRS 9152).

2. When he came a-courtin'
   Fine stories he did tell.
   He told her they'd get married
   And he would treat her well.

3. One night he came and told her,
   They'd meet at Adams's spring.
   He said he'd bring her money
   And lots of pretty things.

4. He didn't bring no money,
   He just brought her one thing.
   He showed her in his pocket
   A golden wedding ring.

5. He said, "Jump up behind me;
   We'll ride a little way.
   We'll go to see the preacher
   And we'll get married today."

6. So she jumped up behind him,
   And ridin' they did go,
   Ridin' up Deep River,
   Where the still waters flow.

7. "Well, Omie, poor Omie,
   I'll tell you my mind,
   My mind is for to drown you,
   And leave you here behind."

8. "Oh, pity me, oh, pity me,
   Oh, pity me," she cried.
   "Just let me go a-mournin'
   And not become your bride."

9. He threw her in the river,
   Just below the dam.
   Then he rode off and left her,
   Just like an innocent man.

10. They found poor Omie's body,
    And it was cold as clay.
    They knew that John was guilty
    And arrested him that day.

11. "Oh, hang me, oh, hang me,
    Oh, hang me," he did cry.
    "I drownded little Omie,
    And now I wanta die."

ON TOP OF OLD SMOKY

This evergreen has been an audience-participation favorite ever since
The Weavers put it at the top of the hit parade in the 1940s. It is closely
associated with "The Wagoner's Lad," and many versions of both contain
similar or identical verses. That courting too slow was something to be
worried about at least as far back as 1869 is shown by these lines from "Courting Too Slow," which appeared in John Ashton's *A Pedlar's Pack of Ballads
and Songs:*

Kiss the pretty girls and give them to know,
You don't mean to lose them by courting too slow.

The version shown here is arranged so that you can feed each new line to
the audience while they are holding the sustained tones at the end of each
phrase. (The Weavers sing it this way on their recording listed below.) If
your audience knows the words well enough, you may speed things up by
taking one measure off the end of each phrase. By all means, do it this way
if you are singing it solo.

256

Recordings: Burl Ives (Columbia, CL 6109); Milt Okun (Baton, BL 1203); Bob Ross (Folkways, FA 2334); Paul Sykes (Crown, CLR 5057); The Weavers (Vanguard, VRS 9013 and 9161).

On top of old Smo - ky, (All covered with snow) All cov-ered with snow (I lost my true lover) I lost my true lov - er (By courtin' too slow) By cour-tin' too slow. (Now, courtin's a pleasure)

2. Now, courtin's a pleasure,
   Parting is grief;
   But a false-hearted lover
   Is worse than a thief.

3. A thief he will rob you
   And take all you have;
   But a false-hearted lover
   Will lead you to the grave.

4. The grave will decay you
   And turn you to dust;
   There ain't one in a million
   A poor girl (boy) can trust.

5. They'll hug you and kiss you
   And tell you more lies
   Than the cross-ties on railroads
   Or the stars in the skies.

6. They'll tell you they love you
   To give your heart ease;
   But soon as your back's turned
   They'll court who they please.

7. Come all you young maidens,
   And listen to me;
   Never place your affection
   On a green willow tree.

8. For the leaves they will wither
   And the roots they will die;
   Your lover will leave you
   And you'll never know why.

By shifting from three beats a measure to four and working out an interesting rhythmic accompaniment (say, in hillbilly or blues idiom), you can create an interesting new sound. For solo work you can add interest by improvising the melody as you go along—changing, building, and embellishing it. Here's one melodic line to get you started:*

*© 1964 by James Leisy Music. Used by permission. Portions of text have been adapted and quoted with permission from *Folk Song Fest* by James F. Leisy, copyright © 1964 by Sam Fox Publishing Company, Inc.

*...wishing her lover
good speed*

And away, hey...

*She crossed the
broad prairies...*

P

*...the leafy
green dome*

*Can she bake
a cherry pie...*

*As I was going
to Derby...*

PAPER OF PINS

Courtship songs are teasing, singing games and are among the oldest and most widespread of all traditional songs. As dialogue songs they are most effective when male and female voices are used (or faked) as indicated. After a couple of verses have been sung, you can encourage audience participation, with reasonable assurance, on the last two lines of each verse. Several different endings are commonly found in folk traditions and some are presented here for your selection.

Recordings: Milt Okun and Ellen Stekert (Riverside, RLP 12 634); Jean Ritchie and Oscar Brand (Elektra, EKL 122, and Riverside, RLP 12 646).

Boy: I'll give to you a pap-er of pins, And that's the way my love be-gins, If you will marry me, me, me, If you will mar-ry me.

Girl:
2. I'll not accept your paper of pins,
   If that's the way your love begins,
   And I'll not marry you, you, you,
   For I'll not marry you.

Boy:
3. I'll give to you a dress of red
   All bound round with golden thread,
   If you will marry me, me, me,
   If you will marry me.

Girl:
4. I'll not accept your dress of red
   All bound round with golden thread,
   And I'll not marry you, you, you,
   For I'll not marry you.

Boy:
5. I'll give to you a little dog
   To take with you abroad, abroad.
   (Refrain)

Girl:
6. I'll not accept your little dog
   To take with me abroad, abroad.
   (Refrain)

Boy:
7. I'll give to you a dappled horse
   So you can ride from cross to cross.
   (Refrain)

Girl:
8. I'll not accept your dappled horse
   And I'll not ride from cross to cross.
   (Refrain)

Boy:
9. I'll give to you the keys to my chest
   And all the money that I possess,
   If you will marry me, me, me,
   If you will marry me.

Girl:
10. Oh, yes, I'll take the keys to your chest
    And all the money that you possess,
    And I will marry you, you, you,
    And I will marry you.

Boy:
11. Oh, now I see that money is all,
    And your love is nothing at all,
    So I won't marry you, you, you,
    No, I won't marry you.

Girl:
12. Then I shall be an old maid,
    And take a chair and sit in the shade,
    And I will marry none at all,
    I'll marry none at all.

    If you want the boy to win the girl use this ending:

    Boy:
9A. I'll give to you the gift of my heart,
    That we may love and never part,
    And I will marry you, you, you,
    Oh, I will marry you.

    Girl:
10A. Oh, I'll accept the gift of your heart,
    And we shall love and never part.
    Yes, I will marry you, you, you,
    Oh, I will marry you.

    Or she can marry someone else:

    Boy:
11A. Well, you love coffee and I love tea;
    You love money, but you don't love me.
    I won't marry you, you, you,
    No, I won't marry you.

    Girl:
12A. Yes, I love coffee and I hate tea;
    Without your money you're not for me;
    And I will marry someone else,
    I'll marry someone else.

PAT WORKS ON THE RAILWAY

In the 1830s and 1840s, the time of the great potato famines in Ireland, many Irish immigrated to America and England. Because this was also the great era of railroad building in the United States, many of these Irish laborers found themselves with pick and shovel in hand "a-working on the railway." Several versions of this song about the Irish railroader may be found in America and England. A popular sea chantey begins:

> In eighteen hundred and sixty-three,
> I came across the stormy sea,
> My dung'ree breeches I put on,
> To work upon the railway, the railway,
> To work upon the railway,
> Oh, poor Paddy, come work on the railway.

College students have delighted in this song because of the simple rhyming opportunities it offers. Although it is difficult to catch a static example of campus wit at work on this song, here are some verses I included in *Songs for Swingin' Housemothers:*

> Eighteen hundred and ninety-one,
> That's the year when I begun.
>
> Eighteen hundred and ninety-two,
> Looking around for something to do.
>
> Eighteen hundred and ninety three,
> Section boss a-drivin' me.
>
> Eighteen hundred and ninety-four,
> Hands and feet were getting sore.
>
> Eighteen hundred and ninety-five,
> Felt like I was more dead than alive.
>
> Eighteen hundred and ninety-six,
> Kicked a couple of dynamite sticks
> (And quickly left the railroad).
>
> Eighteen hundred and ninety-seven,
> Found myself on the way to Heaven.
>
> Eighteen hundred and ninety-eight,
> A-picking the lock on the pearly gate.
>
> Eighteen hundred and ninety-nine,
> I found the angels drinking wine,
> They gave me a harp and a crown divine,
> Overlooking the railroad.
>
> Eighteen hundred and ninety-ten,
> Found myself on the earth again.
>
> Eighteen hundred and ninety-eleven,
> Railroad sent me again to Heaven.
> It wasn't no different than ninety-seven,
> Or workin' on the railroad.

Notice how the dates change with each version. The campus version uses a different chorus, but one which may be sung to the same tune:

> Patsy-ory-ory-aye,
> Patsy-ory-ory-aye,
> Patsy-ory-ory-aye,
> A-workin' on the railroad.

Recordings: Sam Hinton (Decca, DL 8579); Cisco Houston (Folkways, FA 2346); Ewan MacColl (Stinson, SLP 79); Pete Seeger (Stinson, SLP 57).

(Note: Melody in top notes, harmony in bottom notes.)

Chorus:

> Fi-li-me-oo-ree-oo-ree-ay,
> Fi-li-me-oo-ree-oo-ree-ay,
> Fi-li-me-oo-ree-oo-ree-ay,
> A-workin' on the railway.

2. In eighteen hundred and forty-two,
   I left the Old World for the New;
   I rue the luck that brought me through,
   To work upon the railway.

3. In eighteen hundred and forty-three,
   'Twas then I met sweet Biddy Magee;
   An elegant wife she's been to me,
   While workin' on the railway.

4. In eighteen hundred and forty-four,
   Hands and feet were gettin' sore,
   Hands and feet were gettin' sore,
   From workin' on the railway.

5. In eighteen hundred and forty-five,
   I found myself more dead than alive,
   I found myself more dead than alive,
   While workin' on the railway.

6. In eighteen hundred and forty-six,
   I changed my trade to carryin' bricks,
   I changed my trade to carryin' bricks,
   From workin' on the railway.

7. In eighteen hundred and forty-seven,
   Sweet Biddy Magee she went to heaven,
   If she left me a child she left me eleven,
   To work upon the railway.

PICK A BALE OF COTTON

This is one of the field songs popularized by Huddie (pronounced Hugh-dee) Ledbetter, the great Negro folk song artist who was brought to national attention by John A. Lomax. Early in life he earned the nickname Leadbelly, along with the reputation that he could "outsing, outwork, and outlast" anybody else. Leadbelly was born on a blackland farm near Shreveport, Louisiana, about 1888. He learned to play the twelve-string guitar as a boy and developed his unique singing style and extensive repertoire of work songs and shouts, blues, ballads, spirituals, and play songs during the years he worked as a cotton laborer in the South. His fierce competitive spirit and quickness to anger frequently got him into serious trouble. He was an inmate of the Louisiana State Prison in 1933, when John Lomax discovered him, recorded him, and ultimately arranged for his pardon to pursue a new career as a professional singer. From then until his death in 1949, of the same disease that killed Lou Gehrig, he traveled the country singing in concert halls, night clubs, and wherever an audience for his unique talents could be found. Many of his songs are available on recordings issued by various companies. The most extensive catalogue is available from Folkways Records. *The Leadbelly Songbook* by Moses Asch and Alan Lomax contains songs and biographical sketches. Leadbelly's version of this song is available in the album *Take This Hammer* (*Legacy #1*), Folkways Records (FA 2004).

Recordings: Harry Belafonte (RCA Victor, LPM 1150—"Jump Down, Spin Around"); Freedom Singers (Mercury, MG 20879); Leadbelly (Victor, LPV 505); Pete Seeger (Folkways, FA 2412); Sonny Terry (Verve-Folkways Records, VRF FV 9010).

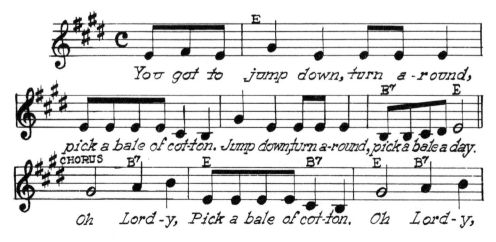

You got to jump down, turn a-round, pick a bale of cotton. Jump down, turn a-round, pick a bale a day.

CHORUS

Oh Lord-y, Pick a bale of cotton. Oh Lord-y,

265

Pick a bale a day Oh Lord-y, Pick a bale of cotton.

Oh Lord-y, Pick a bale a day.

1. Me and my buddy can
   Pick a bale of cotton,
   Me and my buddy can
   Pick a bale a day.

2. I believe to my soul I can
   Pick a bale of cotton,
   I believe to my soul I can
   Pick a bale a day.

3. Me and my buddy and
   My buddy's friend
   Can pick more cotton
   Than a gin can gin.

Zip in: Brother, sister, mother, father, little woman, etc.

PUTTING ON THE STYLE

Just before the turn of the century, "Putting on the Style" became a popular song. Poking fun at people who put on airs is appealing to almost anyone, and it didn't take long for this song to become a part of the folk tradition of this country. Hardly a year goes by without some new verses being added to the song and the old verses being updated to reflect the present scene. In *Songs for Swinging' Housemothers* I contributed verses like:

> Walking down the hallway,
> Swingin' like a gate,
> She gives each boy the eyeball,
> Tryin' to make a date.
> She pretends that she's a princess,
> And her daddy has a pile,
> But we know she's only
> Puttin' on the style.

The verses shown below were sung in the 1890s. You might want to try your hand at bringing them up to date.

Recordings: The Gateway Singers (Decca, DL 8413); Milt Okun (Riverside, RLP 12 603); Pete Seeger (Folkways, FA 2043); Shanty Boys (Elektra, EKL 142); Ellen Stekert (Stinson, SLP 49).

Young man in a car-riage, Driv-ing like he's mad,
With a pair of hors-es He bor-rowed from his dad. He
cracks his whip so live-ly Just to see his la - dy smile,
But she knows he's on -ly Put-ting on the style.

CHORUS
Put-ting on the ag-on-y, Put-ting on the style.
That's what all the young folks Are do-ing all the while. And
as I look a-round me It makes me want to smile, To
see so man-y peo-ple Put-ting on the style.

2. Young man home from college,
   Smokes a dirty pipe;
   He looks like a pumpkin
   That's only half-way ripe.
   Smoking, drinking, chewing,
   And thinking all the while,
   There is nothing equal
   To putting on the style.
   Chorus.

3. Listen to the scholar
   Make a big display
   With a great big jawbreaker
   That he can hardly say.
   It can't be found in Webster

267

And won't be for a while,
But we know he's only
Putting on the style.
Chorus.

4. Preacher in the pulpit
Shouts with all his might,
Glory hallelujah,
Puts you in a fright.
You would think that Satan's
Coming down the aisle,
But it's just the preacher
Putting on the style.
Chorus.

5. Going to a circus
Looking nice and clean,
Fresh as a dew drop
Amongst the garden green,
Gingerbread and candy
Eating all the while,
Going to the circus
Putting on the style.
Chorus.

6. Congressman from Washington
Looking mighty slick,
Wants to get elected
And go back there right quick.
He beats his breast and hollers,
And waves the flag awhile,
But we know he's only
Putting on the style.
Chorus.

*...wishing her lover
good speed*

And away, hey...

*She crossed the
broad prairies...*

R

...the leafy
green dome

Can she bake
a cherry pie...

As I was going
to Derby...

RAILROAD BILL

Conflict between fact and fiction in folk songs is a problem only if you make it one. What are you looking for anyhow? The truth? Or something that will entertain you? No good storyteller, at least of the old school, is going to let the truth get in the way of a good story. Anyhow, there are two stories connected with Railroad Bill—the facts as we know them and the legend that survived.

Railroad Bill was the name picked up by Morris Slater, a Negro outlaw, while robbing freight cars in Alabama and Florida in the 1890s. Law-enforcement officers were unable to apprehend the boxcar bandit for three years, during which his reputation for a charmed life became legendary. Several officers were killed by Slater before he was shot down while munching crackers and cheese in a little country store in Atmore, Alabama. That, however, is a little too pedestrian for storytellers singing about a big, bad railroad robber.

The last verse in this collation of verses seems to have been tacked on somewhere along the line by someone who hoped a listener would make good on Bill's last pledge.

Recordings: Paul Clayton (Folkways, FA 2110); Jack Elliott (Aravel, AB 1003, and Prestige Folklore); Cisco Houston (Folkways, FA 2013).

2. Railroad Bill, mighty bad man,
   Shot all the lamps right off of the stand.
   And it's ride, ride, ride.

3. Railroad Bill, so mean, so bad,
   Took everything the poor farmer had.
   And it's mean old Railroad Bill.

4. Railroad Bill, mighty bad,
   He shot his maw and beat up his dad.
   And it's ride, ride, ride.

5. Somebody told my lovin' wife,
   All about—well, my past life.
   It was Railroad Bill.

6. Railroad Bill led a mighty bad life,
   Always hookin' some other man's wife.
   That's Railroad Bill.

7. Railroad Bill, whistlin' a tune,
   Shot MacMillan by the light of the moon.
   And it's ride, ride, ride.

8. Four policemen dressed in blue,
   Come around the corner two by two,
   Lookin' for Railroad Bill.

9. Everybody told him, he better get back,
   Policemen comin' down the railroad track,
   Lookin' for Railroad Bill.

10. Sheriff went up on number five;
    He went to get him dead or alive;
    So long, Railroad Bill.

11. Railroad Bill, before he died,
    Said he'd build a railroad for the hoboes to ride.
    Ride on, Railroad Bill.

RAISE A RUCKUS

"Raise a Ruckus," usually pronounced "rookus," was popular with Negro minstrels who sang on street corners, at medicine shows, and at fairs, holidays, and picnics. The Negro minstrel operated in the traditional minstrel manner traveling from place to place and performing wherever and whenever anyone would underwrite his performance. He was distinct from the black-faced minstrel of the vaudeville circuit, though probably somewhat influenced by him.

The first verses of this song are more recent and emphasize its protest aspects. They are the ones most frequently used by contemporary folk-style singers. The rest of the verses, which I have picked up from here, there, and everywhere, are from the Negro minstrel tradition.

Recordings: The Folkmasters (Folkways, FA 2028); Folksay, Volume II (Stinson, SLP 6); Michael LaRue and the Drinking Gourd Singers (Esoteric, ES 560); Variation: "Shivaree!" (Esoteric, ES 538); Josh White (Elektra, EKL 102).

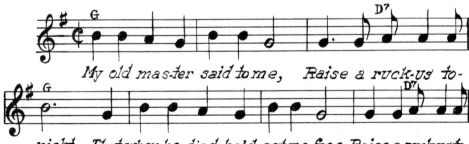

My old master said to me, Raise a ruck-us to-night, That when he died he'd set me free, Raise a ruck-us to-

night, He lived till his head got slick and bald, Raise a ruck-us to-

night, Done give up the notion at dyin' at all, Raise a ruck-us to-

CHORUS

night. Come a-long, lit-tle chil-dren come a-

long. Come, while the moon is shin-ing bright.— Get on

board, little child-ren, get on board.— We're gon-na

raise a ruck-us to-night.—

2. My old mistress said to me,
   Raise a ruckus tonight,
   That when she died she'd set me free,
   Raise a ruckus tonight.

3. Now she's makin' out her will,
   Raise a ruckus tonight,
   To leave me plowin' yonder hill,
   Raise a ruckus tonight.

Continue, as above:

4. That's what they done promised me,
   But they died too slow for me.
   A dose of poison helped them along,
   And the devil preached their funeral song.

5. Way down yonder in Chitlin' Switch
   A bullfrog jumped from ditch to ditch;
   Jumped way down in the bottom of a well,
   Swore he'd jumped all the way to hell.

6. Some folks say a preacher won't steal.
   I caught two in my cornfiel'.
   One had a bushel; one had fo';
   If that ain't stealin', I don't know.

273

7. Rufus Akes and Rastus Payne;
   They got married down in Gaines.
   Now they say them Georgia woods
   Is full of Akes and Paynes.

8. I'm going down to the river now;
   I'll lay me down and then I'll die.
   But if I find the water's wet,
   I'll have to wait until it's dry.

RED APPLE JUICE

If the disjointed verses of this song bother you, just take a few slugs of white lightnin', mountain dew, or even red apple juice and you'll be amazed how well the verses all fit together. The influence of Negro musicians on Anglo-American hillbillies is clearly evident in the words and melody of "Red Apple Juice." With a banjo, fiddle, and guitar you can make this modal mountain song really sound like it ought to. Let the banjo and fiddle take turns between each verse and use the guitar for a fast-paced, strong rhythm.

Recording: Hally Wood (Stinson, SLP 73).

2. Don't give a care for your red rocking chair;
   Ain't got no honey baby now. Lord, Lord,
   Ain't got no honey baby now.

3. Who'll rock your cradle? Who'll sing your songs?
   Who'll rock your cradle when I'm gone? Lord, Lord,
   Who'll rock your cradle when I'm gone?

4. I'll rock the cradle; I'll sing the songs;
   Don't need no man when you're gone. Lord, Lord,
   Don't need no man when you're gone.

5. It's all I can do; it's all I can say;
   Can't get along without you nohow. Lord, Lord,
   Can't get along without you nohow.

6. It's all I can do; it's all I can say.
   Sing it to your mama next payday. Lord, Lord,
   Sing it to your mama next payday.

THE RED LIGHT SALOON

A lot of fascinating songs were made and passed along during the great days (nineteenth century) of logging in the massive woods of the Northeast, the Lake States, and the Pacific Northwest. Many of the songs are lusty and colorful—and so were those hardy, hell-raising men in red flannels and mackinaws who "let daylight into the swamps" with their axes and saws. The men started early in the day and worked long and hard hours, but at sundown the cooks took over and the crews relaxed. In the evenings and on Sundays there were usually enough around who weren't too tired to play cards for tobacco, swap stories, dance a few jigs to the accompaniment of a fiddle, and sing. They made their own entertainment, and anyone with a little talent or imagination was welcome company.

When the crews hit town after a long winter in the tall timber, they would go on a spree to end all sprees, driving the local citizenry off the streets and behind closed doors and barred shutters. The townspeople had to view the carousing and fighting as a mixed blessing, since the men generally left all or most of their hard-earned pay behind when they headed back to the woods. Some of the places where the men congregated—Fan Jones's place or Tom Dixon's cat house in Maine, for instance—were famous (infamous). But the most celebrated hot spot, in song, was "The Red Light Saloon." The saloon of the song is probably only legendary, although there was a real one operated by Johnny Williams in Muskegon, Michigan, in the 1870s.

Most versions of the song I have heard are unprintable. I pieced together this one with the help of Jim McDaniel, an outdoorsman from Minnesota. It leaves enough to the imagination to allow it in print without (we think) distorting the spirit of the song. William Main Doerflinger included a partial version in his book *Shantymen and Shantyboys,* and Oscar Brand has a similar version in his book *Bawdy Songs and Backroom Ballads.*

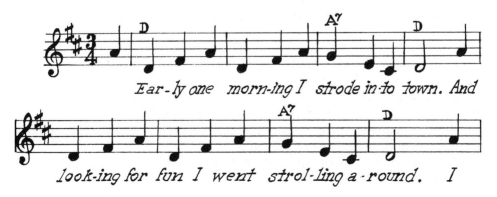

Ear-ly one morn-ing I strode in-to town. And looking for fun I went strol-ling a-round. I

knew I would find me some sport pretty soon, When I saw there a place called the Red Light Sa-loon.

2. I walked in the door and stepped up to the bar.
   A handsome young lady said, "Have a cigar."
   I smoked that cigar while she sang me a tune;
   And I felt right at home at the Red Light Saloon.

3. She mussed up my hair and sat down on my knee,
   Said: "Jack, you're a woodsman, oh, that I can see."
   "Well, that's what I am, tell me, how did you know?"
   "Your muscle is hard from your head to your toe."

4. She felt all my muscles to prove she was right.
   And I smoked my cigar without striking a light.
   Now many a man has been led into ruin [rune],
   From the treatment you get at the Red Light Saloon.

5. Then early next morning I bid her goodbye,
   As she gave me a kiss with a tear in her eye.
   And I didn't discover till early in June
   That she'd slipped me a keepsake from the Red Light Saloon.

6. I'll curse that young lady till the forest turns blue;
   And with whiskey and women, I swear I am through.
   But I know as I swear I would give my fortune
   Just to be back again in the Red Light Saloon.

THE RED RIVER VALLEY

People often adapt a favorite folk song to their own locale. This song has been named and renamed for many different valleys and locations. Most contemporary versions use this title and, at least by implication, place the location at the Red River between Texas and Oklahoma. For a long time, most folk music scholars have gone along with an assumption that the song originated from another, "In the Bright Mohawk Valley" by James J. Kerrigan, published in 1896. But Canadian folk music specialist Edith Fowke, in her article "The Red River Valley Re-examined" (*Western Folklore*, vol. XXIII, No. 3), makes a convincing case for an earlier Canadian birthplace for the song. If she is correct, the original locale of the song may have been the Red River that flows into Lake Winnipeg.

The early versions Edith Fowke refers to and quotes appear to be the lament of a French-Indian maiden for a soldier who came, saw, conquered, and departed. The historical events that took place after 1869 at the Red River Settlement, in what is now the Province of Manitoba, support the story line and make it more powerful in that context. The words of the earlier versions are not particularly stronger than those used today, however – with some exceptions:

> It's a long time, you know, I've been waiting
> For the words that you never did say,
> But alas! all my fond hopes have vanished,
> For they tell me you're going away.
>
> And the dark maiden's prayer for her love
> To the Spirit that rules all this world
> Is that sunshine his pathway may cover
> And the grief of the Red River girl.

The last two lines of the chorus are:

> But remember the Red River Valley,
> And the half-breed that loved you so true.

Contrast those verses with this one from a version I found in Tennessee:

> Now when I am dead and buried,
> In this world never more to be seen,
> There is one little thing, darling, grant me,
> That's to see that my grave is kept clean.

Whether the Red River Settlement version is the original or simply a re-composition of a still earlier song remains to be determined. Edith Fowke provides additional evidence which might lead to the discovery of earlier versions. The text below is from Texas.

Recordings: Marilyn Child and Glenn Yarbrough (Elektra, EKL 143); Woody Guthrie (Stinson, SLP 32); Frank Luther (Decca, DL 5085); Bob Ross (Folkways, FA 2334); Glenn Yarbrough (Tradition, TLP 1019).

277

Verses (same tune as chorus):

2. From this valley they say you are going,
   We will miss your bright eyes and sweet smile,
   For they say you are taking the sunshine
   That has brightened our pathway a while.

3. Won't you think of the valley you're leaving?
   Oh, how lonely, how sad it will be.
   And think of the fond heart you're breaking,
   And the grief you are causing to me.

4. As you go to your home by the ocean,
   May you never forget those sweet hours,
   That we spent in the Red River Valley,
   And the love we exchanged 'mid the flowers.

REUBEN RANZO

In the days when sailors were sailors, whalers were whalers—no self-respecting able-bodied seaman had any respect for a whaler. Conditions were very bad aboard whalers, and, in the opinion of the regular sailors, nobody but bums and misfits would sign aboard them. The fact that a good many whalers were recruited from waterfront riffraff amply supported this belief. This popular chantey grew out of these traditional beliefs.

When a bungling novice came aboard a ship, he was likely to be tagged with the name Reuben, which would stick with him until he proved himself. The ingenuity of many creative chanteymen has gone into the invention of these verses, which show how fast one of the best Reubens of all time was able to climb the ladder of success aboard a whaler. This tongue-in-cheek success story deserves a dead-pan performance with lots of enthusiasm in the choral responses— "RRRRRRanzo, boys, Ranzo,"—where the hauling effort was made.

Recording: A. L. Lloyd and Ewan MacColl (Stinson, SLP 81).

Oh,— pit-y Reu-ben Ran-zo! Ran-zo, boys, Ran-zo! Oh,—

poor old Reu-ben Ran-zo! Ran-zo, boys, Ran-zo!

2. Now, Ranzo was no sailor,
   Ranzo, boys, Ranzo!
   But he shipped on board a whaler.
   Ranzo, boys, Ranzo!

3. And he could not do his duty,
   Ranzo, boys, Ranzo!
   So they took him to the gangway.
   Ranzo, boys, Ranzo!

4. For Ranzo was a tailor,
   Ranzo, boys, Ranzo!
   But Ranzo was no sailor.
   Ranzo, boys, Ranzo!

5. They gave him nine-and-thirty,
   Ranzo, boys, Ranzo!
   Yes, lashes nine-and-thirty.
   Ranzo, boys, Ranzo!

6. The captain being a good man,
   Ranzo, boys, Ranzo!
   Took him into his cabin.
   Ranzo, boys, Ranzo!

7. He gave him wine and water,
   Ranzo, boys, Ranzo!
   Rube kissed the captain's daughter.
   Ranzo, boys, Ranzo!

8. To fit him for his station,
   Ranzo, boys, Ranzo!
   They taught him navigation.
   Ranzo, boys, Ranzo!

9. Though Ranzo was no sailor,
   Ranzo, boys, Ranzo!
   He's first mate of that whaler.
   Ranzo, boys, Ranzo!

In some versions Ranzo rises even higher in his career as a seaman:

He married the captain's daughter,
And sailed across the water.

Oh, Ranzo was a tailor,
But now he is a sailor.

And now he's Captain Ranzo,
Hurrah, for Captain Ranzo!

THE RIDDLE SONG

Riddles in courtship situations have been used frequently as a basis for folk songs. There's "Captain Wedderburn's Courtship" (number 46 in Child's collection of ballads), in which the lady says "I'll not lie in your bed till I get dishes three" and then:

'Tis I maun hae to my supper a chicken without a bane;
And I maun hae to my supper a cherry without a stane;
And I maun hae to my supper a bird without a gaw. . . .

Captain Wedderburn answers:

> Whan the chicken's in the shell, I am sure it has na bane;
> And whan the cherry's in the bloom, I wat it has na stane;
> The dove she is a gentry bird, she flees without a gaw;
> Sae we'll baith lie in ae bed, and ye'll be at the wa.

But the lady dreams up several other riddles to be solved before she finally agrees to lie in his bed—and even then, some of the versions end with him lying against the wall instead of her. Placement next to the wall seems to be of great concern throughout all versions of the ballad. Whether this is a matter of comfort or the elimination of an easy escape route from romantic overtures is not made quite clear.

In the Jewish folk song "Tumbalalaika," a shy boy who is worried about finding a girl asks what can grow without rain, what can burn without burning out, and what can cry without tears. *The* girl (presumably) answers that a stone can grow without rain, love can burn without burning out, and a heart can cry without tears.

The most popular courtship riddle song today is also known by the titles "I Gave My Love a Cherry" and "I Gave My Love an Apple." Versions with the latter title include additional verses:

> I gave my love an apple without a core,
> I gave my love a dwelling without a door,
> I gave my love a palace wherein she might be,
> That she might unlock it without a key.
>
> How can there be an apple without a core?
> How can there be a dwelling without a door?
> How can there be a palace wherein she might be,
> That she might unlock it without a key?
>
> My head it is an apple without a core.
> My mind it is a dwelling without a door.
> My heart it is a palace wherein she might be,
> That she might unlock it without a key.

To extend the song, you may wish to include these verses with those shown below in "The Riddle Song."

In 1960 literary critic Horace Reynolds reported a teen-age parody in the *New York Times Book Review:*

> A cherry in a Manhattan, it has no stone.
> Chicken a la king, it has no bone.
> A story from the Bible, it has no end.
> A baby when it's strangled has no cry-en.

Recordings: Alfred Deller (Vanguard, VRS 479); Cynthia Gooding (Elektra, EKL 131); Burl Ives (Columbia, CL 6109); Jean Ritchie and Oscar Brand (Riverside, RLP 12 646); Julie Felix (London, LL 3395); Pete Seeger (Folkways, FA 2321); Josh White (Decca, DL 8665). "Tumbalalaika": The Gateway Singers (Decca, DL 8413); Ruth Rubin (Riverside, RLP 12 647).

I gave my love a cher-ry that has no stone, I gave my love a chick-en that has no bone, I gave my love a ring— that has no end, I gave my love a ba-by that's no cry-in'.

2. How can there be a cherry that has no stone?
   How can there be a chicken that has no bone?
   How can there be a ring that has no end?
   How can there be a baby that's no cryin'?

3. A cherry when it's bloomin', it has no stone;
   A chicken when it's pippin', it has no bone;
   A ring when it's rollin', it has no end;
   A baby when it's sleepin', it's no cryin'.

ROCK ABOUT MY SARO JANE

The Kingston Trio, both praised and panned, probably did more than anyone to make this Mississippi River-steamboat roustabout song a favorite with folk song revivalists. A couple of decades earlier it had been popularized with hillbilly audiences by Uncle Dave Macon and his Fruit Jar Drinkers. I've always felt that performers should use themselves to show how good a song is—not use the song to show how good they are. "Saro Jane" is one of those songs, however, that seem to bring out the virtuoso impulse in musicians; and they can usually be counted on literally to tear it to pieces with wild strumming and rapid, esoteric chord changes. What you do is your business. The arrangement provided here may not be the best or the most interesting, but it has the virtue of simplicity—melodically, rhythmically, and harmonically. Many performers start with the first verse sung slowly, ad lib (at liberty), and then hit the chorus about ninety miles per hour.

Recordings: The Kingston Trio (Capitol, T 996); Ed McCurdy (Elektra, EKL 205); Odetta (Vanguard, VRS 9059).

I've got a wife and-a five little child-ren, Believe I'll take a trip on the old Mac-mil-lan,— Oh, Sar-o Jane.
Oh, there's noth-ing to do but to set down and sing, nd
rock a-bout my Sar-o Jane.— Oh, rock a-bout my Sar-o—
Jane.— Oh, rock a-bout my Sar-o Jane. Oh, there's noth-ing to
do but to set down and sing And rock a-bout my Sar-o Jane.—

2. Boiler busted and the whistle done blowed,
   The head captain done fell overboard;
   Oh, Saro Jane.
   Chorus.

3. Engine gave a crack and the whistle gave a squall,
   The engineer's gone to the hole in the wall;
   Oh, Saro Jane.
   Chorus.

THE ROCK ISLAND LINE

Huddie "Leadbelly" Ledbetter created a unique talking-singing version of "The Rock Island Line," in which he described the tricking of a depot agent by a man who claimed to have only livestock in his load when in reality he was carrying pig iron. Leadbelly's version became a hit with rock-'n-roll enthusiasts in the 1950s through a recording by Lonnie Donegan of England. The version presented here is equally popular with folk song enthusiasts, but it is less stylized and omits the spoken patter. You can pick that up by listening to Ledbetter's recording.

I've provided a simple arrangement that may be used with a group of three or more voices. If you prefer to sing it solo you will find the melody in the lower staff. You might try your hand at creating new verses for the song or borrowing them from other songs. Any couplet will do since, by custom, the verses have no relation to the chorus.

Recordings: The Gateway Singers (Decca DL 8413); Huddie Ledbetter (Folkways, FA 2034, and Stinson, SLP 19); Milt Okun (Baton, BL 1203); The Weavers (Vanguard, VRS 9010 and 9161).

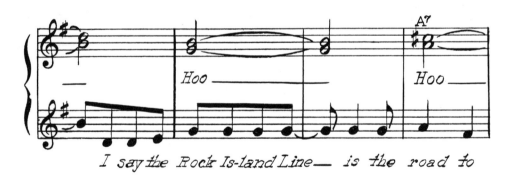

If you want to ride it, got to ride it like you're fly-in'. Buy your

tick-et at the sta-tion on the Rock Is-land Line. I

may be right and I may be right or wrong, I

know you'll miss me when I have gone.—

2. A, B, C, Double-U, X, Y, Z,
   Cat's in the cupboard but he can't see me.

3. Jesus died to save our sins.
   Glory be to God, we're gonna need Him again.

4. I'm gonna ride this railroad line
   Till I get a girl that'll be all mine.

For contrast (while you're riding it like you're flying in the chorus) you can sing some of these verses from "The Dummy Line" by repeating the tune of the verse twice to accommodate the extra two lines:

1. Across the prairie on a streak of rust,
   There's something moving in a cloud of dust.
   It crawls into the village with a wheeze and a whine,
   It's the two o'clock flyer on the Rock Island Line.

2. I got aboard at half-past two,
   Looked out at four and saw the same old view,
   I asked the conductor, "What're we waiting here for?"
   He said, "We've been moving for an hour or more."

3. I asked a man a hundred years old,
   If he'd always worked on this railroad,
   He said he started at twenty-one,
   A mile or two back, and this was his first run.

4. A queer-looking lady across the aisle
   Grabbed up her grips, looked at me with a smile;
   "I must be off," she said to me;
   Said I, "You're off, that's plain to see."

5. I asked the conductor, "Can't we speed up a bit?"
   He said, "You can walk if you don't like it."
   Said I, "Old man, I'd like to take your dare,
   But my folks don't expect me 'til the train gets there."

'ROUND THE BAY OF MEXICO

The men who have logged the sea chanteys of the nineteenth century are all high in their praise of Negro contributions to chanteys and the art of chantey-ing. Bahamian Negroes came up with one chantey, "Round the Bay of Mexico," that adapts tune and ideas from at least two well-known chanteys from the packet-trade days. This chantey was popularized by The Weavers and the Kingston Trio during the height of the commercial era of the folk song revival, and it has remained a favorite with city singers.

Recordings: Eric Andersen (Vanguard, VRS 9157); Folksay: Volume II, with Bob Carey, Erik Darling, and Roger Sprung (Stinson, SLP 6); The Wagoners (Folkways, FC 7030).

'Round the Bay of Mex-i-co, Way, oh Sus-i-an-na;

Mex-i-co is the place that I be-long in, 'Round the Bay of Mex-i-co.

2. When I was a young man in my prime,
   Way, oh Susianna;
   I'd court those Nassau gals two at a time,
   'Round the Bay of Mexico.

3. Nassau girls they love me so,
   Way, oh Susianna;
   'Cause I don't say everything that I know,
   'Round the Bay of Mexico.

4. Nassau gals don't use no combs,
   Way, oh Susianna;
   They comb their hair with whipper-snapper bones,
   'Round the Bay of Mexico.

5. Nassau boys don't use no sleds,
   Way, oh Susianna;
   They slide down the hills on whipper-snapper heads,
   'Round the Bay of Mexico.

6. Goodbye, girls of Nassau town,
   Way, oh Susianna;
   I'm bound away for the fishing ground,
   'Round the Bay of Mexico.

THE ROVING GAMBLER

Here is a popular American version of an old English song. It is known by other titles, including "The Gambling Man" and "Rambling, Gambling Man." Earlier English versions refer to a *gamboling,* traveling man instead of a card shark:

I am a roving traveler and I go from town to town.
Whenever I see a table spread I merrily sit down.

I had not been traveling but a few days, maybe three,
When I fell in love with a London girl, and she in love with me.

She took me to her dwelling and cooled me with her fan.
She whispered low in her mother's ear, "I love this gamboling man."

It is not difficult to see how the transition from *gamboler* to *gambler* was made in oral tradition when the song crossed over to America.

In some versions, the song is extended more or less indefinitely as the mother and daughter discuss other vocations, which the mother thinks more appropriate for a husband in a sensible marriage—all of which, of course, are distasteful to the girl with her heart set on the gambler:

> I wouldn't marry a doctor, they're always gone from home.
> All I want is a gamblin' man 'cause he won't leave me alone.

To follow this tack you zip in a lawyer, a banker, a preacher, and so on, for *doctor* in the first line, make up a reason why they're unsuitable, and then lock it up with a gamblin' man line that rhymes.

Here are two more examples:

> I wouldn't marry a farmer, he's always in the dirt;
> All I want is a gamblin' man who wears a striped shirt.

> I wouldn't marry a sheriff, the kind that's shot and dies;
> All I want is a gamblin' man, who has them pretty blue eyes.

You would probably start this sequence after the sixth verse in the version shown below.

Recordings: Logan English (Riverside, RLP 12 643); Cisco Houston (Folkways, FA 2346); Alan Lomax (Tradition, TLP 1029); Ed McCurdy (Elektra, EKL 124); The New Lost City Ramblers (Folkways, FA 2396); John Jacob Niles (RCA Camden, CAL 219).

I am a rov-ing gam-bler; I've gam-bled all a-round. Wher-ev-er I meet with a deck of cards I lay my mon-ey down.

2. I've gambled in Alaska; I've gambled over in Spain;
   I'm on my way to Georgia to knock down my last game.

3. I had not been in Washington for many more weeks than three,
   When I fell in love with a pretty little girl and she fell in love with me.

4. She took me in her parlor; she cooled me with her fan;
   She whispered soft in her mother's ear: "I love that gamblin' man."

5. "Oh, daughter, my dear daughter, why do you treat me so?
   How can you leave your dear old mother and with a gambler go?"

287

6. "Oh, mother, my dear mother, you know I love you well;
   But the love I have for the gamblin' man no human tongue can tell.

7. "I hear the train a-comin'; she's blowin' 'round the curve;
   She's a-whistlin' and a-blowin' and a-strainin' every nerve.

8. "Oh, mother, my dear mother, I'll tell you if I can;
   If you ever see me comin' back it'll be with a gamblin' man."

RYE WHISKEY

You can sing of the virtues of a good many vices with this popular song. Whether or not it originated as a song of personal protest, it probably satisfied many a man's soul to sing out in defiance of those who would put a stop to his drinking, gambling, and living in sin. "Rye Whiskey" is equally well know by the title "Jack o' Diamonds," usually beginning with the verse, or chorus:

> Jack o' Diamonds, Jack o' Diamonds,
> I know you of old,
> You've robbed my poor pockets
> Of silver and gold.

Sometimes "Rye Whiskey" is sung as a woman's lament:

> My children are crying
> For want of some bread.
> My husband's a gambler.
> I wish I was dead.

There is another "Jack o' Diamonds" song, in the blues idiom, which may have been inspired by at least the opening lines of this older song—or it may not have been. In any event, it is a different song:

> Jack o' Diamonds, Jack o' Diamonds,
> Jack o' Diamonds is a hard card to play.

Blind Lemon Jefferson was the first Negro folk singer to make a commercial record of the blues-style song.

You may browse through *all* of these versions and songs by listening to the suggested recordings.

Recordings: Oscar Brand (Riverside, RLP 12-630); John A. Lomax, Jr. (Folkways, FG 3508); Ed McCurdy (Elektra, EKL 124); Pete Seeger (Folkways, FA 2176). Variation: "Jack o' Diamonds": Bill Bender (Stinson, SLP 18); Logan English (Riverside, RLP 12-643); Blind Lemon Jefferson (Riverside, RLP 1014); John Jacob Niles (RCA Camden, CAL 219); Odetta (Tradition, TLP 1010); Brother John Sellers and Sonny Terry (Vanguard, VRS 7022).

For work I'm too laz-y and beg-gin's too slow, Train rob-bin's too dang'rous, to gamb-ling I'll go. Rye — whis-key, rye — whis-key, rye whis-key I cry. If I don't get rye whis-key, I sure-ly will die.

2. Sometimes I drink whiskey,
   Sometimes I drink wine,
   Ten thousand bottles
   I've killed in my time. *Chorus.*

3. I've no wife to quarrel with,
   No babies to bawl,
   The best way of livin'
   Is no wife at all. *Chorus.*

4. I'll eat when I'm hungry,
   I'll drink when I'm dry,
   If the hard times don't kill me,
   I'll live till I die. *Chorus.*

5. Beefsteak when I'm hungry,
   Red liquor when I'm dry,
   Greenbacks when I'm hard up,
   And religion when I die. *Chorus.*

6. But if I get boozy,
   My whiskey's my own,
   And them that don't like me,
   Can leave me alone. *Chorus.*

7. Oh, whiskey, you villain,
   You've been my downfall,
   You've kicked me, you've cuffed me—
   But I love you for all. *Chorus.*

Additional verses from other versions:

I used to drink bourbon,
But now I drink rye.
If the Indians don't kill me
I'll live till I die.

I'll build me a castle
On the mountain so high.
Where the wild geese will see me
As they do pass by.

If the ocean was whiskey
And I was a duck,
I'd dive to the bottom
And never come up.

But the ocean ain't whiskey,
And I ain't no duck.
I'll play jack o' diamonds
And try to change my luck.

Rye whiskey, rye whiskey,
You're no friend of mine.
You keep me unhappy
And you trouble my mind.

If the ocean was whiskey
And the river was wine,
You'd find me a-fishin'
Most any old time.

...wishing her lover good speed

And away, hey...

She crossed the broad prairies...

S

...*the leafy green dome*

Can she bake a cherry pie...

As I was going to Derby...

SAINT JAMES INFIRMARY BLUES

This blues ballad, sometimes called "The Gambler's Blues," has burial-instruction verses that appear to be derived from "The Unfortunate Rake," an old British street ballad. These verses have led many folk music specialists to regard "Saint James Infirmary Blues" as a derivative of "The Unfortunate Rake" and a relative of "The Cowboy's Lament" ("The Streets of Laredo") and "Wrap Me Up in My Tarpaulin Jacket." Sometime when you have an afternoon or evening to kill, look up "'The Unfortunate Rake' and His Descendants" by Kenneth Lodewick in *Western Folklore,* volume 14, page 98. Conflicting claims of authorship for "Saint James Infirmary Blues" have been made since at least 1920, with no one settling the matter yet.

Singers vary considerably the order of the verses they use. Feel free to change the order shown here to suit yourself. For example, Cisco Houston sings the verses in this order: 3, 4, 1, 5, 6, 7, 8. This order provides for a different interpretation of the story. The "Let her go" verse never quite makes sense in any version I've heard. Most singers probably feel as I do: it's too good a verse to kick out even if it doesn't fit.

Recordings: Clarence Cooper (Elektra, EKL 27); Sam Hinton (Decca, DL .8108); Cisco Houston (Folkways, FA 2346); John A. Lomax, Jr. (Folkways, FA 2319); Pete Seeger (Folkways, FA 2319); Josh White (Elektra, EKL 102); Stan Wilson (Cavalier, Cav 6003).

I went down to the St. James In-firm'ry; To see my ba-by there. She was lyin' on a long white ta-ble, So — sweet, so — cool — so fair.

2. Went up to see the doctor,
   "She's very low," he said;
   Went back to see my baby;
   Great God! She was lyin' there dead.

3. I went down to old Joe's barroom,
   On the corner by the square;
   They were servin' the drinks as usual,
   And the usual crowd was there.

4. On my left stood Joe McKennedy,
   His eyes were bloodshot red;
   He turned to the crowd around him,
   These are the words he said:

5. Let her go, let her go, God bless her;
   Wherever she may be;
   She may search this wide world over
   She'll never find a man like me.

6. Oh, when I die, please bury me
   In my high-top Stetson hat;
   Put a gold piece on my watch chain
   So they'll know I died standin' pat.

7. Get six gamblers to carry my coffin,
   Six chorus girls to sing my song,
   Put a jazz band on my tail gate
   To raise hell as we go along.

8. Now that's the end of my story;
   Let's have another round of booze;
   And if anyone should ask you, just tell them
   I've got the Saint James Infirmary blues.

SALLY, LET YOUR BANGS HANG DOWN

Hang around a few Saturday-night barn dances and jamborees in Tennessee and Kentucky and you're bound to get the lowdown on Sally. Anybody who thinks all the fiddle-dance hollers are about relatively clean-cut girls like Cindy and Sally Goodin just hasn't been to the right (or wrong, if you please) places. A lot of people thought all along that fiddlin' and dancin' was the devil's doin'. Hillbilly singers have used songs like this to help their audiences enjoy feeling guilty as sin at a Saturday-night stomp. I've included the printable verses — you can borrow some more from any fiddle tune. So here's another song from the gifted pen of the celebrated "composer" of "I'm Gonna Put Me a Bar in the Back of My Car and Drive Myself to Drink."

Recordings: Dian and the Greenbriar Boys (Elektra, EKL 233); Ed McCurdy (Elektra, EKL 112); or try to track down an old seventy-eight of the song by Roy Acuff.

2. She's a gal from old Kentucky,
   Always happy and go-lucky.
   Sally, let your bangs hang down.
   Sally knows the way to please 'em,
   First she loves 'em then she leaves 'em.
   Sally, let your bangs hang down.

3. Once I heard old Sal confessin'
   How she always kept 'em guessin'.
   Sally, let your bangs hang down.
   She calls everybody honey
   Just to make 'em spend their money.
   Sally, let your bangs hang down.

4. I saw Sally changin' clothes.
   She was in a perfect pose.
   Sally, let your bangs hang down.
   I found out what Sally's got,
   Makes the men think she's so hot.
   Sally, let your bangs hang down.

SHENANDOAH

Shenandoah is a corruption of the name used by the Iroquois Indians for the mountains on both sides of the Shenandoah Valley in Virginia. It means "land of big mountains." In the nineteenth century, it went to sea as the title of a beautiful chantey used for weighing anchor and, as "The Wild Mizzouri," the same song was popular with cavalrymen. The melodic and rhythmic interpretation of the song varies with the performer and the performance. Sailors, according to an old sailor, used "a very peculiar time, or rather no set time at all, and the singer could make his own rendering of it as far as the solo part was concerned, the heaving stresses of the chorus being dictated by the strain on a rope or anchor cable."

Some versions tell the story of a redskin chief, Shenandoah, and his beautiful daughter. A white trader elopes with the maiden after silencing the chief with firewater. A similar chantey version goes like this:

> The white man loved the Indian maiden,
> Away, you rolling river.
> With notions his canoe was laden,
> Away, we're bound away,
> 'Cross the wide Missouri.

And continues, as above:

> The chief, he made an awful holler,
> He turned away the trader's dollars.

> Along there came a Yankee skipper,
> He winked at her and tipped his flipper.

> He sold the chief some firewater,
> He got him drunk and stole his daughter.

295

I prefer the genuine feeling, and simplicity, of the version I have used below. My setting is designed for group singing with rhythmic regularity, but it may be adapted for solo singing at liberty.

Recordings: Oscar Brand (Riverside, RLP 12 639); Paul Clayton (Tradition, TLP 1005); Terrea Lea (ABC-Paramount, ABC 161); Brownie McNeil (Sonic, B 16847-8); Alan Mills (Folkways, FA 2312); Milt Okun (Baton, BL 1203); Paul Robeson (Vanguard, VRS 9037); Pete Seeger (Folkways, FA 2321; Disc, D 101; and Aravel, AB 1003); Andrew Rowan Summers (Folkways, FA 2348).

2. Oh, Shenandoah's my native valley.
   Away, you rolling river.
   Oh, Shenandoah's my native valley.
   Away, we're bound away,
   'Cross the wide Missouri.

   Continue, as above:

3. Oh, Shenandoah, it's far I wander.

4. Oh, Shenandoah has rushing waters.

5. Oh, Shenandoah, I long to hear you.

6. Oh, Shenandoah, I love your daughter.

7. Oh, Shenandoah, I'll never leave you.

8. Oh, Shenandoah, I'll never grieve you.

THE SHIP THAT NEVER RETURNED

If there ever was a million-dollar tune, this one is it. It has provided three of the biggest commercial successes in the history of popular music—and there is every reason to believe it can ride the charts again when somebody comes up with another great idea. The original tune and words were written by a very popular songwriter, Henry C. Work, in the last half of the nineteenth century. His song "The Ship That Never Returned" (the first big hit) inspired "The Train That Never Returned," which led to "The Wreck of the Old '97" (the second big hit), which later was borrowed for a political campaign song in Boston, "The MTA Song," which became the third big hit as performed by the Kingston Trio. You can pick up the MTA version, written by Jacqueline Steiner and Bess Hawes, from any number of sources including one of the Kingston Trio's Capital LPs and Will Holt's Coral LP (CRL 57114). It might be more interesting today, however, to play around with some of these earlier versions. Recordings of the first two songs (*Ship* and *Train*) are scarce. If you're particularly resourceful and determined, you can track down "The Ship That Never Returned" in the *Archive of American Folk Song* at the Music Division of the Library of Congress. Sprinkle the chorus liberally throughout your performance.

On a sum-mer's day when the waves were rip-pling With a gentle and a peace-ful breeze A ship set sail with a car-go la-den for a port a-cross the sea. Oh, did she ev-er re-turn? No, she nev-er re-turned, And her fate is still un-learned. And one last man set sail, Com-man-der, On a ship that nev-er re-turned.

2. There were sad farewells, there were friends forsaken,
   And her fate is still unlearned.
   But a last poor man set sail, Commander,
   On a ship that never returned.

3. Said a feeble lad to his aged mother,
   "I must cross that deep blue sea,
   For I hear of a land in the far off country,
   Where there's health and strength for me."

4. 'Tis a gleam of hope and a maze of danger,
   And her fate is still to learn.
   And a last poor man set sail, Commander,
   On a ship that never returned.

5. Said a well-built lad to his aged mother,
   As he kissed his weeping wife,
   "Just one more purse of that golden treasure,
   It will last us all through life.

6. "Then we'll live in peace and joy together
   And enjoy all I have earned."
   So they sent him forth with a smile and a blessing
   On a ship that never returned.

THE TRAIN THAT NEVER RETURNED

1. **I was goin' 'round the mountain one cold winter morning;**
   Saw the steam was boiling high.
   It was from a fast train on the C. and O. railroad
   And the engineer waved goodbye.

   Chorus:

   Did she ever return? No, she never returned,
   Though the train was due at one.
   For hours and hours the watchman waited
   For the train that never returned.

2. **His sweet little wife came up to the station,**
   Said "Last night my heart did yearn.
   I dreamed last night there was a wreck on the railroad
   And a train that never returned."

3. **"Go back, sweet wife," said the drunken conductor,**
   And he waved his hat with delight.
   "If the wheels will roll and the engineer stays sober,
   We will all be home tonight."

A real situation inspired another text for the tune. Old 97, a fast mail train running between Washington and Atlanta, began its career in 1902 with a special appropriation from Congress. On the ill-fated run, Joseph A. Broady (nicknamed "Steve" for Steve Brodie who had jumped off the Brooklyn Bridge) took over as engineer at Monroe, Virginia, one hour behind time. The song tells the rest of the story.

In the 1920s Vernon Dalhart made a recording of the song which sold five million copies. This commercial success involved Victor in a lawsuit that lasted almost through the thirties, went to the Supreme Court twice, and never was settled. The question was: Who wrote the song? Although copyrights are still claimed to this day, nobody has yet been established as the legal author. If the man named Dave Graves George deserved the credit and the money, he got neither. George, a 45-year-old telegraph operator at the Southern Railway station in Franklin Junction, Virginia, visited the scene of the wreck north of Danville, Virginia. He claimed that he wrote the verses during the week following the wreck and then recited them in a barbership in Franklin Junction, and that someone later suggested he put them to the tune of "The Ship That Never Returned."

In the version presented here, you will notice that Broady's name has been changed (logically) to Brooklyn by some inventive folk writer.

Recordings: RCA Victor has reissued the original Vernon Dalhart recording in *Folksingers* (RCA Popular Collector's Issue, LPT 6). You can hear a variety of performances by listening to Pink Anderson (Riverside, RLP 12 611); Cisco Houston (Folkways, FA 2013); Merrill Jay Singers (Cabot Records, CAB 503); George Pegram and Walter Parham (Riverside, RLP 21 650); Pete Seeger (Folkways, FA 2320); The Stoneman Family (Folkways, FA 2315).

1. They gave him his orders at Monroe, Virginia,
   Saying, "Steve, you're away behind time.
   This is not Thirty-eight, but it's old Ninety-seven;
   You must put her in Spencer on time."

2. Steve Brooklyn said to his black greasy fireman:
   "Just shovel in a little more coal,
   And when we cross that White Oak Mountain
   You can watch old Ninety-seven roll."

3. It's a mighty tough road from Lynchburg to Danville,
   And a line on a three-mile grade.
   It was on this grade that he lost his air-brakes,
   And you see what a jump he made.

4. He was going down the grade making ninety miles an hour,
   When his whistle began to scream.
   He was found in the wreck with his hand on the throttle,
   And was scalded to death by the steam.

5. Come all you young ladies, you must take warning,
   From this time and now on;
   Never speak harsh words to a loving husband,
   For he may leave you and never return.

SILVER DAGGER

There are several songs with many variants that use a silver-dagger theme. In my version the girl warns her suitor that her mother sleeps with a dagger and that she, the daughter, is going to sleep alone. In some texts both the mother and father are sleeping, each with a silver dagger ready "to pierce the heart that I love best." The suitor then kills himself with *his* silver dagger, and in the last verse the girl kills herself with the same weapon. In another version the girl changes her mind:

> Come back, come back, true-hearted lover,
> Come back and run away with me.
> I will forsake both father and mother.
> And it's all for the sake of thee.

Some folk music scholars have classified this song, with a dagger in every verse, bed, and hand, as "The Drowsy Sleeper" song—presumably because some versions have a first line that says, "Awake, awake, you drowsy sleeper." They don't like to have "The Drowsy Sleeper" confused with another old song that *they* call "The Silver Dagger"—although it barely mentions a silver dagger. In this song, a young lady kills herself with a silver dagger because her boy friend's parents won't let him marry her. He's wandering conveniently nearby when she commits suicide—so

> He then picked up the bloody weapon,
> And pierced it through his own true heart.
> Oh let this be a woeful warning
> To all that would true lovers part.

With apologies to these scholars, I include *their* drowsy-sleeper song under the silver-dagger title they have saved for that other song. And I hope you aren't hopelessly confused at this point because I'm not really sure that it matters at all. Some singers escape the whole argument by calling this song: "Don't Sing Love Songs."

Recording: Joan Baez (Vanguard, VRS 9078).

2. All men are false, says my mother;
   They'll tell you wicked lovin' lies.
   The very next evening they'll court another;
   Leave you alone to pine and sigh.

3. My daddy is a handsome devil.
   He's got a chain five miles long.
   And on every link a heart does dangle
   Of some poor girl he's loved and wronged.

4. Go court another tender maiden
   And hope that she will be your wife,
   For I've been warned and I've decided
   To sleep alone all of my life.

SINNER MAN

"Sinner Man" comes from the singing tradition of the fundamentalist churches of the South. It may have been derived from spiritual tradition, however, since there are several spirituals which treat the same theme. The spiritual-singing Jubilee Singers of Fisk University sang:

Oh! sinner, Oh! sinner man,
Oh! sinner, Oh!
Which way are you going?

Oh! Come back, sinner, and don't go there,
Which way are you going?
For hell is deep and dark despair.
Oh! Which way are you going?

Recordings: Leon Bib (Vanguard, VRS 904); William Clauson (Capitol, T 10158); Folksongs with the Folksmiths (Folkways, FA 2407); Terrea Lea (ABC-Paramount, ABC 161), The Weavers (Vanguard, VRS 9161).

2. Run to the rock, the rock was a-melting, *(3 times)*
   All on that day.

3. Run to the sea, the sea was a-boiling, *(3 times)*
   All on that day.

4. Run to the moon, the moon was a-bleeding, *(3 times)*
   All on that day.

5. Run to the Lord, "Lord, won't you hide me?" *(3 times)*
   All on that day.

6. Oh, sinner man, you oughta been a-praying, *(3 times)*
   All on that day.

7. Run to the Devil, Devil was a-waiting, *(3 times)*
   All on that day.

SKIP TO MY LOU

The folk dance is closely related to, and, of course, quite dependent on, folk music. Folk dancing began with the ceremonial dances of primitive people. Through the ages the custom has been handed down from generation to generation and has evolved into what is now primarily a social and recreational activity.

The play-party, or singing, game thrived in America at a time when dancing was seriously frowned upon. The fiddle was considered an instrument of the devil, and public dancing became practically nonexistent. The play-party game, which was acceptable to all, differs from other forms of folk dancing in that there is no instrumental accompaniment. The players furnish their own simple music by singing "swing arounds" as they go through the dance figures. The spectators add to the rhythmic accompaniment by clapping their hands and stamping their feet as the spirit moves them.

"Skip to My Lou" is one of the most popular of the singing games. In the early part of this century "lou" was a commonly used term for "sweetheart" in some parts of this country. It is quite possibly derived from the Scottish word "loo," meaning "love."

FORMATION: Any number of couples form a circle, facing in, with one boy alone in the center.

ACTION: The boy in the center starts with the first verse, and the rest join in singing and clapping hands. At the end of the verse the boy in the center steals a partner and skips around the circle with her (their clasped right hands crossed by clasped left hands) while the chorus is sung. He then takes her partner's place in the circle. The boy whose girl has been stolen then takes his turn in the center of the circle, and the action is repeated.

Lost my part-ner, What'll I do? Lost my part-ner, What'll I do?
Lost my part-ner, What'll I do? Skip to my Lou, my dar-ling.

Chorus (same tune as verse):

Lou, Lou, skip to my Lou,
Lou, Lou, skip to my Lou,
Lou, Lou, skip to my Lou,
Skip to my Lou, my darling.

2. I'll get another, a better one, too,
   I'll get another, a better one, too,
   I'll get another, a better one, too,
   Skip to my Lou, my darling.

3. I'll find another one just as true,
   I'll find another one just as true,
   I'll find another one just as true,
   Skip to my Lou, my darling.

Continue, as above:

4. Sugar is sweet and so are you.

5. Needle in a haystack; where are you?

6. Can't get a redbird, a bluebird'll do.

7. His big feet don't know what to do.

8. Going to Texas, two by two.

9. I'll get her back in spite of you.

10. Hurry up, slowpoke, let's get through.

11. We'll keep going till half-past two.

THE SLOOP JOHN B.

You may know this song as "The Wreck of the John B. Sails" or simply the "John B." The Weavers got it going in the 1950s, and it has been popular ever since. It had appeared earlier, in *The Island Song Book* (published in the 1920s), and later, in Carl Sandburg's famous *The American Songbag.* In *The Island Song Book,* John and Evelyn McCutcheon said: "Time and usage have given this song almost the dignity of a national anthem around Nassau. The weathered ribs of the historic craft lie imbedded in the sand at Governor's Harbor, whence an expedition, especially set up for the purpose in 1926, extracted a knee of horseflesh and a ring-bolt. These relics are now preserved and built into the Watch Tower."

There is evidence that twentieth-century folk have been at work adding new verses. At our Cable Car Hoots in San Francisco in 1964 there was a girl who sang a verse that began: "The stewardess she got stewed, ran around the deck in the nude; We sent the captain ashore and . . ." She stopped at that point, and I never found out whether it was modesty, intentional lack of further lines, or the outrage of the crowd that stopped her.

Recordings: Cisco Houston (Folkways, FA 2042); The Weavers (Vanguard, VRS 9013); Stan Wilson (Verve, MGV 2051).

Oh, we sailed on the sloop John B., My grand-fath-er and me. 'Round Nas-sau town we did roam. Drink-in' all night, We got in a fight, I feel so break-up, I want-a go home.

Chorus (same tune as verse):
So, hoist up the John B. sails, see how the mains'l's set,
Send for the cap'n ashore, lemme go home!
Lemme go home! Lemme go home!
I feel so break-up, I want to go home!

2. The first mate he got drunk, break up the people's trunk,
Constable come aboard and take him away,
Mr. Johnstone, please let me alone,
I feel so break-up, I want to go home.
Chorus.

3. The poor cook he got fits, throw 'way all the grits,
Then he took and eat up all o' my corn,
Lemme go home, I want to go home!
This is the worst trip, since I been born!
Chorus.

SOLDIER, SOLDIER, WILL YOU MARRY ME?

This old British courting or game song has been collected widely throughout the southern mountains of this country. It has overtones of other songs in this book—see index listing for "Buffalo Boy" and "The Cambric Shirt." A harmony part is included (lower notes) for those places in "Soldier, Soldier" where harmonizing is appropriate.

Recordings: Isla Cameron (Tradition, TLP 1001); Patrick Gainer (Folk Heritage Recording, DB 2122-3); Jean Ritchie (Westminster, WP 6037); Jean Ritchie and Oscar Brand (Riverside, RLP 12 814); Robin Roberts (Stinson, SLP 77); John Runge (Riverside, RLP 12 814); Tom Scott (Coral, CRL 56056).

Harmony on lower notes

"Oh, soldier, soldier, will you marry me With your fife and drum?" "Oh, no, oh, no," the soldier replied, "I have no shoes to put on."

2. Away she flew to the cobbler's shop.
Bought him the very best pair.
Came right back and he put them on,
And she said, "Now there you are. So . . .

3. "Soldier, soldier, will you marry me
With your fife and drum?"
"Oh no, oh no," the soldier replied,
"I have no hat to put on."

4. Away she flew to the hatter's shop,
Got him the very best hat.
Came right back and he put it on,
And she said, "Now look at that. So . . .

5. "Soldier, soldier, will you marry me
With your fife and drum?"
"Oh no, oh no," the soldier replied,
"I have no suit to put on."

6. Away she flew to the tailor's shop,
Got him the very best suit.
Came right back and he put it on,
And she said, "Now that's to boot. So . . .

7. "Soldier, soldier, will you marry me
With your fife and drum?"
"Oh no, oh no," the soldier replied,
"I've a wife and children at home!"

SPRINGFIELD MOUNTAIN

Phillips Barry, one of the most important folk song scholars of the twentieth century, carefully reconstructed the history of "Springfield Mountain" and published the essence of his findings in the *Bulletin of the Folksong Society of the Northeast*. The song, probably the oldest purely American (non-Indian) folk song, was originally a serious memorial to Timothy Myrick of Springfield Mountain, Massachusetts, who died of a rattlesnake bite in 1761.

By the middle of the nineteenth century it had been converted to a comic variety-show song, and in this mood the song is best known today. Alan Lomax includes a rare serious version in *The Folk Songs of North America*.

Recordings: Paul Clayton (Folkways, FA 2106); Bob Gibson (Riverside, RLP 12 806); Sam Hinton (Decca, DL 8108); Bascom Lamar Lunsford (Folkways, FA 2040); Ed McCurdy (Riverside, RLP 12 601).

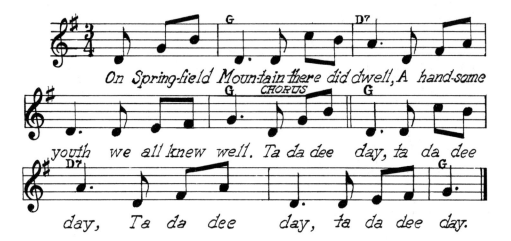

On Spring-field Moun-tain there did dwell, A hand-some youth we all knew well. Ta da dee day, ta da dee day, Ta da dee day, ta da dee day.

2. One Friday morning he did go
   Down to the meadow for to mow.

3. And as he mowed across the field,
   A pizen sarpent bit his heel.

4. They took him to his Molly dear,
   Because he looked so ver-aye queer.

5. His Moll-aye had two rub-aye lips,
   With which the pizen she did sip.

6. But Moll-aye had a rotten tooth,
   Which the pizen struck and killed them both.

7. And all their friends both far and near
   Did cry and howl, they were so dear.

8. The moral is, I'm sure you know,
   When grass is tall you must not mow.

STAGOLEE

The legends surrounding Negro bad man Stagolee, or Stackalee, are legion: He was born in Missouri with a veil over his face. He sold his soul to the devil in his youth for a magic Stetson hat. He shot anyone who tried to steal his hat. He blew San Francisco down when his drink arrived too slowly at a bar. When he killed Billy Lyon in Memphis, his freedom — and his hat — were taken away from him. Eventually he made a big hit in hell, where he felt right at home—taking good care of all his old buddies and organizing a jazz band with the devil on cornet.

A sampling of the recordings below will show you there is a good deal of variation in this blues-ballad in performances. Although the song usually follows a reasonably orthodox blues pattern, there is considerable alteration in melody and text. You'll notice, for example, that Cisco Houston develops the story a little differently and uses "when you lose your money, learn to lose" instead of "he was a bad man," etc., as the repetitive last phrase.

Recordings: Paul Clayton (Riverside, RLP 12 615); Logan English (Riverside, RLP 12 643); Cisco Houston (Folkways, FA 2042); Ed McCurdy (Elektra, EKL 108); Pete Seeger (Folkways, FA 2042).

2. Stagolee shot Billy de Lyons.
   What do you think about that,
   Shot him down in cold blood
   Because he stole his Stetson hat;
   He was a bad man,
   That mean old Stagolee.

3. Billy de Lyons said, "Stagolee
   Please don't take my life,
   I've got two little babes
   And a darling, loving wife;
   You are a bad man,
   You mean old Stagolee."

4. "I care not for your babies
   Nor your darling little wife.
   You done ruined my Stetson hat
   And I'm bound to have your life."
   That bad man,
   That bad man Stagolee.

5. It was no Stetson hat.
   He didn't have a good excuse.
   They say he killed old Billy Lyons
   'Cause he gave his gal abuse.
   He was a bad man,
   That mean old Stagolee.

6. Stago's wench was a good girl;
   She was as true as steel;
   She said, "I'll stand by you, Stag,
   On you I'm never gonna squeal."
   Down at the trial
   Of mean old Stagolee.

7. The judge put on the black cap;
   His voice was stern and cold.
   "I sentence you to be hanged;
   The Lord have mercy on your soul.
   You're a bad man,
   Mean old Stagolee."

STEAL AWAY

In recent years many folk song specialists have pursued a theory that many spirituals were designed with hidden meanings, messages, and signals for the slaves. Support for this idea is found in the documented practice among slaves of talking and singing about their overseers in double-meaning terms that would inform or entertain the Negroes but not their overseers. And if you pursue this theory you can find, among both secular and religious songs, example after example whose words can be interpreted as holding such hidden meanings. "Steal Away" is one of the spirituals frequently cited in support of this theory. An examination of the text can render it, for instance, an invitation to steal away to freedom.

It is quite possible, however, that, rather than being consciously designed for devious purposes, songs of this type simply had a universal appeal among Negroes because of the parallels they found between their situation and the situations in the songs. Harold Courlander comments on this theory in *Negro Folk Music, U. S. A.**:

> If songs of the type of "Steal Away to Jesus" and "Go Down Moses" are to be considered conscious disguises for political, temporal meanings, a large part of the religious repertoire must be placed in the same category. Every reference to crossing the Jordan could be interpreted to mean escape to the North; every battle of the Israelites might be read to mean the battle for Negro freedom; every reference to Elijah's chariot or the gospel train could be seen as allusion to the Underground Railroad; and every trumpet blast interpreted as Emancipation Day. But such a notion would be difficult to accept. Negro religious activity and belief are not based on the principle of secular or situational parallels. Negro religious music must be considered to be, in the main, precisely what it purports to be. . . . A large number of spirituals and anthems were so worded that they could have a disguised

*From *Negro Folk Music, U.S.A.* by Harold Courlander. Copyright © 1963 Columbia University Press, New York.

meaning; but it is not safe to assume (or even take the word of persons who were born to slavery) that they were created as anything else but religious songs.

Recording: Roland Hayes (Vanguard, VRS 494).

Steal a-way, steal a-way, steal a-way to Je-sus! Steal a-way, steal a-way home, I ain't got long to stay here. My Lord calls me, He calls me by the thun-der; The trump-et sounds it in my soul! I ain't got long to stay here.

2. Green trees are bending,
   Poor sinners stand trembling;
   The trumpet sounds it in my soul:
   I ain't got long to stay here.

3. My lord calls me,
   He calls me by the lightning;
   The trumpet sounds it in my soul:
   I ain't got long to stay here.

4. Tombstones are bursting,
   Poor sinners are trembling;
   The trumpet sounds it in my soul:
   I ain't got long to stay here.

SWEET BETSY FROM PIKE

"Pikes" or "Pikers" became a term of derision in the slang of gold-rush days (see "Joe Bowers" listing in Index). Many of the first forty-niners to arrive in California were from Pike County in Missouri. The tune of "Sweet Betsy from Pike," a period-piece companion of "Joe Bowers," is borrowed from "Vilikins and Dinah" (also included here), an earlier humorous mock-ballad from Ireland.

Recordings: John Allison (Ficker, C 10001); Bill Bender (Stinson, SLP 18); Logan English (Folkways, FH 5255); Pat Foster (Riverside, RLP 12-654); Cisco Houston (Folkways, FA 2022); Burl Ives (Columbia, CL 6109); Milt Okun (Baton, BL 1203); Susan Reed (Columbia, ML 54368).

2. They soon reached the desert, where Betsy gave out,
   And down on the sand she lay rolling about,
   While Ike, in great tears, looked on in surprise.
   Said, "Betsy, get up, you'll get sand in your eyes."

3. The rooster ran off and the oxen all died;
   The last piece of bacon that morning was fried.
   Poor Ike got discouraged and Betsy got mad;
   The dog wagged his tail and looked awfully sad.

4. The alkali desert was burning and hot,
   And Ike, he decided to leave on the spot:
   "My dear old Pike County, I'll go back to you."
   Said Betsy, "You'll go by yourself if you do."

5. They swam the wide rivers, they crossed the tall peaks,
   They camped out on prairies for weeks and for weeks,
   Fought hunger and Injuns and big storms of dust,
   Determined to reach California or bust.

6. They crossed the Sierras through mountains of snow,
   And saw California all spread out below.
   Sweet Betsy she hollered and Ike gave a cheer,
   "We'll be millionaires now that we've made it here."

7. Then Ike and Sweet Betsy they went to a dance;
   He wore a pair of his Pike County pants.
   And Betsy was dressed up in ribbons and rings.
   Said Ike, "You're an angel without any wings."

8. A miner asked Betsy: "Will you dance with me?"
   "I will, you old hoss, if you don't make too free.
   And I'll tell you the reason if you want to know why,
   Doggonnit, I'm chuck full of strong alkali."

VILIKINS AND DINAH

1. It is of a rich merchant I am going to tell,
   Who had for a daughter an unkimmon nice young gal.
   Her name it was Dinah, just sixteen years old,
   With a very large fortin in silver and gold.
   Singing, Toorali, toorali, toorali-ay.

2. Now, as Dinah was waliking in the garding one day,
   The father comed up to her and thus to her did say:
   "Go dress yourself, Dinah, in gorgeous array
   And I'll bring you home a husiband both galliant and gay."
   Singing, Toorali, toorali toorali-ay.

3. "O father, dear father," the daughter she said,
   "I don't feel inclined to be marri-i-ed;
   And all my large fortin I'll gladly give o'er,
   If you'll let me live single a year or two more."
   Singing, Toorali, toorali, toorali-ay.

4. "Go, go! boldest daughter," the parient he cried,
   "If you don't feel inclined to be this young man's bride,
   I'll give your large fortin to the nearest of kin,
   And you shan't reap the benefit of not one single pin."
   Singing, Toorali, toorali, toorali-ay.

5. Now as Vilikins was waliking the garding all round
   He spied his dear Dinah laying dead upon the ground,
   And a cup of cold pison all down by her side,
   With a billet-dow which said as how 'twas by pison she died.
   Singing, Toorali, toorali, toorali-ay.

6. Then he kissed her cold corper-ses a thousand times o'er
   And called her his dear Dinah, though she was no more,
   Then he swallowed up the pison, and sung a short stave,
   And Vilikins and his Dinah were laid in one grave.
   Singing, Toorali, toorali, toorali-ay.

7. Now all you young men, don't you thus fall in love, nor
   Do that not by no means disliked by your gov'nor;
   And, all you young maidens, mind who you claps your eyes on;
   Think of Vilikins and his Dinah, not forgetting the pison.
   Singing, Toorali, toorali, toorali-ay.

SWING LOW, SWEET CHARIOT

And it came to pass, as they still went on, and talked, that, behold, there appeared a chariot of fire, and horses of fire, and parted them both asunder; and Elijah went up by a whirlwind into heaven. II Kings, 2:11

Whether it is a symbol of salvation or escape to freedom from bondage, or both, the chariot occurs frequently in Negro spirituals. For more on the subject of symbolism, see the Index page references for other sections of this book where this point is elaborated on.

Recordings: Frances Archer and Beverly Gile (Disneyland, WDL 3006); Big Bill Broonzy (Columbia, WL 111); Lee Charles (Riverside, RLP 12 651); Howard University Choir (RCA Victor, LM 2126); Bascom Lamar Lunsford (Riverside, RLP 12 645); Robert McFerrin (Riverside, RLP 12 812); Paul Robeson (Columbia, ML 2038).

2. If you get there before I do,
   Tell all my friends I'm coming, too.

3. The brightest day that ever I saw,
   When Jesus washed my sins away.

4. I'm sometimes up an' sometimes down,
   But still my soul feels heavenly boun'.

5. I never went to Heaven, but I been told
   The streets in Heaven am paved with gold.

Additional verses:

**Let me tell you what's a matter of fact,
If you ever leave the devil you'll never go back.**

**If salvation was a thing that money could buy,
The rich would live and the poor would die.**

**See that sister dressed so fine?
She ain't got religion on her mind.**

T

...the leafy
green dome

Can she bake
a cherry pie...

As I was going
to Derby...

TALKING BLUES

If you want to be a star let me tell you what to do.
Just buy a guitar and take a lesson or two.
Now, it won't matter if you can't sing;
Just do the talkin' blues while you pick and grin.
It's easy . . . . go to Nashville . . . . . be a hillbilly.

Spoken patter, rhythmic and rhyming, with instrumental or vocal accompaniment, is a familiar device that has been used in many different ways by entertainers. Negroes appear to be more adept at this art than anyone else. I've never heard better improvised patter than from this source, whether it is jive talk:

I'm mellow as a cello and fine as wine.

or a sermon:

I take my text from Genesis two and twenty-one.
Behold de rib!
Now, my beloved,
Behold means to look and see.
Look at dis woman God done made.
But first thing, ah hah!
Ah wants you to gaze upon God's previous works.
Almighty and arisen God, hah!
Peace-giving and prayer-hearing God,
High-riding and strong-armded God
Walking across his globe creation, hah!
Wid de blue elements for a helmet
And a wall of fire round his feet
He wakes de sun every morning from his fiery bed
Wid de breath of his smile
And commands de moon wid his eyes.
And oh —
Wid de eye of faith
I can see him.
Even de lion had a mate.
So God shook his head
And a thousand million diamonds
Flew out from his glittering crown
And studded de evening sky and made de stars.
So God put Adam into a deep sleep
And took out a bone, ah hah!
And it is said that it was a rib.
Behold de rib!
Brothers, if God
Had taken dat bone out of man's head
He would have meant for woman to rule, hah;
If he had taken a bone out of his foot,
He would have meant for us to dominize and rule.
He could have made her out of back-bone
And then she would have been behind us.
But, no, God Almighty, he took de bone out of his side,
So dat places de woman beside us;
Hah! God knowed his own mind,
Behold de rib!

. . . .

or that familiar chant:

> Dry bones, dry bones,
> Well, them bones, dry bones, that are
> Laid in the valley.
> Well, them bones, dry bones, that are
> Laid in the valley.
> You can hear the word of the Lord.
> Or from my toe bone to my
> Foot bone, or from my
> Foot bone to my
> Ankle bone, or from my
> Ankle bone to my
> Leg bone, or from my
> Leg bone to my
> Knee bone. . . .

If Negro entertainers didn't invent the talking blues, and they probably did, they must have provided the inspiration for it.

In the 1920s hillbilly entertainers started talking the blues on records, and the talkin' has been goin' on ever since. We've had "Talking Dust Bowl Blues," "Talking Sailor," "Talking Columbia Blues," "Talking Miner," "Talking Union," "Talking Subway," "Talking Drunk," "Talking Farmer," "Talking Atom," and "Talking Freedom," to name a few.

The instrumental accompaniment for talking blues can be as simple or as complex as you want to make it. You might just want to use a rhythmic strum with a few interesting chord changes, or you might improve on that by throwing in some bass runs. How much farther you go is up to you and your technical abilities. You'll find a lot of ideas on recordings.

Recordings: Oscar Brand (Riverside, RLP 12 825); Pat Foster and Dick Weissman (Counterpoint, CPT 550); John Greenway (Folkways, FH 5232); Cisco Houston (Disc, D 103); The Weavers (Vanguard, VRS 9013). Variations: "Talking Atom": Oscar Brand (Tradition, TLP 1022); Pete Seeger (Folkways, FN 2501). "Talking Columbia Blues": Woody Guthrie (Folkways, FA 2481). "Talking Dust Bowl Blues": Woody Guthrie (Folkways, FA 2011); Sam Hinton (Decca, DL 8418). "Talking Sailor": Woody Guthrie (Stinson, 347–1A). "Talking Union": Almanac Singers (Folkways, FH 5285); Pete Seeger (Hootenanny, HLP 201). Various talking blues on one long-playing recording: Pat Foster and Dick Weissman (Counterpoint, CPT 550); John Greenway (Folkways, FH 523).

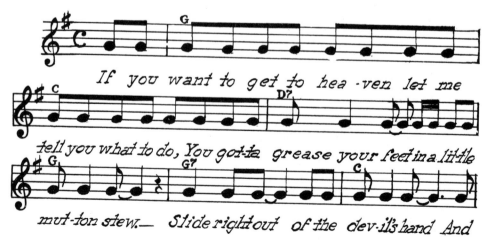

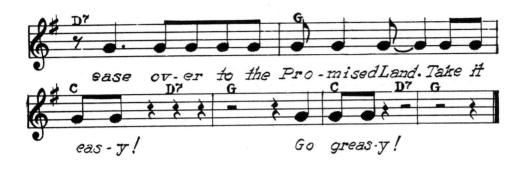

ease ov-er to the Pro-mised Land. Take it
eas-y!   Go greas-y!

2. Down in the wild-wood settin' on a log,
   Finger on the trigger; my eye on a hog.
   I pulled the trigger; gun went zip.
   Jump on the hog with all of my grip.
   Such scramblin' . . . . eatin' hog-eyes . . . . . love chitlins.

3. Behind the henhouse on my knees
   I thought I heard that chicken sneeze.
   Only the rooster sayin' his prayers . . .
   Givin' out hints to the hens upstairs.
   Such preachin' . . . . rooster prayin' . . . hens singin' . . . . payin' off eggs.

4. Make up the beds, gals, make 'em up nice.
   Old preacher Johnson will be here tonight.
   When that preacher starts to eat,
   You never seen such a hungry sight . . .
   He's a chicken eater . . . . loves cake . . . . . likes sisters, too.

5. Standing in the corner by the mantelpiece.
   Standing in the corner by a bucket of grease.
   Grease my feet with axle grease
   Went sliding up that mantelpiece.
   Huntin' matches . . . . . cigarette stubs . . . . . chewing tobacco.

6. Behind the henhouse the other night
   It was awful dark, didn't have no light.
   Fool around got a hold of a goose.
   Somebody hollered better turn him a-loose.
   Jump gullies . . . . . . rose bushes . . . . dodge bullets, too.

7. What's the need of me workin' so hard
   When I've got a woman in the rich folks' yard.
   When she kills me a chicken she saves me the feet.
   She thinks I'm workin'. I'm loafin' down the street.
   Thinkin' about her . . . . . havin' a good time . . . . . . two other women.

It's easy to see you can go anywhere you want to with these verses. Here
are a couple of moonshine verses:

Mama's in the kitchen fixin' the yeast,
Poppa's in the bedroom greasin' his feet,
Sister's in the cellar squeezin' up the hops,
Brother's at the window just a-watchin' for the cops.
Drinkin' home-brew makes you happy.

Now I'm just a city dude a-livin' out of town,
Everybody knows me as Moonshine Brown;

I make the beer, and I drink the slop,
Got nine little orphans that calls me Pop.
I'm patriotic . . . . . . raisin' soldiers . . . . . Red Cross nurses.

This verse starts with a couplet that shows up in "Hey Lidee" and several other make-'em-up-as-you-go-along songs:

I've got a gal lives over the hill.
She don't kiss like her sister will.
Never takes a bath, not even a rub,
Afraid she'll slide through the hole in the tub.
Awful skinny . . . . . . bony . . . . . . cut a man like a razor.

TELL OLD BILL
(This Morning, This Evening, So Soon)

This morning. Just this morning everything was normal. Life was going on in the same old way. Same old work to do. Same old complaints. Same old things to think about, worry about, fuss about. That was only this morning. Then came the unbelievable, shocking, bewildering announcement. There must be a mistake. It can't be true. This morning . . . This evening . . . So soon.

The expressiveness, the power, of this tragic blues lament is captured in the bewilderment of those incomplete sentences. It can't happen to us. . . . But it did.

Recordings: Julie Felix (London, LL 3395); Bob Gibson (Riverside, RLP 12 806); Sam Hinton (Decca, DL 8108).

318

2. Old Sal was baking bread, this morning,
   Old Sal was baking bread, this evening,
   Old Sal was baking bread,
   When she found out her Bill was dead,
   This morning, this evening, so soon.

3. She said, "Oh, no, it can't be so," this morning,
   She said, "Oh, no, it can't be so," this evening,
   She said, "Oh, no, it can't be so,
   My Bill left here about an hour ago,
   This morning, this evening, so soon."

4. She said, "Oh, no, this just can't be," this morning,
   She said, "Oh, no, this just can't be," this evening,
   She said, "Oh, no, this just can't be,
   They killed my Bill in the third degree,
   This morning, this evening, so soon."

5. They brought Bill home in a hurry-up wagon, this morning,
   They brought Bill home in a hurry-up wagon, this evening,
   They brought Bill home in a hurry-up wagon,
   Poor dead Bill, now his toes were draggin',
   This morning, this evening, so soon.

THERE'S A HOLE IN MY BUCKET

Circular rhymes are popular in folklore. When I was in high school a popular circular rhyme went like this:

> You remind me of a man.
> What kind of a man?
> A man with the power.
> Power of what?
> Voodoo.
> Who do?
> You do.
> Do what?
> Remind me of a man.

And there we were back where we started, with nothing else to do but keep it going until somebody quit.

This circularity also shows up in song, as in "Yon Yonson":

> My name is Yon Yonson,
> I come from Visconsin,
> I vork in the lumber mills there;
> Ven I valk down the street,
> All the people I meet,
> Say, "Hello, vot's your name?"
> And I say . . .
> My name is Yon Yonson, *etc.*

or

> 'Round the corner behind the tree
> A sergeant major he said to me:
> "Oh, how'd you like to marry me?

I would like to know,
For every time I look in your eyes,
I feel I'd like to go:
'Round the corner . . . ," *etc.*

"There's a Hole in My Bucket" takes a lot longer to get back where you started, but the principle is the same. Sam Hinton told me it was originally a German song, "Wenn der Topp aber nu en Loch Hat." Korson and others have collected several variants from the Pennsylvania "Dutch," who brought it to this country.

I've used George and Liza as the principals in the cast. Feel free to make up your own road company by substituting your favorite leading man and woman. The straw has been cut with a hoe, as well as with a knife, in some versions. Don't overlook the pun fun of *whetting* as well as *wetting* the stone.

Recordings: Oscar Brand and Fred Hellerman (Tradition, TLP 1014); Ed McCurdy (Tradition, TLP 1027).

There's a hole in my buck-et, dear Liz-a, dear Liz-a, There's a hole in my buck-et, dear Liz-a, a hole.

2. Then mend it, dear Georgie, dear Georgie, dear Georgie,
   Then mend it, dear Georgie, dear Georgie, mend it.

3. With what shall I mend it, dear Liza, dear Liza,
   With what shall I mend it, dear Liza, with what?

4. With a straw, dear Georgie, dear Georgie, dear Georgie,
   With a straw, dear Georgie, dear Georgie, a straw.

5. The straw is too long, dear Liza, dear Liza,
   The straw is too long, dear Liza, too long.

6. Then cut it, dear Georgie, dear Georgie, dear Georgie,
   Then cut it, dear Georgie, dear Georgie, cut it.

7. With what shall I cut it, dear Liza, dear Liza,
   With what shall I cut it, dear Liza, with what?

8. With a knife, dear Georgie, dear Georgie, dear Georgie,
   With a knife, dear Georgie, dear Georgie, a knife.

9. The knife is too blunt, dear Liza, dear Liza,
   The knife is too blunt, dear Liza, too blunt.

10. Then sharpen it, dear Georgie, dear Georgie, dear Georgie,
    Then sharpen it, dear Georgie, dear Georgie, sharpen it.

11. With what shall I sharpen it, dear Liza, dear Liza,
    With what shall I sharpen it, dear Liza, with what?

12. With a stone, dear Georgie, dear Georgie, dear Georgie,
    With a stone, dear Georgie, dear Georgie, a stone.

13. The stone is too dry, dear Liza, dear Liza,
    The stone is too dry, dear Liza, too dry.

14. Then wet it, dear Georgie, dear Georgie, dear Georgie,
    Then wet it, dear Georgie, dear Georgie, wet it.

15. With what shall I wet it, dear Liza, dear Liza,
    With what shall I wet it, dear Liza, with what?

16. With water, dear Georgie, dear Georgie, dear Georgie,
    With water, dear Georgie, dear Georgie, with water.

17. In what shall I get it, dear Liza, dear Liza,
    In what shall I get it, dear Liza, in what?

18. In a bucket, dear Georgie, dear Georgie, dear Georgie,
    In a bucket, dear Georgie, dear Georgie, in a bucket.

19. There's a hole in my bucket, dear Liza, dear Liza,
    There's a hole in my bucket, dear Liza, a hole.

THIS TRAIN

Chariots, ships, and trains have all served as symbols of a means of escape to freedom, or redemption, in Negro religious songs. "This Train" belongs to the gospel tradition of Negroes and whites and is derived from earlier spiritual tradition. Woody Guthrie, the man who wrote "two or three ballads for breakfast every morning," didn't write this one, but he sure could pour a lot of life into singing it. And he used the train's destination for the title of his autobiography, *Bound for Glory*. Despite the fact that one verse frequently sung in recent years states

> This train, you don't pay no transportation,
> No Jim Crow and *no discrimination*

most of the verses *discriminate* against someone — prostitutes, hypocrites, or anyone who isn't righteous and holy. I wonder who decides who is righteous and holy.

Recordings: Big Bill Broonzy (Folkways, FG 3586); Bob Gibson (Riverside, RLP 830); Alan Lomax (Kapp, KL 1110); Sister Rosetta Tharpe (Decca, DL 8782). Variation: "The Cisco Special": Cisco Houston (Vanguard, VRS 9057).

This train is bound for glor-y, This train,—

This train is bound for glor-y, This train,—

This train is bound for glory, Don't ride nothin' but the righteous and the holy.

This train is bound for glor-y, this train.—

2. This train don't carry no gamblers, this train,
   This train don't carry no gamblers, this train,
   This train don't carry no gamblers,
   No hypocrites, no midnight ramblers.
   This train is bound for glory, this train.

3. This train is built for speed now, *etc.*
   Fastest train you ever did see.
   This train is bound for glory, this train.

4. This train don't carry no liars, *etc.*
   No hypocrites and no high flyers.
   This train is bound for glory, this train.

5. This train don't carry no rustlers, *etc.*
   Sidestreet walkers, two-bit hustlers.
   This train is bound for glory, this train.

THE TITANIC

When the *Titanic* collided with an iceberg and sank on her maiden voyage in 1912, with a loss of over fifteen hundred lives, the balladeers went to work immediately (as they do with every great tragedy). Soon broadsides about the event were being sold on front and back streets around the country. The most widely sung version that survives today is usually sung in a lighthearted, enthusiastic manner which fails to take the tragedy seriously. Other versions take the matter a little more soberly:

It was on a Monday morning just about at one o'clock,
When that great *Titanic* began to reel and rock.
Folks began to scream and cry, sayin' "Lord, am I gonna die?"
It was sad when that great ship went down.

And ending:

You know that it was bad with those people on the sea.
They say they were singin' "Nearer My God to Thee."
They all were homeward bound; sixteen hundred had to drown.
It was sad when that great ship went down.

Meanwhile, back on the campus, they've tacked on an ending that goes like this:

Now, the moral of this story, as you can plainly see:
Is to wear a life preserver and never go out to sea.
Keep your feet upon the ground; ever pure and faithful be.
It was sad when that great ship went down.

Recordings: Bob Gibson (Riverside, RLP 12 830); Pete Seeger (Folkways, FA 2319); Songs of Camp (Folkways, FC 7510); Stan Wilson (Verve, MGV 2076). Other versions: Pink Anderson (Riverside, RLP 12 611); Rolf Cahn (Folkways, FA 2416); Huddie "Leadbelly" Ledbetter (Folkways, FA 2914); William and Versey Smith (Folkways, FH 2951).

sad when that great ship went down,(to the bot-tom of the)
Hus-bands and wives, lit-tle child-ren lost their lives, It was
sad — when that great— ship went down.

2. Oh, they sailed from England, and were almost to the shore,
   When the rich refused to associate with the pore,
   So they put them down below, where they were the first to go.
   It was sad when that great ship went down.

3. The boat was full of sin, and the sides about to burst,
   When the captain shouted: "Women and children first!"
   Oh, the captain tried to wire, but the lines were all afire.
   It was sad when that great ship went down.

4. When they swung the lifeboats out on the deep and raging sea,
   And the band struck up with "Nearer My God to Thee,"
   Little children wept and cried, and the waves swept o'er the side.
   It was sad when that great ship went down.

TOM DOOLEY

On May 1, 1868, after various trials and appeals and a pre-execution confession, Thomas C. Dula was hanged for the murder of Laura Foster. Later that year Ann Melton, charged as his accomplice, was acquitted. The evidence showed that Dula was running around with both girls and, in the process, picked up a disease from Laura and passed it on to Ann. According to a newspaper description "a state of immorality unexampled in the history of any country exists among these people, and such a general system of free loveism prevails that it is 'a wise child that knows its father!'" Whether or not this was sensational or biased journalism, the community did draw the line at murder. Or maybe they just objected to Dula's looks. A reporter for the *New York Herald* described him as follows:

> Thomas Dula, the condemned man, is about twenty-five years old, five feet eleven inches high, dark eyes, curly hair, and though not handsome might be called good looking. He fought gallantly in the Confederate service, where he established a reputation for bravery, but since the war closed, has become reckless, demoralized and a desperado, of whom the people in this community had a terror. There is everything in his expression to indicate the hardened assassin—a fierce glare of the eyes, a great deal of malignity, and a callousness that is revolting.

Recordings: Paul Clayton (Riverside, RLP 12 615); New Lost City Ramblers (Folkways, FA 2397); Frank Warner (Elektra, EKLP 3); Doc Watson (Vanguard, VRS 9152).

Hang down your head, Tom Dooley, Hang down your head and cry. You killed poor Laura Foster; Now you're bound to die. I met her on the hill-top. There I took her life. I met her on the hill-top, And stabbed her with my knife.

2. I killed her on the hilltop,
   God Almighty knows.
   I killed her on the hilltop
   And there I hid her clothes.

3. Tonight I'll pick my banjo.
   I'll pick it on my knee.
   Tomorrow I'll be hangin'
   From a white oak tree.

4. This day and one more,
   Do you reckon where I'll be?
   This day and one more
   And I'll be in eternity.

5. I had my trial at Wilkesboro.
   Oh, what do you reckon they done?
   They bound me over to Statesville,
   And that's where I'll be hung.

6. Daddy, oh my Daddy,
   What shall I do?
   I have lost all my money,
   And killed poor Laury, too.

7. Mother, oh dear Mother,
   Oh, don't you weep and cry.
   I have killed poor Laury Foster,
   And you know I'm bound to die.

8. Oh, what my mother told me
   Is about to come to pass:
   That drinkin' and the women
   Would be my ruin at last.

THE TWELVE DAYS OF CHRISTMAS

It just wouldn't be a real Christmas without someone's testing his memory and endurance with this favorite cumulative counting song. It extends the Christmas season from Christmas Day to the Feast of the Epiphany twelve days later, and thus preserves the memory of a time when this custom prevailed in England.

In earlier days singers would start at twelve, count down to one, and then count back up to twelve; today most singers are satisfied to work their way up from one through twelve. In recent years there has been a trend toward inventing twelve gifts appropriate to contemporary Christmas giving (transistor radios, television sets, and so on), but most singers still prefer to adhere to the traditional gifts. Which gifts are traditional? Although they vary according to the singer's memory or source, here's a chart that indicates most of the possibilities currently in use:

12 ships a-sailing	hunters hunting	drummers drumming	bulls a-bellering	ladies dancing
11 drums a-beating	ladies leaping	pipers piping	lords a-limping	lords a-leaping
10 ladies dancing	tailors stitching	lords a-leaping	drummers drumming	
9 lords a-knitting	fiddlers fiddling	ladies dancing	wolves a-howling	pipers piping
8 bulls a-roaring	lords a-dancing	maids a-milking	deers a-running	
7 swans a-swimming	swa-ans swimming			
6 geese a-laying				
5 gold rings	golden rings			
4 Cornish hens	calling birds	colored birds	colley birds	
3 French hens	French horns			
2 turtle doves				

1 partridge in a pear tree.

I include the variations not to confuse the issue but to provide an aid to settling arguments—or to inspire additional variations. If you're bothered by visions of "lords a-knitting" and "colley birds," blame it on folk distortion.

Recordings: Tom Glazer (Mercury, MG 2007); Burl Ives (Decca, DL 8391); Randolph Singers (Westminster, WP 6023).

On the first day of Christ-mas my true love sent to me A

part-ridge_ in a pear tree. On the sec-ond day of Christ-mas my

true love sent to me Two tur-tle doves, And a part-ridge_ in a pear

tree. On the third day of Christ-mas my true love sent to me

Three French_hens, Two tur-tle doves, And a part-ridge_ in a pear

tree. On the fourth day of Christmas my true love sent to me

Four col-ly birds, Three French_hens, Two tur-tle doves, And a

part-ridge_ in a pear tree. On the fifth day of Christ-mas my

true love sent to me Five gold_rings, Four_col-ly birds,

Three French_hens, Two-tur-tle doves, And a part-ridge_in a pear

tree. On the sixth day of Christ-mas my true love sent to me, Six geese a-laying

7. *Seven swans a-swimming,*
8. *Eight maids a-milking,*
9. *Nine ladies dancing,*
10. *Ten lords a-leaping,*
11. *Eleven pipers piping,*
12. *Twelve drummers drumming,*

Five gold rings, Four col-ly birds, Three French hens,

Two turtle doves, And a part-ridge in a pear tree.

1. On the first day of Christmas
   My true love sent to me
   A partridge in a pear tree.

2. On the second day of Christmas
   My true love sent to me
   Two turtle doves, and
   A partridge in a pear tree.

3. On the third day of Christmas
   My true love sent to me
   Three French hens,
   Two turtle doves, and
   A partridge in a pear tree.

4. On the fourth day of Christmas
   My true love sent to me
   Four colly birds,
   Three French hens,
   Two turtle doves, and
   A partridge in a pear tree.

5. On the fifth day of Christmas
   My true love sent to me
   Five gold rings,
   Four colly birds,
   Three French hens,
   Two turtle doves, and
   A partridge in a pear tree.

6. On the sixth day of Christmas
   My true love sent to me
   Six geese a-laying,
   Five gold rings,
   Four colly birds,
   Three French hens,
   Two turtle doves,
   And a partridge in a pear tree.

7. On the seventh day of Christmas
   My true love sent to me
   Seven swans a-swimming,
   Six geese a-laying,
   Five gold rings,
   Four colly birds,
   Three French hens,
   Two turtle doves,
   And a partridge in a pear tree.

8. On the eighth day of Christmas
   My true love sent to me
   Eight maids a-milking,
   Seven swans a-swimming,
   Six geese a-laying,
   Five gold rings,
   Four colly birds,
   Three French hens,
   Two turtle doves,
   And a partridge in a pear tree.

9. On the ninth day of Christmas
   My true love sent to me
   Nine ladies dancing,
   Eight maids a-milking,
   Seven swans a-swimming
   Six geese a-laying,
   Five gold rings,
   Four colly birds,
   Three French hens,
   Two turtle doves,
   And a partridge in a pear tree.

10. On the tenth day of Christmas
    My true love sent to me
    Ten lords a-leaping,
    Nine ladies dancing,
    Eight maids a-milking,
    Seven swans a-swimming,
    Six geese a-laying,
    Five gold rings,
    Four colly birds,
    Three French hens,
    Two turtle doves,
    And a partridge in a pear tree.

11. On the eleventh day of Christmas
    My true love sent to me
    Eleven pipers piping,
    Ten lords a-leaping,
    Nine ladies dancing,
    Eight maids a-milking,
    Seven swans a-swimming,
    Six geese a-laying,
    Five gold rings,
    Four colly birds,
    Three French hens,
    Two turtle doves,
    And a partridge in a pear tree.

12. On the twelfth day of Christmas
    My true love sent to me
    Twelve drummers drumming,
    Eleven pipers piping,
    Ten lords a-leaping,
    Nine ladies dancing,
    Eight maids a-milking,
    Seven swans a-swimming,
    Six geese a-laying,
    Five gold rings,
    Four colly birds,
    Three French hens,
    Two turtle doves,
    And a partridge in a pear tree.

THE TWO SISTERS

"The Two Sisters" ballad tells the story of a jealous girl who drowns her younger sister. In earlier British versions the older sister's guilt is discovered through a supernatural revelation from a musical instrument the miller made of the victim's corpse:

What did he do with her breast bone?
He made him a violl to play thereupon.

What did he do with her fingers so small?
He made him pegs to his violl withall.

What did he do with her veynes so blew?
He made him strings to his violl thereto.

. . . . . .

Then bespake the second string,
"O yonder sits my mother the queen."

And then bespake the strings all three,
"O yonder is my sister that drowned mee."

In the American version shown below, this part of the story has been dropped; in fact, in one single verse the story leaps from the theft portion to the climax, allowing no time for courtroom drama. In addition, the last line is ambiguously phrased: the guilty sister probably was hanged "there close by"; but she may have escaped and been a spectator at the hanging of the miller. I doubt, however, that the latter interpretation was the intent of the ballad reporter.

Some ballads (and this is one of them) have refrains that have nothing to do with the ballad story. A clue to the reason for the refrain lies in its text: In some parts of Scandinavia ballads are used to accompany dancing, and some specialists believe that this may have been a fairly wide practice in earlier days. The refrain, with or without dancing, provided the singer with a pause to remember in and a break from the demands of the story.

Recordings: Loman Cansler (Folkways, FA 2112); Paul Clayton (Folkways, FA 3210); Richard Dyer-Bennet (Dyer-Bennet, DYB 6000); Cynthia Gooding (Elektra, EKL

131); Artus Moser (Folkways, FA 2112); John Jacob Niles (RCA Camden, CAL 219); Ellen Stekert (Folkways, FA 2354); Andrew Rowan Summers (Folkways, FA 2044).

There lived an old lord by the North-ern Sea, Bow down, bow down. There lived an old lord by the North-ern Sea, Bow and bal-ance to me! There lived an old lord by the North-ern Sea, And he had daugh-ters one, two, three. I'll be true to my love If my love'll be true to me!

2. A young man came a-courting there,
   Bow down, bow down.
   A young man came a-courting there,
   Bow and balance to me!
   A young man came a-courting there,
   And he made a choice of the youngest fair,
   I'll be true to my love
   If my love'll be true to me!

Continue, as above:

3. He made her a present of a beaver's hat,
   And the oldest sister didn't like that.

4. Oh, sister, oh, sister, please walk out,
   To see those vessels a-sailing about.

5. As they walked down to the water's brim,
   The oldest pushed the youngest in.

6. Oh, sister, oh, sister, lend me your hand,
   And I'll give you my house and land.

331

7. I will not give you my hand,
   But I will marry that young man.

8. She floated down to the miller's dam,
   The miller drew her safe to the land.

9. The miller picked up his drab hook,
   And then he fished her out of the brook.

10. And off her fingers took five gold rings,
    And into the water he plunged her again.

11. The miller was hanged on a gallows so high,
    The oldest sister there close by.

*...wishing her lover
good speed*

And away, hey...

*She crossed the
broad prairies...*

V

...the leafy green dome

Can she bake a cherry pie...

As I was going to Derby...

THE VICAR OF BRAY

How to succeed in politics—that's the message in one of the best-known ballads of political opportunism. It was a favorite in the British broadsides of the eighteenth century. Ballad scholar Frank Kidson says it was written by Edward Ward and published in his *Miscellanies* in 1712. Chappell thinks it was written by an officer in Colonel Fuller's troop of dragoons during the reign of King George I. In any event, in the words of the song, the Vicar's own account—though oversimplified—is historically accurate.

In 1660, after a period of Puritan domination, Charles II was restored to the throne and the Anglican Church (the "high church") became the official church of England. Catholics and dissenting protestants were expected, by law, to take communion in the Anglican Church. When James II, a Roman Catholic, came to the throne in 1685, he issued his Declaration of Indulgence (referred to in the second stanza of the song) granting religious freedom to *all* groups and sects. His act was taken as evidence of pro-Catholic leanings— and altogether his Catholicism was feared. Primarily for this reason, in 1688 English aristocrats secretly invited William of Orange (whose wife, Mary, was James' older daughter) to come to England and take the throne. As a result of the "Glorious Revolution," James was deposed and fled to France. During the next half century, however, his son and grandson—known respectively as the "Old Pretender" and the "Young Pretender"—occasionally threw scares into protestant Englishmen, who feared they might seize power.

During William's reign, Parliament emerged as the strong policy maker (instead of the previously autonomous monarchs). Two major parties—Tory (predominantly high church and conservative) and Whig (more generally liberal)—battled for control of Parliament. When, after the death of William, Mary's sister Anne came to the throne, the Tories held control. The occasional conformists referred to in the fourth stanza are protestants who adhered to the old law (the Test Act) by taking communion once or twice a year but attending their own churches the rest of the time.

George I, of the "illustrious house of Hanover," came to the throne in 1714—and for a time the more liberal Whigs were in power. "Protestant succession," which the Vicar now espouses, was from this time assured by act of Parliament.

Recordings: Theodore Bikel (Elektra, EKL 250); Richard Dyer-Bennet (Dyer-Bennet, DYB 1000).

In good King Charles's gold-en days, when loy-al-ty no
harm meant, A zeal-ous high church-man I was and

335

so I gained pre-fer-ment. To teach my flock I never missed, kings

are by God ap-point-ed. And damned are those who

dare re-sist or touch the Lord's a-nointed. And

this is law I will main-tain un-til my dy-ing day, sir, that

what-so-ev-er king shall reign I'll be the Vic-ar of Bray, sir!

2. When Royal James possessed the crown,
And popery came in fashion,
The penal laws I hotted down,
And read the Declaration.
The church of Rome I found did fit
Full well my constitution;
And I had been a Jesuit,
But for the Revolution.

3. When William was our king declared
To heal the nation's grievance,
With this new wind about I steered,
And swore to him Allegiance:
Old principles I did revoke,
Set conscience at a distance;
Passive obedience was a joke,
A jest was non-resistance.

4. When gracious Anne became our queen,
The Church of England's glory,
Another face of things was seen—
And I became a Tory:
Occasional conformists base,
I scorned their moderation,
And thought the church in danger was
From such prevarication.

5. When George in pudding time came o'er,
And moderate men looked big, Sir,
My principles I changed once more,
And so became a Whig, Sir.

336

And thus preferment I procured
From our new faith's defender,
And almost every day abjured
The Pope and the Pretender.

6. The illustrious house of Hanover
And Protestant succession,
To these I do allegiance swear,
While they can keep possession.
For in my faith and loyalty
I never more will falter,
And George my lawful king shall be
Until the times do alter.

I found "The Courtier," with the same idea and sung to the same tune, in
A Pedlar's Pack of Ballads and Songs by W. H. Logan, with these notes:

The hero of the following Ballad is unmistakeably the Honourable Anne
Poulett, who for four successive Parliaments sat as Member for the Borough
of Bridgewater. He was first elected in 1769, when he petitioned against
the election of J. James Viscount Perceval, and claimed the seat; secondly
in 1774; thirdly in 1781, and fourthly in 1784. *See Oldfield's Representative
History*, 8vo. 1816, vol. 4th, pp. 442–3.

In Dodsley's Annual Register, of date 24th March 1784, we find this para-
graph;—"The Right Honourable Charles James Fox was presented by the
Mayor, Aldermen, and capital burgesses, with the freedom of the Borough of
Bridgewater, Somerset; and therewith chosen Recorder for the same, in the
room of Vere Poulett, brother to Anne Poulett, member for the said Borough,"
&c. Two days afterwards, Mr Fox was elected member for the northern
district of the Boroughs in Scotland.

Mr Vere Poulett is the gentleman referred to in the opening stanza, who
"first bought the place." He was one of the members for Bridgewater from
1741 to 1747, when he retired in favour of an elder brother Peregrine. . . .

Hinton House, to which allusion is made in the second stanza, was the
family seat.

The youngest son of the first Earl, and brother of the three last mentioned
Pouletts, was, by command of the Queen, his Godmother, christened Anne.
He was born 11th July 1711, and died 5th July 1785.

The title still exists in the male descendant of Vere, the third Earl. The
family seat is still Hinton St George. . . .

Mr Fox, of whom mention is made in stanza four, being in the spring of
1785 at the Levee, the King passed by him in the Drawing-Room with a
"How do you do, Mr Fox?" and walked on without waiting for an answer.
Fox seeing Lord Mansfield, asked him if his Lordship knew what he had
done to the King that had made his majesty so abrupt and laconic. "My good
friend" (replied Lord Mansfield, with a smile) "if you expect that the king
shall make long speeches to you in the Drawing-Room, you must make short
speeches in St Stephen's Chapel."

THE COURTIER

1. In good Sir Robert's golden days,
   When Brib'ry had no harm in't,
   My brother Vere first bought this place,
   And sought for Court preferment:
   And Hinton House, unto this hour,
   Doth hold it mortal sin, sir,

To side with him that's out of pow'r;
   Or turn from him that's in, sir.
     And this is law, I will maintain,
      Until my dying day, sir,
     Whatever minister shall reign,
      I will be in his pay, sir.

2. When Scottish Councils rul'd this land,
    And tarnish'd England's glory,
  I join'd Lord Bute with heart and hand,
    And was a rank old Tory.
  I stuck by North, when North came in,
    Thro' his Administration,
  Voted with him through thick and thin,
    And help'd to damn the nation.
     And this is law, *etc., etc.*

3. When good Lord Rockingham appeared,
    And honest men looked big, sir;
  With this new wind about I veer'd,
    And would have been a Whig, sir;
  To him I wing'd, and made my Court,
    But found 'twas all in vain, sir,
  He scorned such paltry mean support,
    So I whipp'd back again, sir.
      And this is law, *etc., etc.*

4. When Fox and North at length agreed
    To turn all blunderers out, sir,
  I then, in duty to my creed,
    Once more turned North about, sir,
  Receipt-tax, India-Bill, and all,
    With them I stoutly voted;
  At backstairs' Council learn'd to bawl,
    And secret influence hooted.
      And this is law, *etc., etc.*

5. When North disdained all views of power,
    I left such politicians,
  And turn'd to Thurlow, Pitt, and Gower,
    Yet curs'd all coalitions:
  For this once more the Treasury
    Have backed me at Bridgewater;
  And Master Pitt my man shall be,
    Until the times shall alter.
      And this is law, *etc., etc.*

I can only think what a field day a good student of contemporary politics could have updating these grand old songs.

...wishing her lover good speed

And away, hey...

She crossed the broad prairies...

W

*...the leafy
green dome*

*Can she bake
a cherry pie...*

*As I was going
to Derby...*

THE WABASH CANNONBALL

One of the great all-time favorites of hillbilly-music fans is "The Wabash Cannonball," the Flying Dutchman of hobo lore. And there's probably not one serviceman left over from World War II who is not familiar with it. I've included two popular versions for your choice. The second verse of the first version may be sung as a refrain in either version.

Recordings: Roy Acuff (Columbia, HL 9004); John Greenway (Riverside, RLP 12 619), Pete Seeger (Folkways, FA 2320).

2. Listen to the jingle,
   The rumble and the roar
   As she glides along the woodland,
   Through the hills and by the shore,
   Hear the mighty rush of the engine,
   Hear that lonesome hobo squall,
   You're traveling through the jungles on
   The Wabash Cannonball.

3. She come down from Birmingham
   One cold December day,
   As she rolled into the station,
   You could hear the people say,
   There's a girl from Birmingham,

341

She's long and she is tall,
She come down from Birmingham on
The Wabash Cannonball.

4. Here's to Daddy Claxon,
   May his name forever stand,
   And always be remembered in
   The courts of Alabam,
   His earthly race is over
   And the curtains round him fall,
   We'll carry him home to victory on
   The Wabash Cannonball.

The hobo versions of this song summed up all the places you could hit on the mythical Wabash Cannonball. You might want to switch versions or interpolate some of the hobo verses from the following:

1. Great cities of importance
   We see along the way:
   Chicago and St. Louis,
   Rock Island, so they say.
   Springfield and Decatur,
   Peoria above all.
   You can reach your destination
   On The Wabash Cannonball.

2. This train she runs to Quincy,
   Monroe, and Mexico.
   She runs to Kansas City,
   And she's never running slow.
   She runs right into Denver
   Where she makes an awful squall.
   They all know by the whistle
   She's The Wabash Cannonball.

3. There's many other cities
   That you can go to see:
   St. Paul and Minneapolis,
   Ashtabula, Kankakee,
   The lakes of Minnehaha,
   Where the laughing waters fall;
   You'll reach them by no other
   But The Wabash Cannonball.

4. Now here's to (*insert name*),
   May his name forever stand.
   He'll be honored and respected
   By the hoboes 'cross the land.
   And when his days are over
   And the curtains round him fall,
   We'll ship him off to hell and on
   The Wabash Cannonball.

THE WAGONER'S LAD

According to this popular Anglo-American ballad, a poor girl just hasn't got a chance. First she suffers trying to get a man to marry her, but if she succeeds she's a slave to her husband the rest of her life. Married or not, she can't win.

Verses and ideas have been interchanged so freely between "The Wagoner's Lad," "On Top of Old Smoky," "The Cuckoo," "Rye Whiskey," and other southern mountain songs that it is difficult to decide where to stop. If you took all the verses that have been used in one version or another of "The Wagoner's Lad," there'd be no audience left when you finished. I suggest you use fewer verses than I have included below. If the last verse annoys you as much as it does me, substitute:

> Young ladies, young ladies, take warning from me,
> Never cast your affection on a young man so free.
> He will hug you and kiss you and tell you more lies
> Than the leaves on the green trees or stars in the skies.

The wagoners moved freight around the country before the railroads were built. Their reputation with the ladies is embodied in the ballad.

Recordings: Buell H. Kazee (Folkways, FS 3810); The Kossoy Sisters (Tradition, TLP 1018); Peggy Seeger (Folkways, FA 2049); Pete Seeger (Folkways, FA 2320).

Oh, I am a poor girl, my for-tune's been bad, For a long time I've court-ed the wag-on-er's lad. He court-ed me fair-ly by night and by day, But now he has load-ed and is go-ing a-way.

2. I loved him so dearly, I thought he loved me,
   But now he is leaving, he wants to be free.
   "Go put up your horses and feed them some hay,
   Come sit down beside me for as long as you can stay."

3. "My horses ain't hungry, they won't eat your hay,
   So fare you well darling, I'm going away."
   "It's raining, it's hailing, the moon gives no light,
   Your horses can't travel that dark road tonight."

4. "My horses are harnessed, my whip's in my hand,
   So fare you well, darling, my horses won't stand."
   "Oh, must you then leave me to see you no more,
   To stay here a-weeping on the wild river shore?"

5. "Your parents don't like me, they say I'm too poor,
   They say I ain't worthy to enter your door.
   Yes, your parents are against me and you are the same,
   Dig deep in your heart, dear, and blot out my name."

6. "I know they don't like you, but what do you care?
   For I am your true love and I am your dear,
   And I would have consented your bride for to be,
   But my parents aren't willing for you to have me."

7. "I came to your city to stay for awhile,
   I left my dear parents, went many a mile.
   But you want a freeholder and I have no land.
   Now, that is your true love as I understand.

8. "I earn my own living, my money's my own,
   And if they don't like me, they can leave me alone.
   So early this morning I did then arise
   To cross the wild river with tears in my eyes.

9. "I'm going to Georgia and there I will roam,
   And then I'll make Georgia to be my new home.
   On top yonder mountain I'll look back this way,
   With tears in my eyes my last goodbye I will say."

10. "But when you get to Georgia you'll cry there I fear,
    When you think of the loved one you left waiting here."
    "I'll ride on to Georgia and write you my mind,
    For I mean to marry and leave you behind."

11. And that is the fortune of poor womankind,
    Forever controlled and forever confined,
    Controlled by their parents till they are made wives,
    Then slaves to their husbands the rest of their lives.

WANDERIN'

This blues-oriented ballad expressed the sentiments of many a homeless wanderer who traveled around the country during the depression days of the 1930s. The first verse seems to have something in common with one of the verses from "My God, How the Money Rolls In":

My mother makes beer in the bathtub,
My father makes synthetic gin.
My sister makes fudge for a quarter,
My, God, how the money rolls in.

Alan Lomax cites "Me Father's a Lawyer in England" as a possible source of inspiration for the idea of naming off family occupations to get the song going. A strong lyric and interesting chords make this song a memorable one.

Recordings: Alfred Drake (Decca, DL 8023); Milt Okun (Baton, BL 1203); Walt Robertson (Folkways, FA 2046); Josh White (London, LPB 338); Stan Wilson (Cavalier, Cav 5505 and 6002).

2. I've been a-wanderin'
   Early and late,
   New York City
   To the Golden Gate,
   An' it looks like
   I'm never gonna cease my wanderin'.

3. Been a-workin' in the army,
   Workin' on a farm,
   All I got to show for it
   Is the muscle in my arm,
   An' it looks like
   I'm never gonna cease my wanderin'.

4. Snakes in the ocean,
   Eels in the sea,
   Red-headed woman
   Made a fool out of me,
   An' it looks like
   I'm never gonna cease my wanderin'.

THE WATER IS WIDE

Some of this song is derived from the same old British song ("Waly, Waly") that provided the inspiration for "Must I Go Bound" (see Index). It appears to be a merger of floating verses and another tune.

Recordings: Isla Cameron (Tradition, TLP 1001); John Runge (Riverside, RLP 12 814); Pete Seeger (Folkways, FA 2321).

Oh, the water is wide, I cannot cross over,—
— And neither have I wings to fly.—
— But give me a boat that will carry two,—
— And both shall row, my love and I.—

2. A ship there is and it sails the sea.
   It's loaded deep as deep can be.
   But not so deep as this love I am in,
   I know not how I sink or swim.

3. I put my finger into the bush
   To pluck a rose of fairest kind.
   The thorns they pierced me at a touch,
   And so I left that rose behind.

4. I leaned my back against an oak,
   Thinking that it was a trusty tree.
   But first it bended and then it broke,
   As did my false lord to me.

5. Oh, love is sweet and love is fair,
   Fresh as the dew when first it is new,
   But love grows old and waxeth cold
   And fades away like morning dew.

6. Oh, the water is wide, I cannot cross over.
   And neither have I wings to fly.
   But give me a boat that will carry two,
   And both shall row, my love and I.

WE WISH YOU A MERRY CHRISTMAS

The observance of Christmas dates back to about 200 A.D. and it became the great popular festival of Western Europe during the Middle Ages. The singing of carols at Christmas time is a typically English custom. But the carol is not exclusively a Christmas song, nor is it in any way related to the hymn.

The *carole* was a French round dance which was accompanied by leader-chorus singing in the same manner as other familiar folk music presented in this book. It was most closely associated with the festive celebrations occasioned by the incidence of holy days. Despite the religious impulse and theme of the *caroles*, they were essentially a carry-over of pagan practices and were associated with immorality in general.

From its origin in France, carol singing spread throughout all of Europe, and was well established by the time it became popular in England during the fifteenth century. The church opposed the practice for a long time. The carols spoke in the common language of the people, whereas the hymns of the church were austere and written in a foreign tongue. Ultimately, the carol, without dancing, worked its way into the good graces of the church, and soon carols were being written, both inside and outside the church, for ceremonial occasions.

The sixteenth century brought the Reformation, and the carol was swept out of the sanctuary along with everything else that smacked of "idolatry and superstition." It was then that the practice of singing carols on festive occasions from house to house in minstrel bands grew and flourished. "We Wish You a Merry Christmas" is probably more closely associated with this custom (particularly because of its text) than any other carol we sing at Christmas.

Recordings: Alan Mills (Folkways, FP 709); The Weavers (Vanguard, VRS 9013).

2. Oh, bring us some figgy pudding,
   Oh, bring us some figgy pudding,
   Oh, bring us some figgy pudding,
   With a cup of good cheer.

   As above:

3. We won't go until we get it,
   So bring it out here.

4. We all love our figgy pudding
   With a cup of good cheer.

5. We wish you a merry Christmas
   And a happy New Year.

THE WEE COOPER OF FIFE

This ballad is derived from a much older one, "The Wife Wrapped in Wether's Skin," which, in turn, is known by several similar titles. In *English and Scottish Popular Ballads,* ballad scholar George Lyman Kittredge describes the folk tale "The Wife Wrapped in Morrell's Skin":

> Here a husband, who has put up with a great deal from an excessively restive wife, flays his old horse Morrell and salts the hide, takes the shrew down cellar, and, after a sharp contest for mastery, beats her with birchen rods till she swoons, then wraps her in the salted hide: by which process the woman is perfectly reformed.

In one of the versions collected by Francis James Child, the words are:

> He took the skin and laid it on his wife's back,
> And with a good stick went whikety whack.

In the version below, the Wee Cooper settles for the threat "I'll no be shamin' your gentle kin, but I will skelp my ain sheepskin." And that, he obviously believes, is enough to do the trick.

Recordings: Marilyn Child and Glenn Yarbrough (Elektra, EKL 143); Burl Ives (Columbia, CL 6109); Ewan MacColl and A. L. Lloyd (Riverside, RLP 12 623).

There was a wee coop-er who lived in Fife,

Nick-e-ty, nack-e-ty, noo, noo, noo; And he had got-ten a

gen-tle wife, Hey, wil-ly wal-lack-y,

hey, John Doug-al, A-lane, quo rush-e-ty, roo, roo, roo.

348

2. She would na bake nor would she brew,
   For spilin' o' her comely hue.

3. She would na caird nor would she spin,
   For shamin' o' her gentle kin.

4. The cooper has gone to his woo' pack,
   And he's laid a sheep's skin on his wife's back.

5. "I'll no be shamin' your gentle kin,
   But I will skelp my ain sheepskin."

6. "O I will bake and I will brew,
   And think nae mair o' my comely hue.

7. "O I will wash and I will spin,
   And think nae mair o' my gentle kin."

8. A' ye what hae gotten a gentle wife,
   Send ye for the wee cooper o' Fife.

WHERE ARE YOU GOING, MY GOOD OLD MAN?

Songs like "Buffalo Boy," "There's a Hole in My Bucket," and this one provide great material for a boy and a girl to team up for a comedy routine. Ad libbing or rehearsed patter and horseplay between the verses is customary. You may also want to work out some personalized verses of your own. One of the verses in my version grew out of an early-morning incident with my sleepy-headed wife: half-awake and out of butter, she anointed my eggs with vinegar instead of the cooking-oil substitute she thought she was using.

Recordings: Burl Ives (Decca, DL 5013); Jean Ritchie and Oscar Brand (Elektra, EKL 22).

Spoken: Goin' to the saloon where I always go.

2. Oh, why are you goin' there, my good old man?
   Why are you goin' there, my honey lovey lamb?
   Oh, why are you goin' there, my good old man,
   The best old man in the world?
   Spoken: To get drunk like I always do.

   Continue, as above:

3. Won't you go after supper, my good old man?
   Spoken: All right, if you'll quit jawin' and fix it.

4. Oh, what'll you have for supper, my good old man
   Spoken: A bushel full of eggs like I always have.

5. How do you want 'em cooked, my good old man?
   Spoken: Fry 'em in vinegar like you always do.

6. Ain't you afraid they'll kill you, my good old man?
   Spoken: I don't care if they do.

7. Where shall I bury you, my good old man?
   Spoken: In the chimney corner where you always do.

8. Ain't you afraid of sniffin' ashes, my good old man?
   Spoken: I don't care if I do.

9. Why do you want to be buried there, my good old man?
   Spoken: So I can ha'nt you.

10. A ha'nt can't ha'nt a ha'nt, my good old man.
    A ha'nt can't ha'nt a ha'nt, my honey lovey lamb.
    A ha'nt can't ha'nt a ha'nt, my good old man;
    Meanest old devil in the world.

WHISTLE, DAUGHTER, WHISTLE

This plot, and variations on it, occurs in several humorous songs that have been found in Europe and America. For instance, there are a German, a Flemish, and a French round from the fifteenth or sixteenth century, in which a nun or a monk is tempted to dance by similar offers. A similar gimmick is used in "The Deaf Woman's Courtship," in which a woman is suddenly able to hear clearly and distinctly when the right questions are asked:

Old woman, old woman, will you go a-shearing?
Speak a little louder, sir, I'm rather hard of hearing.

Old woman, old woman, are you good at weaving?
Speak a little louder, sir, my hearing is deceiving.

Old woman, old woman, will you go a-walking?
Speak a little louder, sir, or what's the use in talking.

Old woman, old woman, will you let me court you?
Speak a little louder, sir, I just begin to hear you.

Old woman, old woman, may I kiss you dearly?
Lord have mercy on my soul, now I hear you clearly!

Recordings: A. L. Lloyd (Riverside, RLP 12 614); Jean Murai (Stinson, SLP 75); Peggy Seeger (Folkways, FA 2049); Ellen Stekert (Stinson, SLP 49).

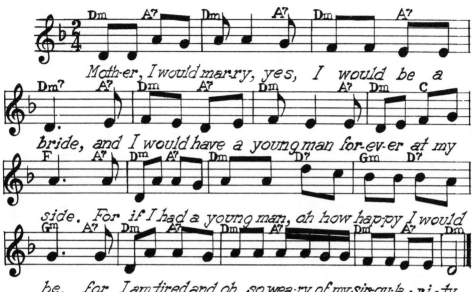

Mother, I would marry, yes, I would be a bride, and I would have a young man for-ev-er at my side. For if I had a young man, oh how happy I would be, for I am tired and oh, so wea-ry of my sin-gu-la-ri-ty.

2. "Whistle, daughter, whistle, and you shall have a cow."
"I cannot whistle, mother, I guess I don't know how.
But if I had a young man, oh, how happy I would be,
For I am tired and so weary of my propriety."

3. "Whistle, daughter, whistle, and you shall have a sheep."
"I cannot whistle mother, I can only weep.
But if I had a young man, oh, how happy I would be,
For I am tired and oh, so weary of my virginity."

4. "Whistle, daughter, whistle, and you shall have a man."
"I cannot whistle, mother, . . ." (*whistles*)
"You impudent little daughter, what makes you whistle now?"
"I'd rather whistle for a man than for a sheep or cow."

In some versions the mother puts the daughter down at this point, but the daughter still has the last word:

"You nasty impudent Jane; I'll pull your courage down.
Take off your silks and satins and put on your working gown.
I'll send you to the fields, a-tossing of the hay,
With your fork and rake the hay to make; and then hear what you say."

"Mother, don't be so cruel, to send me to the fields
Where young men will entice me and to them I may yield.
For mother, it's quite well-known I am not too young grown.
And it is a pity a maid so pretty as I should lay alone."

351

WHEN THE SAINTS
GO MARCHING IN

"The Saints," perhaps as much as any song of Negro origin, represents the transition from the spiritual to jazz. It was a favorite of Dixieland groups, and remains a favorite of jazz musicians, whether cool or hot. It's a staple item for audience participation in singing. Just call out the new line for each verse at the end of the previous verse. If this doesn't work, repeat the first verse as a chorus frequently.

Recording: The Weavers (Vanguard, VRS 9010).

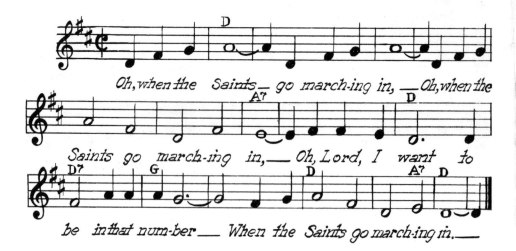

2. And when the revelation comes,
   And when the revelation comes,
   Oh, Lord, I want to be in that number,
   When the revelation comes.

   Continue, as above:

3. Oh, when the new world is revealed.
4. Oh, when they gather 'round the throne
5. And when they crown Him King of Kings.
6. And when the sun no more will shine.
7. And when the moon has turned to blood.
8. And when the earth has turned to fire.
9. And on that hallelujah day.
10. Oh, when the Saints go marching in.

For those who are brave enough to defy convention and risk the wrath of those who wish to hear or sing only familiar texts, a somewhat different version of "The Saints" is provided below. Many of us who have been worn down by frequent performances of this song will enjoy the Bahamian words, which appeared in *The Island Song Book.*

WHEN THE SAINTS GO MARCHING HOME

Oh, I had a dar-ling sis-ter,— She's dead an' gone be-fore. An' I'd like to meet her in the num-bers— When the Saints go march-ing home. When the Saints— go march-ing home, When the Saints go march-ing home, Oh, I'd like to meet her in the num-bers When the Saints go march-ing home.

Continue, as above:

2. **Oh, I had a darling brother.**

3. **Oh, I had a darling mother.**

4. **Oh, I had a darling father.**

WHISKEY JOHNNY

For hoisting yards and other heavy pulling work, the halyard chanteys were called upon. One of them, "Whiskey Johnny," was popular for both its praise and deprecation of drinking, and as a suggestion to the skipper to break out a reward for his men. You'll notice similarities between verses in this song and those in "Rye Whiskey" and other landsman folk songs.

Recordings: Oscar Brand (Riverside, RLP 12 630); Paul Clayton (Folkways, FA 2106); A. L. Lloyd (Tradition, TLP 1026).

Oh, whis-key is the life of man, Whis-key John-ny! Oh,
I'll drink whis-key when I can, Oh, whis-key for my John-ny!

2. Whiskey makes me pawn my clothes,
   Whiskey Johnny,
   And whiskey gave me this red nose,
   Whiskey for my Johnny.

3. Oh, whiskey killed my poor old dad,
   Whiskey Johnny,
   And whiskey drove my mother mad,
   Whiskey for my Johnny.

4. Oh, whiskey up and whiskey down,
   Whiskey Johnny,
   And whiskey all around the town,
   Whiskey for my Johnny.

5. I drink whiskey and my wife drinks gin,
   Whiskey Johnny,
   And the way she drinks it is a sin,
   Whiskey for my Johnny.

6. My wife and I cannot agree,
   Whiskey Johnny,
   For she drinks whiskey in her tea,
   Whiskey for my Johnny.

Additional verses, sung as above:

I had a girl, her name was Lize,
She put whiskey in her pies.

Whiskey's gone and I'll go, too,
For without whiskey I can't do.

Oh, some likes gin and some likes beer,
I wish I had a barrel here.

If whiskey was a river and I could swim,
I'd say here goes and dive right in.

Oh, whiskey straight and whiskey strong,
We'll raise the yard to this old song.

I drink it hot and I drink it cold,
I drink it new and I drink it old.

Oh, bring a glass to the chanteyman,
In a glass or cup or an old tin can.

Here comes the cook with a whiskey can,
And a glass of grog for everyman.

A glass of grog for everyman,
And a bottle full for the chanteyman.

WHISKEY IN THE JAR
(Kilgary Mountain)

This is an American version of an Irish street ballad. In American versions the title, or at least the point of reference, often is the "Gilgary" or "Kilgary" Mountain—probably a mistaken, or folk-adapted, reference to the far-famed Kerry Mountains of Ireland (since there is no Gilgary or Kilgary Mountain in Ireland). In the Kingdom of Kerry you will find some of the most beautiful country in the world: a profusion of peninsulas surrounded by a rugged, restless sea; lakes and glens; and towering, majestic mountains. Jenny, not Molly, is the deceiving woman in most Irish versions. And in the Irish songs our rakish hero fails to escape from the law when he is caught.

With all the above facts at hand you might try reweaving the lyric into a version that would be more widely appreciated in Killarney. Replace "Gilgary" with "Kerry" in the first line, let Jenny take Molly's place, and throw out verses four and five in favor of:

> And if anyone can help me it's my brother in the army.
> If I only knew his station, it's in Cork or Killarney.
> And if he'd come and join me we'd go rovin' in Kilkenny.
> I know he'd treat me fairer than my darlin', sportin' Jenny.

An Australian version introduces still another mountain and ties in the story with Australian history. Sir Frederick Pottinger was police inspector for the Lachlan gold field in New South Wales. Because he tried to put down bushranging (outlawry), he became a frequent target for bushrangers and satirists; he died in 1865 when one of his own pistols accidentally exploded.

> As I was a-crossin' the Abercrombie Mountains,
> I met Sir Frederick Pottinger, and his money he was countin'.
> I first drew me blunderbuss and then I drew me sabre,
> Sayin', "Stand and deliver-oh! for I'm your bold decayver."
> With my mush-a-ring-a-dah,
> Ri-tooral-addy-ah
> Ri-tooral-addy-ah
> There's whiskey in the jar.

> I robbed him of his money; it was a pretty penny,
> I robbed him of it all and I took it home to Jenny;
> I took it home to Jenny and I thought she'd ne'er deceive me.
> Oh, the divil's in the wimmin for they never can be aisy.

Some versions are more elegant and serve the "whiskey in the bar."

Recordings: The Clancy Brothers (Elektra, EKL 249); Patrick Galvin (Riverside, RLP 12 613); Ewan MacColl (Riverside, RLP 12 632). Variations: "Kilgary Mountain": Burl Ives (Decca, DL 8444). "Gilgarry Mountain": Frank Warner (Elektra EKLP 3).

355

As I was a-go-in' o-ver Gilgary Moun-tain, I
met Colo-nel Pep-per and his mon-ey he was count-in'. I
drew forth my pis-tol and I rattled out my sa-bre say-ing;
"Stand and de-liv-er for I am a bold de-ceiv-er."
CHORUS
Mush-a-rig-gum dur-um dye. Whack fol di dad-dy-o,
Whack fol di dad-dy-o, There's whis-key in the jar.

2. Those gold and silver coins they sure did look inviting;
So I picked up the money and I took it home to Molly.
She promised and she swore that she never would deceive me;
But the Devil's in the women and they never can be easy.
Chorus.

3. When I awoke, 'twas between six and seven,
The guards they were around me, in numbers odd and even.
I sprang for my pistols, but alas I was mistaken;
For Molly took my pistols and a prisoner I was taken.
Chorus.

4. They threw me in jail, without a judge or writin',
For robbin' Colonel Pepper on that damn Gilgary Mountain.
But they didn't take my fists, so I knocked the sentry down,
And bid a fond farewell to that jail in Salem town.
Chorus.

5. Now, some take delight in fishing and in bowling,
Others take delight in the carriages a-rolling.
But I take delight in the juice of the barley,
And courtin' pretty maidens in the morning, bright and early.
Chorus.

WHO'S GONNA SHOE
YOUR PRETTY LITTLE FOOT?

A few centuries back the British were singing about "The Lass of Roch Royal" like this:

O who will shoe my bonny foot?
Or who will glove my hand?
Or who will bind my middle jimp
With the broad lily band.

The lass was worried about who was going to look after her while "love Gregor" was many a mile away. During the next thirty or forty verses, depending on the strength and resources of both singer and audience, the lass would go looking for Gregor, find his home, and get turned away by his "false" mother, and die in a shipwreck on her broken-hearted way back home. When Gregor got wind of what had happened, he went after his Anny but was unable to catch up until he saw her with his young son in her arms "baith tossed aboon the tide." After he paused to "wrang his hands" he "catched her by the yellow hair an drew her to the strand, but cauld an stiff was every limb before he reached the land."

Singers today have cut out all of these details and dropped the ballad form entirely. The've taken the first couple of verses from this ballad and used them as floating lyric material. They show up as the first two verses in this popular song from southern mountain country.

Recordings: Alfred Deller (Vanguard, VRS 1001); Shep Ginandes (Elektra, EKL 7); Herta Marshall (Folkways, FA 2333); Milt Okun and Ellen Stekert (Riverside, RLP 12 634).

Who's gonna shoe your pretty little foot?
Who's gonna glove your hand? Who's gonna
kiss your red ruby lips? Who's gonna be your man?
Who's gonna be your man? Who's gonna be your man?
Who's gonna kiss your red ruby lips? Who's gonna be your man?

2. Papa's gonna shoe my pretty little foot,
   Mama's gonna glove my hand.
   Sister's gonna kiss my red ruby lips,
   I don't need no man,
   I don't need no man,
   I don't need no man.
   Sister's gonna kiss my red ruby lips,
   I don't need no man.

3. The longest train I ever did see
   Was a hundred coaches long.
   The only woman I ever did love
   Was on that train and gone,
   Was on that train and gone,
   Was on that train and gone.
   The only woman I ever did love
   Was on that train and gone.

WHOOPEE TI YI YO

In *The Log of a Cowboy,* Andy Adams describes an unusual all-night drive to get across a long stretch of dry land:

> . . . . Within a short time, someone in the lead wig-wagged his lantern; it was answered by the light in the rear, and the next minute the old rear song — "Ip-e-la-ago, go 'long little doggie, You'll make a beef-steer by-and-by" — reached us riders in the swing, and we knew the rear guard of cattle was being pushed forward. . . .
>
> . . . Trailing by moonlight was a novelty to all of us, and in the stillness of those splendid July nights we could hear the point men chatting across the lead in front, while well in the rear, the rattling of our heavily loaded wagon and the whistling of the horse wrangler to his charges reached our ears. The swing men were scattered so far apart there was no chance for conversation amongst us, but every once in a while a song would be started, and as it surged up and down the line, every voice, good, bad, and indifferent, joined in. Singing is supposed to have a soothing effect on cattle, though I will vouch for the fact that none of our Circle Dots stopped that night to listen to our vocal efforts.

Slim Critchlow, of Berkeley, California, formerly a working cowboy in Utah, sings cowboy songs the way they were sung by the "real" cowboys. Ever since I first heard him, I haven't been satisfied with the tame, prettified renditions of cowboy songs as they are typically performed. As Slim says, "There was never a bunch of cows driven anywhere without somebody behind them a-whoopin' and a-yellin'."

The surest way to kill this song is to sing the written text verbatim. When Slim Critchlow sings this song "like it ought to be sung," he uses without restraint — and in a manner that is impossible to describe in print — the yells that come naturally to him: "Hee hi!" "Hippeeee!" "Yippee ti ay ay!" "Hee hoo!"

Recordings: Woody Guthrie and Cisco Houston (Folkways, FA 2484); John A. Lomax, Jr. (Folkways, FG 3508); Frank Luther (Decca, DL 5035); Pete Seeger (Folkways, FA 2003).

As I was a-walkin' one morning for pleasure, I
spied a cow-punch-er a-rid-ing a-long, His hat was throwed back and his
spurs was a-jing-ling, And as he ap-proached he was sing-in' this song;
Whoo-pee ti yi yo,— git a-long lit-tle do-gies, It's your mis-for-tune and
none of my own; Whoo-pee ti yi yo,— git a-long lit-tle do-gies, You
know that Wy-om-ing will be your new home.

2. It's early in spring that we round up the dogies,
   And mark 'em and brand 'em and bob off their tails;
   We round up our horses and load the chuck wagon,
   And then throw the dogies out onto the trail.

3. It's whoopin' and yellin' and a-drivin' them dogies,
   Oh, how I wish that you would go on;
   It's a-whoopin' and punchin' and go on-a, little dogies,
   For you know Wyoming is to be your new home.

4. Some cowboys go up the trail just for pleasure,
   But that's where they get it most awfully wrong,
   For nobody knows what trouble they give us,
   As we go driving them all along.

WILDWOOD FLOWER

This famous mountain tune has long been a favorite of backwoods guitar
pickers. When a guitar player graduates from using simple strums in accom-
panying songs and begins to explore the fascinating world of melody picking,
"Wildwood Flower" is often the first song he tries. The tune is especially

easy to pick out on the guitar in the key of C, because so many notes fall on open strings, strings fretted to form the chord, and neighboring frets. For those who wish to try, I am including in this section a simple arrangement in tablature. The lines of the tablature represent the six strings of the guitar (in this order from top to bottom: E, B, G, D, A, E). The numbers above the tablature represent the frets to be depressed. The letters above represent the chords to be depressed. The letters and arrows below the tablature tell you what strum to use. "T" indicates a thumb pluck—as part of a bass run. An arrow gives the direction of a finger scratch. An "H" specifies a hammer-on. The notes on the tablature mark the strings to be played. If you need additional help, see *The Folksingers Guitar Guide* by Jerry Silverman and listen to the Folkways record, by Pete Seeger, on which the *Guide* is based.

The lyric of this song may seem a little soupy to some; apparently it struck Woody Guthrie that way, for he ignored the words altogether when he borrowed the tune for his World War II diaster ballad, "Reuben James."

Recordings: Joan Baez (Vanguard, VRS 9078); The Carter Family (Harmony, HL 7280); Eugene and Veronica Cox (Folkways, FA 2314); Lester Flatt and Earl Scruggs (Columbia, CL 1664); Mickey Miller (Folkways, FA 2393); Artus Moser (Folkways, FA 2112); Tom Paley (Elektra, EKL 12); Obray Ramsey (Riverside, RLP 12 649). Variation: "Reuben James": Pete Seeger (Disc, D 101).

I will twine with your min-gles of ra-ven black hair, With the ros-es so red and the lil-ies so fair, With myr-tle as bright as the em-e-rald dew, The pale and the lyd-er and eyes of light blue.

2. Oh, he promised to love me; he promised to love;
   And to cherish me always all others above.
   I woke from my dream and my idol was clay;
   My passion for loving had vanished away.

3. Oh, he taught me to love him; he called me his flower;
   A blossom to cheer him through life's weary hour.
   But now he is gone and left me alone;
   The wild flowers to weep and the wild birds to mourn.

4. I'll dance and I'll sing and my life shall be gay;
   I'll charm every heart in the crowd I survey.
   Though my heart now is breaking he never shall know
   How his name makes me tremble, my pale cheeks to glow.

5. I'll dance and I'll sing and my heart will be gay;
   I'll banish this weeping; drive troubles away.
   I'll live yet to see him regret this dark hour
   When he won and neglected this frail wildwood flower.

WILLIE THE WEEPER

Willie the Weeper is the most famous legendary "hero" of dope addiction. His song has been around, in many versions, for just about as long as "Frankie and Johnnie." Vance Randolph, the well-known collector of Ozark folk songs, remembers hearing it in a Kansas coal camp in 1908. In the 1920s the *Adventure* magazine's "Old Songs That Men Have Sung" department received thirty versions with about a hundred different verses, and variations have appeared here and there in many popular song books and on records. In the 1930s, Cab Calloway popularized a Broadway adaptation entitled "Minnie the Moocher"; but it failed to pass the test of time and faded away—while Willie continued to weep.

The two most popular tunes to which the song is sung are both presented here, so you can pick the one you like best. Feel free to depart from either of these melodies and to adapt to the natural accents of the verses, in which considerable variation takes place. The chorus in the first tune version is optional. You may wish to omit the chorus entirely or sing it only with the first, last, or an occasional verse, particularly if you decide on a longer version for performance. The song calls for a slow, syncopated, blues-style (or, as Carl Sandburg says, "insinuating") accompaniment. (I've also included the lyric version "Cocaine Lil" for distaff singers.)

In the established tradition, Willie dreams of amorous adventures and high living—going places, doing things, and getting rich quick. He hobnobs with kings, sultans, and potentates. His love affairs include women of note from Cleopatra and the Queen of Sheba to movie actresses. He wins millions gambling and lights his pipe with hundred-dollar bills. You may create further adventures for Willie by turning your imagination loose on the contemporary scene, history, or your own friends and surroundings. It's high time someone came up with adventures in outer space, scientific explorations, involvement in international intrigue, and affairs with contemporary sex symbols. I'd hate to think that all the action ended for him twenty or thirty years ago.

Recording: Sam Hinton (Decca, DL 8418).

Note: The optional chorus (see headnotes) is arranged here for audience participation. For solo performance omit the responses in the third and fourth, seventh and eighth, eleventh and twelfth, and fifteenth and sixteenth measures.

He had the hab-it and he had it bad.___

Lis-ten while I tell you 'bout the dream he had.___

CHORUS

Teet tee dee dee dee.__ (Teet tee dee dee dee.)__

Toot too doo doo doo.__ (Toot too doo doo doo.)__Yah dah

dah dee dah (Yah dah dah dee dah.) Yah yah yah.(Yah yah yah.)

2. He went to a hop house the other night,
   Where the lights were always shining bright.
   I guess he smoked a dozen pills or more.
   When he woke up he was on a foreign shore.

3. The Queen of Sheba was the first he met.
   She called him her darlin' and her lovin' pet.
   She gave him a fancy automobile
   With a diamond headlight and a golden wheel.

4. He landed with a splash in the river Nile,
   A-ridin' a sea-goin' crocodile.
   He winked at Cleopatra—she said, "Ain't he a sight!
   How about a date for next Saturday night?"

5. He went to Monte Carlo where he played roulette.
   He couldn't lose a penny and he won every bet.
   He played and he played till the bank went broke.
   Then he turned around and took another smoke.

6. He went off to Turkey by special request.
   He stayed seven years as the Sultan's guest.
   But when he got in with that harem crew,
   What was a poor fellow like Willie to do?

7. He had a million cattle and he had a million sheep.
   He had a million vessels on the ocean deep.
   He had a million dollars all in nickles and dimes.
   Well—he knew it 'cause he'd counted them a million times.

8. He landed in New York one evening late.
   He asked his sugar to make a late date.
   He started to kiss her then he made her pout.
   When bing bang bing, the dope gave out.

9. Now, this is the story of Willie the Weeper.
   He's got a job as a chimney sweeper.
   Someday a pill too many he will take,
   And dreaming he's dead he'll forget to awake.

Here are some additional verses on Willie's gambling exploits, more or less in sequence:

He rolled and he smoked about a million pills.
He said, "These'll cure all my aches and ills."
It wasn't long until he fell asleep,
And dreamed he was sailing on the ocean deep.

He played draw poker as he left the land,
And won a million dollars on the very first hand.
He played and he played until the crew went broke.
Then he turned around and took another smoke.

He sailed till he came to the isle of Siam.
He rubbed his eyes and said, "I wonder where I am?"
Played craps with the king and won a million more.
Then he left for Monte Carlo when the king got sore.

He played gin rummy with the King of Iran.
He busted the king with the very first hand.
When he looked around and everybody was broke.
He bought a million dollars worth of hop to smoke.

Here are some additional miscellaneous verses and a different ending for you to pick and choose from to develop your own version:

Down in Honolulu Willie fell into a trance
Watching the dusky beauties do a hula-hula dance.
His sweety got in jail, and Willie sure did shout
When he got the news that she had wriggled out.

He bought an ocean liner, all his own,
He loaded it with money and he started to roam.
He said he'd let it go until it wants to stop,
While he counts his money and he smokes his hop.

Then he went to Paris to buy up all the wine.
For a whole carload he paid a measly dime.
He bought a ruby bush and a diamond tree,
And a whole lot of friends to keep him company.

One day while Willie took a quiet smoke,
The ship struck a rock and Willie awoke.
His money was gone and his dream was o'er.
Now he's sweepin' chimneys like he was before.

The first three verses are provided for the second tune version along with a different ending. You will have to borrow verses from the first version to complete the song, and adapt them to the melodic variation.

Did you ev-er hear the stor-y of Wil-lie the Weep-er?—

Wil-lie the Weep-er was a chim-ney sweep-er.

Had the dope hab-it and he had it bad.—

Lis-ten while I tell you 'bout the dream he had.—

Around a lay-out table a couple of hop-fiends lay.
Listen and I'll tell you what they had to say:
Tales of the money they were goin' to make
And faro banks they were goin' to break.

Oh, Willie was the biggest dreamer of them all.
Dreamin' that the world was at his beck and call.
When he had smoked a dozen pills or more
He dreamed he was living on a foreign shore.

Insert verses from first version.

Now you've heard the story of Willie the Weeper.
Willie the Weeper was a chimney sweeper.
Went to sleep on his hall-room flop
And dreamed he had a million dollars worth of hop.

COCAINE LIL

"Cocaine Lil" may have been invented by someone to provide a female counterpart to Willie. It may be sung to either tune given for "Willie the Weeper."

Did you ever hear about Cocaine Lil?
She lived in a house on a cocaine hill.
She had a cocaine dog and a cocaine cat.
They fought all night with a cocaine rat.

She had cocaine hair on her cocaine head.
She had a cocaine dress that was poppy red.
But the cocaine blues, they made her sad.
Oh, the cocaine blues they made her feel bad.

She went to a snow party one cold night.
The way she sniffed it was a fright.
There was Hophead Mag with Dopey Slim,
Kankakee Liz and Ye She Jim.

Along in the morning 'bout half-past three,
They were all lit up like a Christmas tree.
Lil went home and started for bed;
She took another sniff and it knocked her dead.

They laid her out in her cocaine clothes.
She wore a snowbird hat with a crimson rose.
And they wrote on her tombstone this refrain:
"She died as she lived, sniffing cocaine."

THE WILLOW GARDEN

Although it has a story similar to other murder ballads of Irish and English origin, "The Willow Garden," also known as "Rose Connelly," seems to have originated in America. (For melodic source see Index for "Acres of Clams.")

Recordings: Paul Clayton (Riverside, RLP 12 615); Ian and Sylvia (Vanguard, VRS 9104); The Kossoy Sisters (Tradition, TLP 1018); Herta Marshall (Folkways, FA 2333); Harry and Jeanie West (Stinson, SLP 36).

2. I stabbed her with my dagger,
   Which was a bloody knife.
   I threw her in the river,
   Which was a dreadful sight.
   My father often told me
   How money would set me free,
   If I did murder that dear little girl
   Whose name was Rose Connelly.

3. Now he stands in his cabin door,
   Watching with grieving eyes,
   Watching his only son
   Mounting the scaffold so high.
   My race is run beneath the sun
   And hell awaits for me,
   For I did murder that dear little girl
   Whose name was Rose Connelly.

You may replace the last four lines of the last stanza with this warning to young ladies that appears in some versions:

Come all of you young ladies
And take this warning from me,
Don't never sit a-courtin'
Down under the willow tree.

THE WILLOW TREE

"The Willow Tree" is the most popular American version (particularly with college students) of the famous British ballad, also included here, "Lady Isabel and the Elf-Knight." It tells the story of how a bright young maiden turned the tables on a would-be Bluebeard-type thrill killer. The symbolic use of the willow tree in British songs probably reflects an ancient belief that the soul passes into a living tree at death.

Recordings: Paul Clayton (Stinson, SLP 70); Richard Dyer-Bennet (Decca, DLP 5046).

There was a youth, a cru-el youth; He lived be-side the sea.— Six love-ly maid-ens he drown-ed there By the lone-ly wil-low tree.—

367

2. As he went out with Sally Brown,
   And they walked by the sea,
   An evil thought it came to him
   By that lonely willow tree.

3. "Now turn your back to the waterside,
   Your face to the willow tree;
   Six pretty maidens I've drownded them here,
   And you the seventh shall be."

4. "But first take off your golden gown,
   Take off your gown," said he;
   "For though I am going to murder you,
   I would not spoil your finery."

5. "Then turn around, you false young man,
   Then turn around," said she;
   "For it is not proper that such a youth
   A naked woman should see."

6. Then 'round he turned, that false young man,
   Around about turned he,
   And seizing him boldly in both her arms,
   She cast him into the sea.

7. "Lie there, lie there, you false young man,
   Lie there, lie there," said she;
   "For six pretty maidens you've drownded them here.
   Go, keep them company."

8. He sank beneath the icy waves,
   He sank down into the sea;
   No living thing wept a tear for him
   Save that lonely willow tree.

Here is the traditional version of "Lady Isabel and the Elf-Knight" as it is sung without accompaniment:

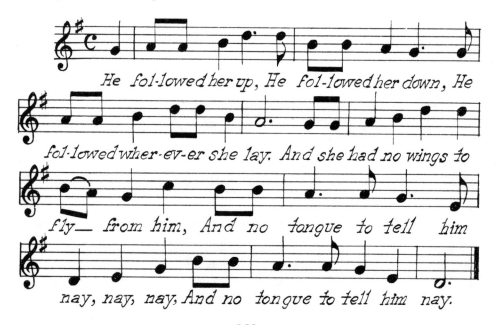

He fol-lowed her up, He fol-lowed her down, He fol-lowed wher-ev-er she lay. And she had no wings to fly__ from him, And no tongue to tell him nay, nay, nay, And no tongue to tell him nay.

2. She got on her pony, her pony of brown;
   He got on the iron-gray.
   They rode till they came to the blue-water sea
   At the end of a long summer day, day, day,
   At the end of a long summer day.

Continue, as above:

3. "Get down, get down, my pretty young Miss,
   Get down, these words I say.
   For here I've drownded eight maidens fair,
   And you the ninth shall be.

4. "Pull off, pull off, your fine silken gown,
   And lay it on yonder stone,
   For it cost your father much too much
   To rot in the salt sea foam."

5. "Turn your face around and about,
   And look at the leaves on the tree,
   For it is not right that a man like you
   A naked lady should see."

6. She picked him up and she plunged him in,
   He sank to the depths of the sea.
   "Lie there, lie there, you false-hearted man,
   Lie there instead of me."

An anticlimax occurs in "The Outlandish Knight" version included in Frank Kidson's supplement to Chappell's *Old English Popular Music.* After she has drowned the would-be killer, the resourceful young lady rides away:

> She mounted on her milk-white steed,
> And led the dapple grey;
> She rode till she came to her own father's hall,
> Three hours before it was day.
>
> The parrot being in the window so high,
> Hearing the lady, did say:
> "I'm afraid that some ruffian has led you astray,
> That you have tarried so long away."
>
> "Don't prittle nor prattle, my pretty parrot,
> Nor tell any tales of me;
> And thy cage shall be made of glittering gold,
> Although it is made of the tree!"
>
> The king being in the chamber so high,
> And hearing the parrot, did say—
> "What ails you, what ails you, my pretty parrot,
> That you prattle so long before day?"
>
> "It's no laughing matter," the parrot did say,
> "That so loudly I call unto thee;
> For the cats have got into the windows so high,
> And I'm afraid they will have me."
>
> "Well turned, well turned, my pretty parrot,
> Well turned, well turned for me;
> Thy cage shall be made of the glittering gold,
> And the door of the best ivory."

THE WINNSBORO COTTON MILL BLUES

When an immigrant English mechanic named Samuel Slater built a yarn-making mill in Pawtucket, Rhode Island, in 1798, he started the modern American textile industry—and, in fact, the industrialization of our country. Before his venture the British had a half-century lead, and a virtual monopoly, in mechanization. Slater's first employees were nine children under twelve years of age. He set a pattern, borrowed from England, for using child labor for long hours. By 1820 half the textile industry labor force was composed of children under eleven, and the other half was made up mostly of women from farms. Many of the mills were located in mining areas and in the South. The work was monotonous, and 75-hour weeks were common. Extensive labor unrest—and therefore, an abundance of protest songs—naturally resulted from these conditions.

This song uses several technical terms and refers to a traditional folk belief: A spool is a reel used to wind yarn. A knotter is used to tie the ends of the yarn together. A doffer is the worker who takes filled bobbins from spinning frames.

A man who steals the coppers from a dead man's eyes has long been considered the lowest form of thief. This is one of the curiosities of folk beliefs. The folk have often sung in praise and admiration of those who take dollars from the living. Why is it worse, then, to take money from a man who cannot use it? The practice of closing a dead man's eyes is ancient. There is a reference to this custom in Genesis (46:4). The large English copper coin or penny existed long before the smaller American penny, and this saying probably originated with English coin and custom. Taking candy from a baby refers to ease rather than baseness of crime and is evidently more respected in folk traditions. In more modern times, as conspicuous consumption has become more and more the practice of a status-seeking society, the ante has been upped. The nickel replaced the penny in "Winnsboro Cotton Mill Blues" at a time when a nickel would buy a coke or an Eskimo Pie. According to *Reveille in Washington* by Margaret Leech, when Lincoln died, a doctor laid half-dollars on his eyelids.

Recordings: Pete Seeger (Folkways, FH 5251). There is also a Library of Congress recording of this song made by Bill Wolff at the Southern School for Workers in North Carolina in 1939.

He'd take the nickels off a dead mans eyes to buy Co-ca Cola and Es-ki-mo pies.— I got the blues,— I got the blues,— I got the Winns-bo-ro cotton mill blues.— Lor-dy, Lor-dy, spool-in's hard. You know and I know, I don't have to tell you work for Tom Wat-son, well, you work like hell.— I got the blues,— I got the blues,— I got the Winns-bo-ro cotton mill blues.

2. When I die, don't bury me at all,
   Just hang me up on the spool-room wall;
   Place a knotter in my hand,
   So I can spool in the Promised Land.

3. When I die, don't bury me deep,
   Bury me down on Six Hundred Street.
   Place a bobbin in each hand,
   So I can doff in the Promised Land.

WORRIED MAN BLUES

When hillbilly singers came into contact with Negro blues, songs like this one began to emerge. The verses make it seem likely that the song originated with someone on a chain gang. And this may well be how it started. But once the famous Carter Family of singers got hold of it, the hillbillies took over and made it one of their own. Later on the folk revivalists picked it up, too.

Recordings: The Carter Family (Harmony, HL 7280); Lester Flatt and Earl Scruggs (Columbia, CL 1664); Cisco Houston (Folkways, FA 2013); Ed McCurdy (Dawn, DLP 1127).

371

It takes a wor-ried man to sing a wor-ried song, It takes a wor-ried man to sing a wor-ried song, It takes a wor-ried man to sing a wor-ried song. I'm wor-ried now ____ but I won't be wor-ried long. ____

2. I went across the river and I lay down to sleep. (*3 times*)
When I awoke there were shackles on my feet.

3. Twenty-one links of chain wrapped around my leg. (*3 times*)
And on each link an initial of my name.

4. I asked the judge what might be my fine. (*3 times*)
Twenty-one years on the R. C. mountain line.

5. Twenty-one long years to pay my awful crime. (*3 times*)
Twenty-one years, but I got ninety-nine.

6. The train arrived, sixteen coaches long. *(3 times)*
The girl I love is on that train and gone.

7. I looked down the track as far as I could see. (*3 times*)
Little bitty hand was waving after me.

8. If anyone should ask you who composed this song. (*3 times*)
Tell 'em it was me and I sing it all day long.

9. It takes a worried man to sing a worried song. (*3 times*)
I'm worried now but I won't be worried long.

...wishing her lover good speed

And away, hey...

She crossed the broad prairies...

Y

*...the leafy
green dome*

*Can she bake
a cherry pie...*

*As I was going
to Derby...*

YOUNG CHARLOTTE

Phillips Barry, the prominent New England folklorist, traced this early American ballad to "A Corpse Going to a Ball" by Seba Smith, published in *The Rover* in 1843. The author evidently based the ballad on an incident reported in the religious column of *The New York Observer* of February 8, 1840, in which a girl was said to have frozen to death while riding to a ball on a bitterly cold night.

Recording: Ed McCurdy (Elektra, EKL 124).

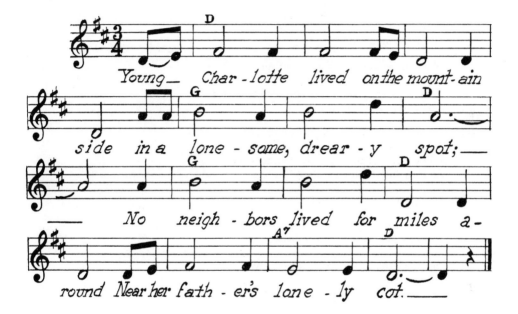

Young_ Char-lotte lived on the mount-ain side in a lone-some, drear-y spot;_ _ No neigh-bors lived for miles a-round Near her fath-er's lone-ly cot._

2. 'Twas on those cold and wintry nights
   Young swains would gather there.
   Her father kept a social place
   And Charlotte was very fair.

3. Her father liked to see her dressed
   Like any city belle;
   She was the only child he had,
   And he loved his daughter well.

4. On a New Year's Eve when the sun went down,
   She watched with wishful eye,
   Out through the frosty windowpane
   As the merry sleighs went by.

5. In a village fifteen miles away
   There was a ball that night;
   And though the air was piercing cold
   Her heart was warm and light.

6. How brightly gleamed her loving eyes
   As a well-known voice she heard;
   And dashing up to her cottage door
   Young Charlie's sleigh appeared.

7. "Oh, Charlotte, dear," her mother said,
   "This blanket 'round you fold;
   It is a dreadful night, you know,
   You'll catch your death of cold."

8. "Oh, no, oh, no," young Charlotte said,
   And she laughed like a gypsy queen,
   "To ride in blankets muffled up,
   I never would be seen.

9. "My silken cloak is quite enough,
   It is lined, you know, throughout;
   Besides I have my silken scarf
   To tie my head about."

10. Her bonnet and her gloves put on,
    She leaped into the sleigh,
    And away they went o'er the mountain top
    And the hills so far away.

11. There was music in the sound of bells
    As o'er the hills they'd go.
    What a crackling noise the runners made
    As they bit the frozen snow.

12. With faces muffled silently,
    For five long miles they rode,
    Until at length with a few frozen words,
    Young Charles the silence broke.

13. "Such a dreadful night I never saw,
    The reins I scarce can hold."
    Young Charlotte faintly then replied,
    "I am exceeding cold."

14. He cracked his whip; he urged his steed,
    Much faster than before;
    And thus five other weary miles
    In silence were passed o'er.

15. Said Charles: "How fast the shivering ice
    Is gathering on my brow."
    And Charlotte then more faintly cried,
    "I'm growing warmer now."

16. Thus on they rode through frosty air
    And the glittering cold starlight,
    Until at last the village lamps
    And the ballroom came in sight.

17. They reached the door and Charles sprang out;
    He reached his hand to her.
    "Why sit you there like a monument
    That has no power to stir?"

18. He called her once; he called her twice;
    She answered not a word.
    He asked her for her hand again,
    But still she never stirred.

19. He took her hand all in his own;
    It was cold and hard as stone;
    He tore the mantle from her face,
    And the cold stars on her shone.

20. Then quickly to the lighted hall
    Her lifeless form he bore.
    Young Charlotte's eyes had closed for all;
    Her voice was heard no more.

21. He threw himself down on his knees
    And the bitter tears did flow.
    He said, "My young, intended bride,
    No more with me you'll go."

22. He threw himself down by her side,
    And he kissed her marble brow,
    And his thoughts ran back to the place she said,
    "I'm growing warmer now."

BIBLIOGRAPHY

Abbie, A. G., Muir, John, Innes, J. Alexander, and Buchan, D. Campbell, *The British Students' Song Book*. London & Glasgow: Bayley Ferguson, 1913.

Adams, Andy, *The Log of a Cowboy*. Boston: Houghton Mifflin Company, 1903.

Allen, Jules Verne, *Cowboy Lore*. San Antonio, Texas: Naylor Company, 1933.

Allen, William Francis, Ware, Charles Pickard and Garrison, Lucy McKim, *Slave Songs of the United States*. Originally published 1867. Reprinted, New York: Oak Publications, 1965.

Ames, Russell, *The Story of American Folk Song*. New York: Grossett & Dunlap, 1955.

Anderson, Nels, *The Hobo*. Chicago: University of Chicago Press, 1923.

Baring-Gould, Sabine, *An Historical Sketch of English National Song*. London: Acorn Edition, printed privately at Messrs. Lowe & Brydone, undated (originally published 1895).

Barry, Phillips, *British Ballads from Maine*. New Haven: Yale University Press, 1950.

——, *The Maine Wood Songster*. Cambridge, Massachusetts: Powell Printing Company, 1939.

Beck, E. C., *Songs of the Michigan Lumberjacks*. Ann Arbor: University of Michigan Press, 1941.

Belden, H. M., *Ballads and Songs Collected by the Missouri Folk-Lore Society*. Columbia, Missouri: University of Missouri Studies, 1940.

Bestic, Captain A. A., *Kicking Canvas*. New York: Viking Press, 1957.

Blair, Walter, *Native American Humor*. New York: American Book Company, 1937.

——, *Tall Tale America*. New York: Coward-McCann, 1944.

Bone, David W., *Capstan Bars*. New York: Harcourt, Brace & Company, 1932.

Botkin, B. A., *A Treasury of American Folklore*. Foreword by Carl Sandburg. New York: Crown Publishers, 1944.

——, *Treasury of Mississippi Lore*. New York: Crown Publishers, 1955.

——, *Treasury of New England Folklore*. New York: Crown Publishers, 1944.

——, *Treasury of Southern Folklore*. New York: Crown Publishers, 1949.

——, *Treasury of Western Folklore*. New York: Crown Publishers, 1951.

——, with Harlow, Alvin, *A Treasury of Railroad Lore*. New York: Crown Publishers, 1953.

Brand, Oscar, *Singing Holidays*. New York: Alfred A. Knopf, 1957.

————, *The Ballad Mongers.* New York: Funk & Wagnalls, 1962.

Bronson, Bertrand, *The Traditional Tunes of the Child Ballads.* Princeton, N.J.: Princeton University Press, 1959–62.

Buchan, Norman, *101 Scottish Songs.* Glasgow and London: William Collins Sons and Company, 1962.

Bulletin of the Folksong Society of the Northeast, bibliographical and special series. MacEdward Leach, general editor. Vol. XI. Philadelphia: The American Folklore Society, 1960.

Burt, Olive F. Woolley, *American Murder Ballads and Their Stories.* New York: Oxford University Press, 1958.

Cazden, Norman, *The Abelard Folk Song Book.* New York: Abelard-Schuman, 1958.

Chappell, William, *Old English Popular Music.* Originally published 1838. Reprinted, New York: Jack Brussel, 1961.

Chase, Richard, *American Folk Tales and Songs.* New York: The New American Library of World Literature, 1956.

Child, Francis James, *English and Scottish Popular Ballads.* Boston: Houghton Mifflin, 1885–86.—Reprints available from Folk Lore Press and Dover.

Coffin, Tristram P., *The British Traditional Ballad in North America.* Revised edition. Philadelphia: The American Folklore Society, 1963.

Colcord, Joanna, *Songs of American Sailormen.* New York: W. W. Norton, 1938. Various reprints available including one in paperback from Oak Publications.

Courlander, Harold, *Negro Folk Music, U.S.A.* New York, Columbia University Press, 1963.

Cox, Edward Godfrey, *The Medieval Popular Ballad.* Boston: Ginn and Company, 1914.

Cox, John Harrington, *Traditional Ballads Mainly from West Virginia.* New York: National Service Bureau, 1939.

Cray, Ed, *Songs from the Ash Grove.* Los Angeles: Ash Grove, 1959.

Creighton, Helen, *Songs and Ballads from Nova Scotia.* Toronto and Vancouver: J. M. Dent, 1933.

————, *Traditional Songs of Nova Scotia.* Toronto: The Ryerson Press, 1950.

Davis, A. K., *Traditional Ballads from Virginia.* Cambridge: Harvard University Press, 1929.

Dearmer, Percy, with Vaughan Williams, Ralph, and Shaw, Martin, *The Oxford Book of Carols.* London: Oxford University Press, 1926.

Dett, R. Nathaniel, *Religious Folk-Songs of the Negro as Sung at Hampton Institute.* Hampton, Virginia: Hampton Institute Press, 1927.

Doerflinger, William Main, *Shantymen and Shantyboys.* New York: The Macmillan Company, 1951.

Dolph, Edward Arthur, *"Sound Off!" Soldier Songs from Yankee Doodle to Parley Voo.* New York: Cosmopolitan Book Corporation, 1929. Various reprints available.

Dorson, Richard M., *American Folklore.* Chicago: University of Chicago Press, 1959.

Douglas, Ronald Macdonald, *The Scots Book of Lore and Folklore.* New York: E. P. Dutton & Company, undated.

Dundes, Alan, *The Study of Folklore.* Englewood Cliffs; New Jersey: Prentice-Hall, 1965.

Dunn, Sinclair, *The Auld Scotch Sangs.* London and Glasgow: Bayley and Ferguson, undated (probably 1865).

D'urfey, Thomas, *Wit and Mirth: Or Pills to Purge Melancholy.* Originally published 1719–20. Reprinted, New York: Folklore Library Publishers, 1959.

Edwards, Charles L., *Bahama Songs and Stories.* New York: G. E. Stechert & Company, 1895.

Farmer, John S., *National Ballad and Song.* Privately printed in five volumes for subscribers only, 1897.

Flanders, Helen Hartness, *Ballads Migrant in New England.* New York: Farrar and Strauss, 1953.

————, *New Green Mountain Songster.* New Haven: Yale University Press, 1939.

————, *Vermont Folk Songs and Ballads.* Brattleborough, Vermont: Stephen Daye Press, 1931.

Fowke, Edith, with Glazer, Joe, *Songs of Work and Freedom.* Chicago: Roosevelt University, Labor Education Division, 1960.

————, with Johnston, Richard, *Folk Songs of Canada*. Waterloo, Ontario: Waterloo Music Company, 1954.

Frank C. Brown Collection of North Carolina Folklore, The. The folklore of North Carolina collected by Dr. Frank C. Brown during the years 1912 to 1943 in collaboration with the North Carolina Folklore Society. In seven volumes. General Editor, Newman Ivey White. Durham, North Carolina: Duke University Press, 1952–

Friedman, Albert B., *The Viking Book of Folk Ballads of the English Speaking World*. New York: The Viking Press, 1956.

Gerould, Gordon Hall, *The Ballad of Tradition*. New York: Oxford University Press, 1932.

Gordon, Robert, *Folk Songs of America*. New York: National Service Bureau Publication, W. P. A., 1938.

Graves, Robert, *English and Scottish Ballads*. New York: The Macmillan Company, undated.

Greenway, John, *American Folksongs of Protest*. New York: A. S. Barnes and Company, 1960.

Gummere, Francis B., *The Popular Ballad*. New York: Dover Publications, 1959.

Guthrie, Woody, *Bound for Glory*. New York: E. P. Dutton & Co., 1943. Reprinted, Garden City: Dolphin Books, Doubleday & Company.

Harlow, Frederick Pease, *Chanteying Aboard American Ships*. Barre, Massachusetts: Barre Gazette, 1962.

Haywood, Charles, *A Bibliography of North American Folk Lore and Folk Song*. New York: Greenburg, 1951.

Henry, Mellinger E., *Still More Ballads and Folk-Songs from the Southern Highlands*. Reprinted from the *Journal of American Folk-Lore*. Volume 45. January–March 1932. No. 175.

Hille, Waldemar, *The People's Song Book*. New York: Boni and Gaer, 1948.

Holbrook, Stewart H., *The Story of American Railroads*. New York: Crown Publishers, 1947.

Hughes, Langston, *The Book of Negro Folklore*. New York: Dodd, Mead and Company, 1959.

Hutchinson, William G., *Songs of the Vine with a Medley for Malt-Worms*. London: A. H. Bullen, 1904.

Ives, Burl, *Wayfaring Stranger*. New York: Whittlesey House, 1948.

Jackson, George Pullen, *Spiritual Folk-Songs of Early America*. New York: J. J. Augustin Publisher, 1937.

————, *Down East Spirituals*. New York: J. J. Augustin, 1941.

————, *White and Negro Spirituals*. New York: J. J. Augustin, 1944.

————, *White Spirituals of the Southern Uplands*. Chapel Hill: University of North Carolina Press, 1933.

Jekyll, Walter, *Jamaican Song and Story*. London: David Nutt, 1907.

Johnson, James, *The Scots Musical Museum*. Originally published 1853. Reprinted, Hatboro, Pennsylvania: Folklore Associates, 1962.

Johnson, James Weldon, *The Book of American Negro Spirituals*. New York: The Viking Press, 1925.

————, *The Second Book of Negro Spirituals*. New York: The Viking Press, 1926.

Journal of American Folk-Lore. Since 1888.

Journal of the English Folk Dance and Song Society. Since 1899.

Kornfield, Barry, *Buck's Rock Sings*. Buck's Rock: Privately printed, 1960.

Korson, George, *Coaldust on the Fiddle*. Philadelphia: University of Pennsylvania Press, 1943.

————, *Minstrels of the Mine Patch*. Philadelphia: University of Pennsylvania Press, 1938.

————, *Pennsylvania Songs and Legends*. Philadelphia: University of Pennsylvania Press, 1949.

Krehbiel, Henry Edward, *Afro-American Folksongs, A Study in Racial and National Music*. New York: Frederick Ungar Publishing Company, republished 1962.

Larkin, Margaret, *Singing Cowboy*. New York: Alfred A. Knopf, 1931.

Lawless, Ray M., *Folksingers and Folksongs in America*. New York: Duell, Sloan and Pearce, 1960.

Laws, G. Malcolm, Jr., *American Balladry from British Broadsides.* Philadelphia: The American Folklore Society, 1957.

———, *Native American Balladry.* A Bibliographical Survey. Philadelphia: The American Folklore Society, 1950.

Leach, Maria, *Standard Dictionary of Folklore, Mythology, and Legend.* New York: Funk & Wagnalls, 1949.

Linscott, Eloise Hubbard, *Folk Songs of Old New England.* New York: The Macmillan Company, 1939.

Lochlainn, Colm O., *Irish Street Ballads.* New York: A Corinth Book distributed by Citadel Press, 1960.

Logan, W. H., *A Pedlar's Pack of Ballads and Songs.* Edinburgh: William Paterson, 1869.

Lomax, Alan, *The Folk Songs of North America.* Garden City, New York: Doubleday & Company, 1960.

Lomax, John, *Adventures of a Ballad Hunter.* New York: The Macmillan Company, 1947.

———, *Cowboy Songs and Other Frontier Ballads.* New York: Stirgis and Walton Company, 1910.

———, and Lomax, Alan, *American Ballads and Folk Songs.* New York: The Macmillan Company, 1934.

———, *Folk Song: U.S.A.* New York: Duell, Sloan and Pearce, 1947.

———, *Leadbelly.* A Collection of World-Famous Songs by Huddie Ledbetter. New York: Folkways Music Publishers, 1959.

———, *Our Singing Country.* New York: The Macmillan Company, 1941.

Marsh, J. B. T., *The Story of the Jubilee Singers; with Their Songs.* Revised edition. Boston: Houghton Mifflin Company, 1881.

Martinengo-Cesaresco, Countess Evelyn, *Essays in the Study of Folk-Songs.* London: George Redway, 1886.

Morgan, Murray, *Skid Road.* Revised edition, New York: The Viking Press, 1960.

Morris, Alton C., *Folksongs of Florida.* Gainesville: University of Florida Press, 1950.

Nettl, Bruno, *An Introduction to Folk Music in the United States.* Detroit: Wayne State University Press, 1960. Subsequently reprinted in a revised paperback edition.

Nicholson, Sidney H., *British Songs for British Boys.* London: The Macmillan Company, 1930.

Nye, Hermes, *How to Be a Folksinger.* New York: Oak Publications, 1965.

Odum, H. W., with Johnson, G. B., *The Negro and His Songs.* Chapel Hill: University of North Carolina Press, 1925.

———, *Negro Workaday Songs.* Chapel Hill: University of North Carolina Press, 1925.

———, *Rainbow Round My Shoulder.* Indianapolis: Bobbs Merrill, 1928.

Owens, William A., *Texas Folk Songs.* Austin and Dallas: The Texas Folklore Society and University Press, 1950.

Parrish, Lydia, *Slave Songs of the Georgia Sea Islands.* New York: Creative Age Press, 1942.

Pittman J., with Colin Brown and Charles MacKay, *The Songs of Scotland.* London: Boosey & Company, 1878.

Randolph, Vance, *Ozark Folksongs.* Edited for the State Historical Society of Missouri by Floyd C. Shoemaker, Secretary, and Frances G. Emberson, Research Associate. Four volumes. Columbia, Missouri: The State Historical Society of Missouri, 1946–50.

Reeves, James, *The Idiom of the People.* London: Heinemann, 1958.

Reprints from Sing Out!. Several volumes available from the publisher of *Sing Out!,* the folk music magazine.

Reprints from the People's Song Bulletin. 1946–49. Foreword by Pete Seeger. Edited by Irwin Silber. New York: Oak Publications, 1961.

Richardson, Ethel Park, *American Mountain Songs.* Edited and arranged by Sigmund Spaeth. New York: Greenberg: Publisher, 1927.

Rickaby, Franz, *Ballads and Songs of the Shanty-Boy.* Cambridge: Harvard University Press, 1926.

Ritchie, Jean, *Singing Family of the Cumberlands.* London: Oxford University Press, 1955.

Roberts, John S., *The Legendary Ballads of England and Scotland*. London: Frederick Warne and Company, undated.

Routley, Erik, *The English Carol*. New York: Oxford University Press, 1959.

Rubin, Ruth, *A Treasury of Jewish Folksong*. New York: Schocken Books, 1950.

Sandburg, Carl, *The American Songbag*. New York: Harcourt, Brace and Company, 1927.

Sargent, Helen Child, and Kittredge, George Lyman, *English and Scottish Popular Ballads*. Cambridge: The Riverside Press; Houghton Mifflin Company, 1904.

Scarborough, Dorothy, *On the Trail of Negro Folk Songs*. Cambridge: Harvard University Press, 1925.

———, *A Song Catcher in Southern Mountains*. New York: Columbia University Press, 1937.

Sharp, Cecil J., *English Folk Songs*. Reprinted, London: Novello & Company, 1959.

———, *English Folk-Songs from the Southern Appalachians*. Edited by Maud Karpeles. Two volumes. London: Oxford University Press, 1932.

Shay, Frank, *A Sailor's Treasury*. New York: W. W. Norton & Company, 1951.

Silber, Irwin, *Lift Every Voice! The Second People's Song Book*. New York: Sing Out, 1953.

———, *Songs of the Civil War*. New York: Columbia University Press, 1960.

Silverman, Jerry, *Folk Blues*. New York: The Macmillan Company, 1958.

Sing Out! The Folk Song Magazine. Published by Sing Out, Inc., New York.

Stone, Christopher, *Sea Songs and Ballads*. London: Oxford at the Clarendon Press, 1906.

Taylor, Cyril, *The Hawthorn Book of Christmas Carols*. New York: Hawthorn Books, 1957.

Taylor, Marshall W., *A Collection of Revival Hymns and Plantation Melodies*. Cincinnati: Marshall W. Taylor and W. C. Echols, Publishers, 1882.

Thompson, Harold W., *Body, Boots and Britches*. Philadelphia: J. B. Lippincott, 1940.

Williams, Ralph Vaughan, *National Music*. London: Oxford University Press, 1934.

Weavers, *The Weavers' Song Book*. New York: Harper & Brothers, 1960.

Wells, Evelyn Kendrick, *The Ballad Tree*. New York: The Ronald Press Company, 1950.

Western Folklore, Journal of the California Folklore Society. Berkeley: University of California Press.

Whall, W. B., *Sea Songs and Shanties*. Glasgow: James Brown & Son, 1910.

White, Newman I., *American Negro Folk Songs*. Cambridge: Harvard University Press, 1928.

Whiting, Bartlett Jere, *Traditional British Ballads*. New York: Appleton-Century-Crofts, 1955.

Wimberly, Lowry C., *Folklore in the English and Scottish Ballads*. New York: Frederick Ungar Publishing Company, 1928.

Work, John W., *American Negro Songs and Spirituals*. New York: Crown Publishers, 1940.

INDEX

386

Marry Me?," 304
"Water is Wide, The," 346
"Who's Gonna Shoe Your Pretty Little Foot?," 357
"Wildwood Flower," 359
Lovell, John, Jr., 6
Lunsford, Bascom Lamar, 21, 80, 128, 148, 186, 306, 312
Luther, Frank, 137, 165, 176, 249, 277, 358

McClintock, "Haywire Mac," 27
MacColl, Ewan, 36, 37, 47, 51, 111, 128, 148, 157, 158, 234, 253, 264, 278, 348, 355
McCurdy, Ed, 21, 22, 31, 32, 42, 47, 54, 60, 67, 76, 111, 137, 169, 176, 186, 190, 234, 251, 255, 281, 287, 288, 294, 306, 307, 320, 371, 375
McCutcheon, John and Evelyn, 78, 303
McDaniel, Jim, ix, 275
McFerrin, Robert, 312
McGhee, Brownie, 26, 54, 190
McNeil, Brownie, 22, 67, 114, 128, 296
Macon, Uncle Dave, 281
"Maid Freed from the Gallows, The," 153
"Maid of Constant Sorrow, The," 226
Makem, Tommy 42, 148, 195
"Mama Don't Allow," 225
"Man of Constant Sorrow," 226
Marais, Josef and Miranda, 56, 57, 72, 114, 125, 232
Marsh, J. B. T., 122
Marshall, Herta, 174, 357, 366
"Maryanne," 227
"Mary Golden Tree, The," 128
"Mary Hamilton," 108
Matthews, Inez, 133
"Men of the West," 3
Merrill Jay Singers, 299
Meyer, Friedrich Wilhelm, 111
"Michael, Row the Boat Ashore," 229
"Midnight Special," 230
"Mill-boy of the Slashes, The," 3
Miller, Harry S., 56
Miller, Mickey, 360
Mills, Alan, 13, 31, 32, 37, 80, 88, 155, 176, 234, 239, 296, 347

"Miss Bailey," 232
"Mister Froggie Went A-Courtin'," 234
"Molly Malone," 61
Moonshine songs:
    "Copper Kettle," 64
    "Darlin' Corey," 76
    "Old Mountain Dew," 251
Moore, Juanita, 226
Moser, Artus, 222, 331, 360
Mountain music, xvi
"M.T.A. Song, The," 297
Murai, Jean, 351
Murder and outlaw ballads:
    "Banks of the Ohio," 20
    "Brennan on the Moor," 42
    "Delia's Gone," 78
    "Florella," 102
    "Four Maries, The," 108
    "Frankie and Johnny," 115
    "Hangman, Hangman," 153
    "Jesse James," 186
    "Lord Randall," 221
    "Omie Wise," 255
    "Railroad Bill," 271
    "Silver Dagger," 299
    "Stagolee," 306
    "Tom Dooley," 324
    "Two Sisters, The," 330
    "Whiskey in the Jar," 355
    "Willow Garden, The," 366
    "Willow Tree, The," 367
"Must I Go Bound," 235

Negro music, xvii
Negro songs, miscellaneous (see also Spirituals; Blues):
    "Crawdad Song, The," 70
    "Deep Blue Sea," 76
    "Delia's Gone," 78
    "Follow the Drinking Gourd," 106
    "Goin' Down the Road Feelin' Bad," 127
    "In the Pines," 180
    "John Henry," 189
    "Kum Ba Ya," 209
    "Michael, Row the Boat Ashore," 229
    "Nine Hundred Miles," 240
    "Nine-Pound Hammer," 241
    "Pick a Bale of Cotton," 265
    "Railroad Bill," 271
    "Raise a Ruckus," 272
    "Rock About My Saro Jane," 281
    "Rock Island Line, The," 282
    " 'Round the Bay of Mex-

ico," 285
    "The Sloop John B.," 303
    "Stagolee," 306
    "Tell Old Bill," 318
    "This Train," 321
Nettl, Bruno, xi
New Lost City Ramblers, The, 117, 287, 324
"New River Train," 239
Newmark, Burton, ix
Niles, John Jacob, 22, 108, 148, 153, 190, 222, 234, 287, 288, 331
"Nine Hundred Miles," 240
"Nobody Knows the Trouble I've Seen," 242
Nye, Hermes, vii, 4, 19, 31, 39, 108

O'Bryant, Joan, 47, 167, 177
Odetta, 77, 93, 114, 146, 153, 160, 179, 190, 198, 215, 231, 281, 288
Odum, Howard, 189
Ogan, Sarah, 226
"Oh Mary, Don't You Weep," 245
"Oh, No, John," 246
Ohliger, Dorothy, ix
Okun, Milt, 13, 27, 32, 51, 58, 91, 96, 105, 114, 148, 169, 177, 190, 232, 235, 246, 257, 261, 266, 283, 296, 310, 345, 357
"Old Ark's A-Moverin'," 247
"Old Chisholm Trail, The," 249
"Old Hal of the West," 3
"Old Maid's Song, The," 250
"Old Mountain Dew," 251
"Old Rosin the Beau," 3
"Old Stormalong," 253
Olsen, Dorothy, 94
"Omie Wise," 255
"On Top of Old Smoky," 256
"Our Goodman," 111
Owens, William, ix
"Oxford Girl, The," 20
Packet ships, trade, xiv, 37
Paley, Tom, 102, 217, 360
"Paper of Pins," 261
Parham, Walter, 52, 299
"Pat Works on the Railway," 263
Peacock, Ken, 86
Pegram, George, 52, 299
Pepys Ballads, 166
"Pick a Bale of Cotton," 265
Pike, 187, 309
Pikers, 187, 309
Play-party songs, discussion, 302
Poole, Charlie, 117
Primitive music, xii

THE AUTHOR AND HIS BOOK

JAMES F. LEISY was born in Illinois but his family moved to Dallas, Texas, when he was six months old. His father was Professor of American Literature at Southern Methodist University, and was active in folklore research, scholarship and societies. As a child Mr. Leisy's interest in folk music was inspired by the visits to his home of folk music specialists, including John Lomax, Carl Sandburg, and William Owens. He learned to play every musical instrument he could get his hands on and by the time he was out of high school he had played professionally with dance bands, hillbilly bands, Dixieland bands and symphony orchestras, activities he continued during and after attending Southern Methodist University.

Mr. Leisy became an arranger for several musical organizations, and musical director for a small independent recording company. His compositions have been recorded by many successful performers, including Betty Johnson, the Mariners, Kitty Kallen, Rusty Draper, Jim "Green Door" Lowe, and Tommy Sands. His hillbilly songs include several standards recorded by Hank Snow, Homer and Jethro, Hank Locklin, Anita Carter, the Louvin Brothers, the Davis Sisters, and Hawkshaw Hawkins.

Mr. Leisy has collected and studied folk music since the 1930s and has written several books, including the bestsellers *Songs for Swingin' House-mothers, Songs for Pickin' and Singin'* and *Hootenanny Tonight*. His books have sold over 600,000 copies, his recordings several million. His "Classic Ballad Series" has been featured for several years in *Playboy* Magazine.

In recent years he has lectured on recreational music and folk music and appeared as a performer and master of ceremonies at colleges and universities, schools, clubs, churches and professional meetings. He organized the Cable Car Hoots, which have been held in the North Beach area of San Francisco for several years and which have, Mr. Leisy says, "contributed much to the musical depreciation of that city."

He is president and a director of the Wadsworth Publishing Company, which specializes in college textbooks. He is a member of Broadcast Music (Performance Society), American and California Folklore Societies, Music Industries Council and the Music Educators National Conference. Mr. Leisy lives in rustic Portola Valley with his wife, Emily, and three young musicians, Jamie, Scot and Becky.

THE FOLK SONG ABECEDARY was composed by the Poole Clarinda Company, Chicago, Ill., employing the modern process which includes computer setting and photography. The text is set in Century Schoolbook, an open and highly legible face. The book was printed by the New York Lithographic Corp., New York City, and bound by American Book–Stratford Press, Brattleboro, Vermont.

A HAWTHORN BOOK